Counting

1 Next to each number write its name.

a	47		e	51	
b	73		f	34	
c	69		g	95	
d	82		h	26	

2 Write these numbers as figures.

a three hundred and sixty ☐   c eight hundred and fifty ☐

b five hundred and two ☐   d one thousand ☐

3 Write the five numbers immediately before and after 503 in order on the number track below.

					503					

4 Give the numbers which come nine before and six after each of these numbers.

a	☐	15	☐	d	☐	91	☐
b	☐	64	☐	e	☐	27	☐
c	☐	43	☐	f	☐	106	☐

Counting

1 Count on in tens from the number in the first box.

a | 45 | | | | | | | | |

b | 376 | | | | | | | | |

2 Count back in tens from the number in the last box.

| | | | | | | | | | 129 |

3

Count on in 2s from 43. → | 43 | | | | |

Count on in 5s from 38. → | 38 | | | | |

Count back in 3s from 57. → | | | | | 57 |

Count back in 4s from 95. → | | | | | 95 |

4 Answer these questions.

a How many steps of ten are there from 30 to 100? | |

b How many steps of 100 are there from 200 to 800? | |

c How many steps are there from 25 to 85 in 5s? | |

Counting

1 Circle the even numbers and draw a box around the odd numbers.

39	74	253	424	61	568	724	268	141	144
32	97	45	96	725	392	682	537	88	806

2 Fill in these charts.

a

+	14	40	22	58	36
12			34		
26					62

b

+	25	13	49	37	51
15					66
23		36			

3 Cross out the word which is wrong in each sentence.

a   If you add two even numbers the answer is (odd, even).

b   If you add two odd numbers the answer is (odd, even).

4 Multiply each of these numbers by 2.

a	31		c	44		e	36		g	47	
b	26		d	53		f	23		h	19	

What do you notice about the answers?

3

Place Value & Ordering

1   What number does each abacus show?

a   H   T   U

b   H   T   U

c   H   T   U

d   H   T   U

2   How many does the digit 4 stand for in:

a   456   ☐

c   749   ☐

b   24   ☐

d   4003   ☐

3   Mark each of these numbers on the abacus below it.

a   582   **b**   904   **c**   36   **d**   477

H   T   U   H   T   U   H   T   U   H   T   U

4   Write down first the largest and then the smallest number you can make using the digits from the number given.

a   231 | 321 | 123 | **c**   759   ☐☐   **e**   648   ☐☐

b   627   ☐☐   **d**   435   ☐☐   **f**   819   ☐☐

Place Value & Ordering

1 Give the numbers that are ten less and ten more than these numbers.

a ☐ 472 ☐   c ☐ 659 ☐   e ☐ 700 ☐

b ☐ 398 ☐   d ☐ 510 ☐   f ☐ 803 ☐

2 Do these addition problems in your head. Write in the final answer.

a 650 + 100 + 10 + 100 + 10 + 100 + 1 = ☐

b 395 + 10 + 100 + 100 + 10 + 1 + 100 = ☐

3 Now do these subtraction problems. Write in the final answer.

a 548 – 100 – 10 – 100 – 10 – 100 – 1 = ☐

b 231 – 10 – 100 – 10 – 100 – 1 – 10 = ☐

4 Write the correct number in each box.

		100 more is			100 less is	
a	900	→	☐	☐	→	300
b	528	→	☐	☐	→	635
c	96	→	☐	☐	→	47

5

Place Value & Ordering

1 Arrange these numbers in order in the boxes.

131   201   231   321   123   302   102   312   213

☐ ☐ ☐ ☐ ☐ ☐ ☐ ☐ ☐

Lowest   Highest

2 Fill in the empty boxes so that there are eight numbers in order.

a | 98 | | 112 | | 160 | | | 163 |

b | 500 | | | 425 | 350 | | 348 | |

3 Answer these questions.

a How many odd numbers lie between 50 and 62? ☐

b Which number is halfway between thirty and seventy? ☐

c Which even numbers lie between 103 and 109? ☐

4 Reorder these numbers.

546   456   654   506   645   405   465   564   605

☐ ☐ ☐ ☐ ☐ ☐ ☐ ☐ ☐

Highest   Lowest

6

Estimating

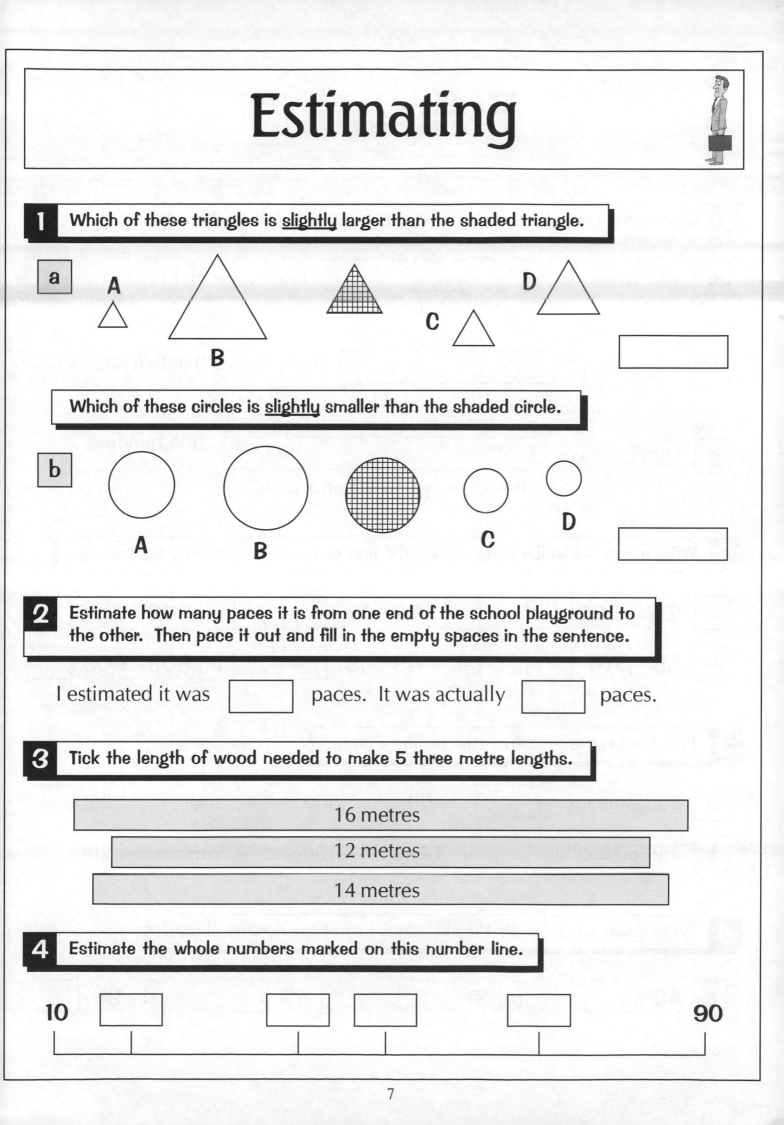

1 Which of these triangles is <u>slightly</u> larger than the shaded triangle.

a

A

B

C

D

Which of these circles is <u>slightly</u> smaller than the shaded circle.

b

A

B

C

D

2 Estimate how many paces it is from one end of the school playground to the other. Then pace it out and fill in the empty spaces in the sentence.

I estimated it was [ ] paces. It was actually [ ] paces.

3 Tick the length of wood needed to make **5** three metre lengths.

16 metres

12 metres

14 metres

4 Estimate the whole numbers marked on this number line.

10   90

Estimating

1   Choose the correct words from those given to complete each sentence.

a   142 sweets is [_____] to fill a jar that holds 150.

       enough   not enough

b   12 apples is [_____] to give 7 people two apples each.

       too few   too many

c   Ninety-nine is [_____] one hundred.

       the same as   approximately

2   Write a number which is more than the first number but less than the second.

a   219   222 [ ]   **c**   399   405 [ ]   **e**   998   1000 [ ]

b   657   701 [ ]   **d**   449   451 [ ]   **f**   609   906 [ ]

3   Pick the best answer from the numbers given.

a   986 is nearly [ ]   100   500   1000   2000

b   149 is roughly [ ]   140   150   940   200

4   Write down a number that is about one half of the number shown.

a   43 [ ]   **b**   31 [ ]   **c**   49 [ ]   **d**   95 [ ]

Estimating

1 Round these numbers to the nearest 10.

| a | 58 | | b | 63 | | c | 72 | | d | 49 | |

Round these numbers to the nearest 100.

| e | 814 | | f | 348 | | g | 499 | | h | 750 | |

2 Connect the sums in the rectangle to their answers in the circle.
Connect the answers in the circle to their nearest 10 in the square.

19 + 19	36 − 9
48 ÷ 2	60 − 7
2 × 31	50 + 26

Circle: 24 38 27 76 62 53

Square: 80 40 50 60 20 30

3 Circle the number that is closest to the number in the box.

| a | 37 | 40 30 | b | 175 | 100 200 | c | 321 | 300 400 |

4 Write your answer to each problem in the first box.
In the second box write the answer to the nearest 100.

| a | 200 − 70 = | | | c | 3 × 60 = | | |
| b | 330 ÷ 3 = | | | d | 300 + 290 = | | |

9

Fractions

1 Arrange these fractions in order in the boxes.

¹/₄   ¹/₁₀   ¹/₃   ¹/₂   ¹/₅   ¹/₈

[ ]   [ ]   [ ]   [ ]   [ ]   [ ]

Smallest   Largest

2 The fraction tells you the amount to shade in.

a [   ] ⁴/₅

b [   ] ³/₄

c [   ] ²/₃

3 Solve these problems.

a Which number is halfway between forty and eighty? [   ]

b How many is one fifth of twenty? [   ]

c Five is one tenth of which number? [   ]

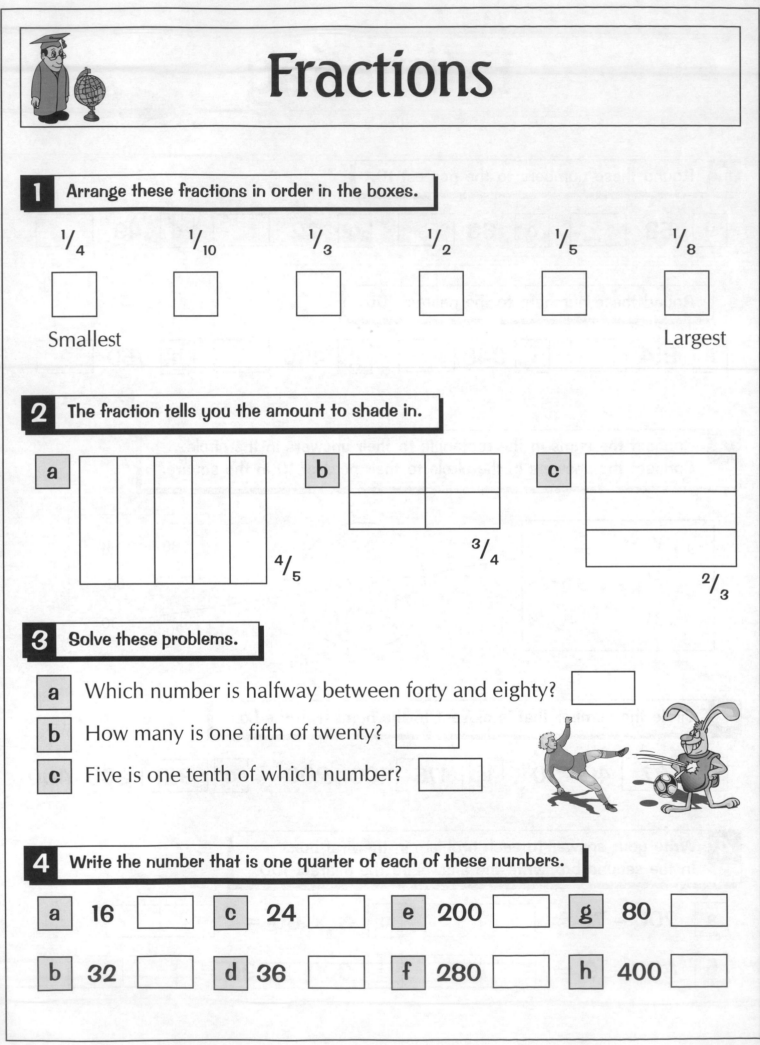

4 Write the number that is one quarter of each of these numbers.

a	16	[ ]	c	24	[ ]	e	200	[ ]	g	80	[ ]
b	32	[ ]	d	36	[ ]	f	280	[ ]	h	400	[ ]

Fractions

1. What fraction of each shape is shaded?

a

b

c

d

2. Think carefully and fill in the missing numbers.

a | Eight tenths is the same as [ ] fifths.

b | Two sixths is the same as [ ] third.

c | Six eights is the same as [ ] quarters.

3. What fraction of each set is ringed?

a

b

4. Write the number that is one fifth of each of these numbers.

a 25 [ ]   c 15 [ ]   e 300 [ ]   g 200 [ ]

b 40 [ ]   d 35 [ ]   f 450 [ ]   h 500 [ ]

Fractions

1 Circle the shape that is divided into fifths.

A

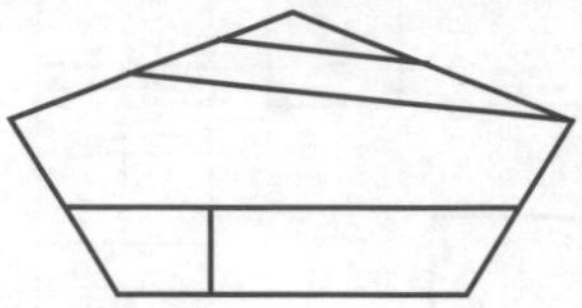

B

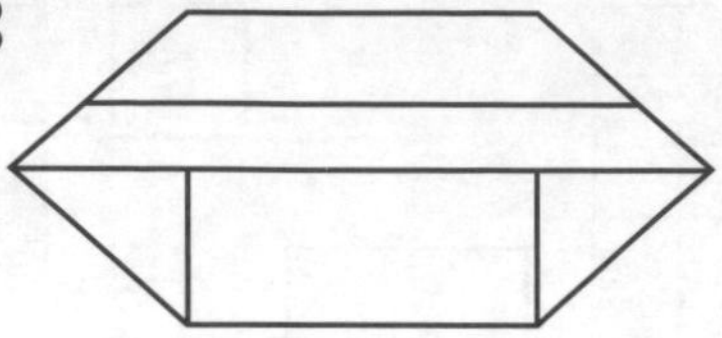

C

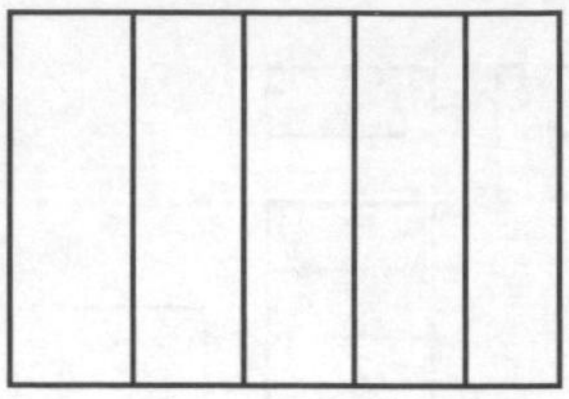

2 Use the fraction strip to help you answer the questions.

1 whole one							
½				½			
¼		¼		¼		¼	
⅛	⅛	⅛	⅛	⅛	⅛	⅛	⅛

How many:

a halves in a whole one?

d eighths in one half?

b quarters in two halves?

e quarters in six eighths?

c eighths in three quarters?

f halves in four eighths?

3 How many whole ones in:

a 20 fifths?

b 24 quarters?

c 15 thirds?

4 Write the number that is one tenth of each of these numbers.

a 30

b 70

c 200

d 600

Adding

1 Write five different pairs of numbers that total eleven.

2 Double each of these numbers.

a 7 ☐   **c** 15 ☐   **e** 18 ☐   **g** 13 ☐

b 9 ☐   **d** 16 ☐   **f** 19 ☐   **h** 12 ☐

3 Use the number line to help you with the questions.

```
0        25        50        75        100
|__|__|__|__|__|__|__|__|__|__|__|__|__|__|__|__|__|__|__|__|
```

How many steps of five are there from:

a 25 to 75? ☐   **b** 20 to 55? ☐   **c** 15 to 90? ☐

4 Complete these calculations.

a ☐ + 600 = 1000   **c** 200 + ☐ = 1000

b ☐ + 300 = 1000   **d** 900 + ☐ = 1000

Adding

1 Add together each pair of numbers.

a 17 13 ☐   **c** 14 12 ☐   **e** 11 18 ☐

b 15 14 ☐   **d** 10 16 ☐   **f** 12 19 ☐

2 Use all these numbers to make eight addition sums. You must only use each number once.

☐ + ☐ = ☐

☐ + ☐ = ☐

☐ + ☐ = ☐

☐ + ☐ = ☐

36	31	11	20
23	24	32	27
16	15	12	39
35	40	28	19

☐ + ☐ = ☐

☐ + ☐ = ☐

☐ + ☐ = ☐

☐ + ☐ = ☐

3 Solve these problems. Write the answers in words.

a How many altogether is 42 and 28? ☐

b Fifty-nine plus twenty-nine. ☐

4 Find the total of these groups of numbers.

a 6, 8, 4, 2 ☐   **b** 3, 8, 7, 5 ☐   **c** 8, 5, 5, 9 ☐

Adding

1 Work out the missing answers.

| a | 2 4
+2 3 | b | 2 9
+5 8 | c | 3 3
+3 9 | d | 2 8
+6 3 | e | 4 5
+3 7 |

2 Complete these addition tables.

a

+	25	37	48
29	54		
35		72	
43			91

b

+	52	65	78
59			137
67		132	
73	125		

3 Try these more difficult sums.

| a | 6 4 1
+2 3 2 | b | 2 1 7
+7 6 8 | c | 4 9 7
+1 9 6 | d | 3 2 8
+2 9 6 |

4 Here is a challenge for your calculation skills.

a 14 + 59 + 19 = ☐   c 36 + 17 + 39 = ☐

b 64 + 87 + 99 = ☐   d 87 + 29 + 37 = ☐

Subtracting

1 Take away the smallest number from the largest number.

a 12, 4 ☐   c 6, 13 ☐   e 17, 8 ☐   g 9, 18 ☐

b 5, 20 ☐   d 14, 9 ☐   f 7, 15 ☐   h 16, 5 ☐

2 How many do you need to subtract from each number to leave forty?

a 57 ☐   c 85 ☐   e 66 ☐   g 99 ☐

b 82 ☐   d 74 ☐   f 63 ☐   h 71 ☐

3 Use the number line to help you with the questions.

0   10   20   30   40   50

How many steps of five are there from:

a 40 to 10? ☐   b 35 to 0? ☐   c 45 to 5? ☐

4 Complete these calculations.

a ☐ – 700 = 300   b 800 – ☐ = 600

16

Subtracting

1 | Do these word problems.

a Take nine from fourteen. ☐ **c** Subtract ten from forty–six. ☐

b Eighty–three subtract fifty. ☐ **d** Sixteen take away seven. ☐

2 | Use all these numbers to make eight subtraction sums. You must only use each number once.

☐ – ☐ = ☐

☐ – ☐ = ☐

☐ – ☐ = ☐

☐ – ☐ = ☐

90	40	13	70
14	17	20	16
60	15	10	50
11	30	12	80

☐ – ☐ = ☐

☐ – ☐ = ☐

☐ – ☐ = ☐

☐ – ☐ = ☐

3 | Solve these problems. Write the answers in words.

a What is the difference between 85 and 35? ☐

b How many more than 6 is 69? ☐

4 | Subtract the two smallest numbers from the largest one.

a 34, 8, 6 ☐   **b** 9, 47, 5 ☐   **c** 8, 9, 58 ☐

Subtracting

1 Work out the missing answers.

a
```
  6 9
- 3 5
─────
```

b
```
  7 0
- 2 9
─────
```

c
```
  7 8
- 3 9
─────
```

d
```
  5 3
- 2 6
─────
```

e
```
  8 5
- 4 9
─────
```

2 Complete these subtraction tables.

a

–	51	65	79
23	28		
35		30	
48			31

b

–	110	130	150
84			66
72		58	
46	64		

3 Try these more difficult subtractions.

a
```
  9 8 7
- 5 4 2
───────
```

b
```
  8 5 0
- 4 3 2
───────
```

c
```
  6 9 1
- 5 1 3
───────
```

d
```
  4 5 8
- 3 7 2
───────
```

4 Here's a challenge for your calculation skills.

a 114 – 18 – 24 = ☐

b 129 – 32 – 17 = ☐

c 151 – 16 – 47 = ☐

d 206 – 25 – 83 = ☐

18

Multiplying

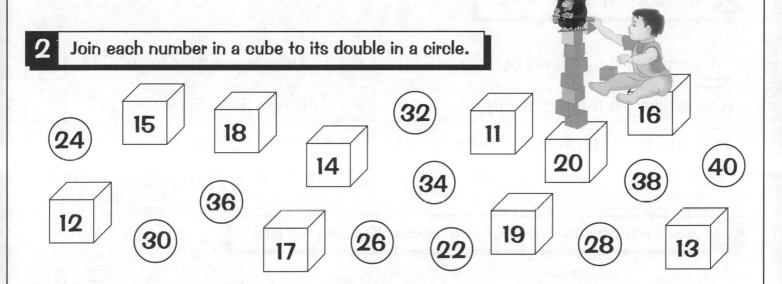

1 Complete this multiplication chart.

×	4	9	1	6	0	5	3	8	10	2	7
2				12					20		
5	20										35

2 Join each number in a cube to its double in a circle.

15 18 (32) 11 (16)
(24)   14   (20) (38) (40)
    (36)   (34)
(12) (30) 17 (26) (22) 19 (28) 13

3 Shade in the numbers that are multiples of 3.

30	12	19	23	21	11	6	17
24	26	9	14	18	36	29	15

4 Fill in the multiplication fact for this addition sum.

4 + 4 + 4 + 4 + 4 + 4 + 4 + 4 = ☐ × ☐ = ☐

Multiplying

1 Multiply each pair of numbers.

a 2, 48 ☐   **c** 19, 5 ☐   **e** 3, 16 ☐   **g** 14, 5 ☐

b 17, 4 ☐   **d** 3, 13 ☐   **f** 12, 5 ☐   **h** 2, 42 ☐

2 Do these word problems.

a Multiply nineteen by four. ☐   **d** How many is four times 21? ☐

b Make 18 five times larger. ☐   **e** Thirteen times five. ☐

c Thirty multiplied by three. ☐   **f** Nine fours times two. ☐

3 Join each two-digit number to a number 10 times the size.

81   28   63   280   54
55
550   810   630   46   540
37   370   72
720   460   90   900

4 Multiply these numbers by five and write your answer in the bottom box.

a 120 ☐   **b** 170 ☐   **c** 130 ☐   **d** 190 ☐   **e** 150 ☐   **f** 180 ☐

Multiplying

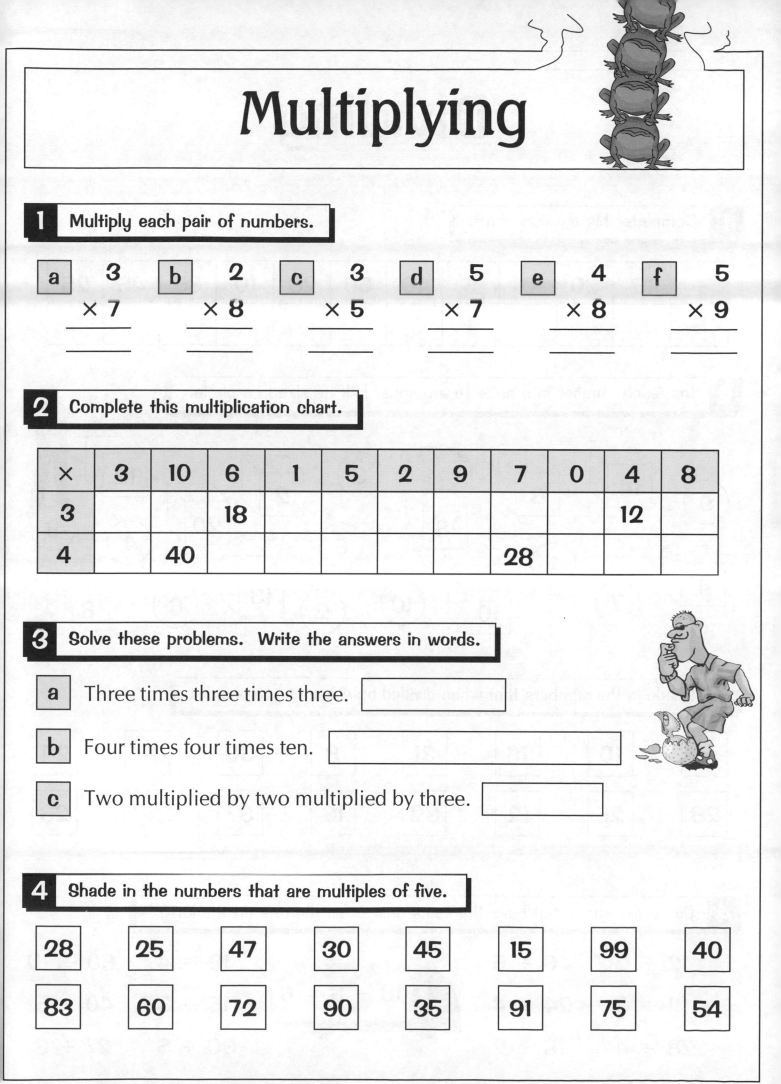

---

1 Multiply each pair of numbers.

a	3 × 7	b	2 × 8	c	3 × 5	d	5 × 7	e	4 × 8	f	5 × 9

---

2 Complete this multiplication chart.

×	3	10	6	1	5	2	9	7	0	4	8
3			18							12	
4		40						28			

---

3 Solve these problems. Write the answers in words.

a Three times three times three.

b Four times four times ten.

c Two multiplied by two multiplied by three.

---

4 Shade in the numbers that are multiples of five.

28	25	47	30	45	15	99	40
83	60	72	90	35	91	75	54

Dividing

1 Complete this division chart.

÷	15	30	0	5	40	50	20	10	35	45	25
5				1					7		

2 Join each number in a cube to a number half its size in a circle.

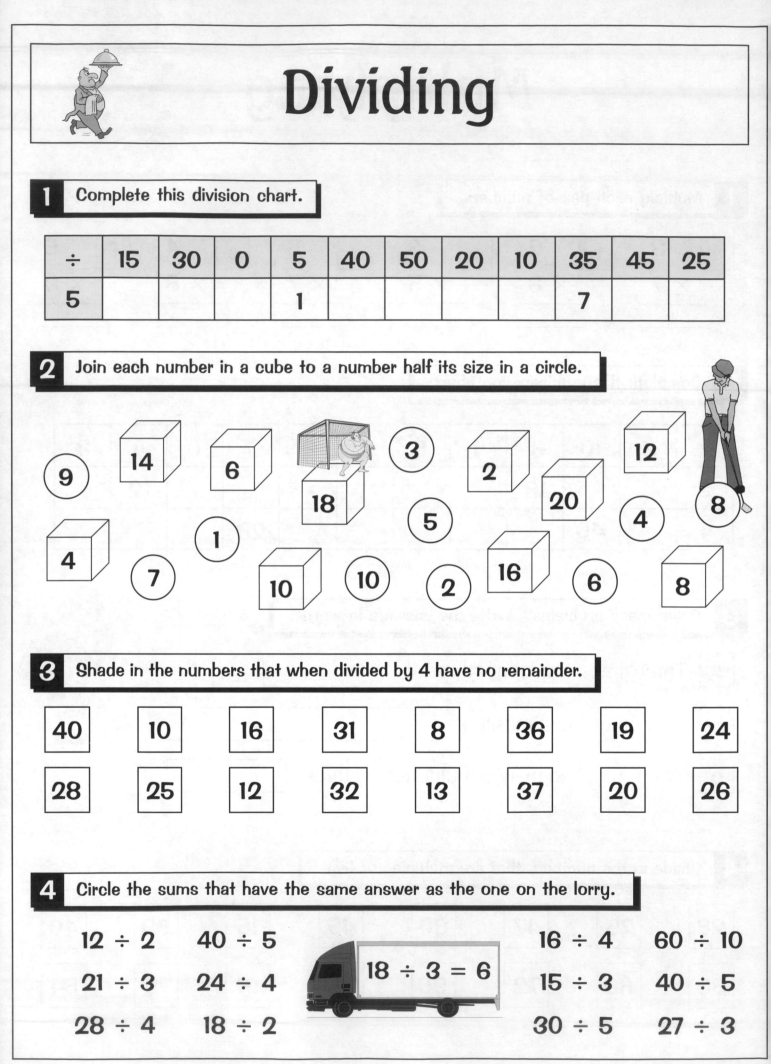

3 Shade in the numbers that when divided by 4 have no remainder.

40	10	16	31	8	36	19	24
28	25	12	32	13	37	20	26

4 Circle the sums that have the same answer as the one on the lorry.

12 ÷ 2	40 ÷ 5		16 ÷ 4	60 ÷ 10
21 ÷ 3	24 ÷ 4	18 ÷ 3 = 6	15 ÷ 3	40 ÷ 5
28 ÷ 4	18 ÷ 2		30 ÷ 5	27 ÷ 3

Dividing

1 Fill in the missing numbers.

a [ ] ÷ 2 = 8   c 15 ÷ [ ] = 5   e 28 ÷ 4 = [ ]

b [ ] ÷ 4 = 10   d 12 ÷ [ ] = 6   f 27 ÷ 3 = [ ]

2 Do these word problems.

a Divide eighteen by two. [ ]   d How many fives make thirty? [ ]

b A half of 14 is how many? [ ]   e Share 24 between three. [ ]

c Share sixty between ten. [ ]   f What is a quarter of 20? [ ]

3 Join each three–digit number to a number 10 times smaller.

20   90   80   60   800   40

700   400   100   70   600

30   900   500   50   10   300

200

4 Complete this division chart.

÷	24	9	30	3	18	12	0	27	6	21	15
3				1				9			

23

Dividing

1 Divide the larger number by the smaller.

a 39, 3 ☐   d 70, 5 ☐   g 2, 50 ☐   j 3, 66 ☐

b 3, 81 ☐   e 2, 30 ☐   h 85, 5 ☐   k 2, 80 ☐

c 65, 5 ☐   f 90, 5 ☐   i 2, 60 ☐   l 54, 3 ☐

2 Complete this division chart for the ×4 and extended ×2 tables.

÷	20	0	36	8	24	16	4	40	32	12	28
4			9								7
2			18								14

3 Fill in the answers and how many left over.

a 10 ÷ 3 = ☐ r ☐   c 13 ÷ 3 = ☐ r ☐   e 32 ÷ 3 = ☐ r ☐

b 25 ÷ 3 = ☐ r ☐   d 22 ÷ 3 = ☐ r ☐   f 17 ÷ 3 = ☐ r ☐

4 Circle the sum that has the same answer as the large number.

a **30** | 80 ÷ 2 | 60 ÷ 2

b **50** | 100 ÷ 2 | 200 ÷ 2

c **70** | 170 ÷ 2 | 140 ÷ 2

Money Problems

1 How much change from 50p will you get if you spend...

a 19p? ____   c 27p? ____   e 45p? ____   g 34p? ____

b 33p? ____   d 42p? ____   f 28p? ____   h 16p? ____

2 Complete this addition chart.

+	23p	34p	54p	25p	14p	32p	45p	12p	52p	43p	55p
24p		58p							76p		
39p	62p						84p				

3 Work out these problems.

a Claire spent 15p and had 11p left. How much had she at first? ____

b Ben has a 10p piece, a 20p piece and three 5p pieces. ____
How much has he altogether?

c A ham roll costs 55p. Write the cost in pence of two ham rolls. ____

4 Complete this subtraction chart. Try to work out the answers in your head.

−	13p	17p	22p	16p	11p	23p	15p	18p	12p	21p	14p
28p			6p							7p	
39p		22p								18p	

Money Problems

1 Solve these problems.

a How many 5p pieces have the same value as a £1 coin? ☐

b A bar of chocolate costs 24p. Find the cost of four bars. ☐

c Share £1.20 equally among three girls.
How many pence does each girl receive? ☐

2 Work out the missing amounts in your head.

a 3 × 7p = ☐   **c** ☐ ÷ 4 = 21p   **e** 6p × ☐ = 30p

b 50p ÷ ☐ = 10p   **d** 4 × 4p = ☐   **f** ☐ ÷ 2 = 21p

3 Complete both of these tables.

×	6p	9p	7p	8p
3			21p	
4		36p		
5	30p			

÷	40p	80p	60p	£1
2		40p		
5			12p	
10				10p

4 Treble the value of each coin and write your answer in the first box.
Divide that answer by two and write the final result in the second box.

a 2p | 6p | 3p   **c** 20p ☐ ☐   **e** £1 ☐ ☐

b 10p ☐ ☐   **d** 50p ☐ ☐   **f** £2 ☐ ☐

Money Problems

1 How many...

a 1p coins make 40p? ⬜

b 2p coins make 50p? ⬜

c 5p coins make 80p? ⬜

d 10p coins make £2.00? ⬜

e 20p coins make £5.00? ⬜

f 50p coins make £10? ⬜

2 Solve these problems. Write the answer in words.

a By how much is 29p more than 14p? ⬜

b Work out half of £30 and add £4.00 to your answer. ⬜

3 Find the total value of each set of coins.

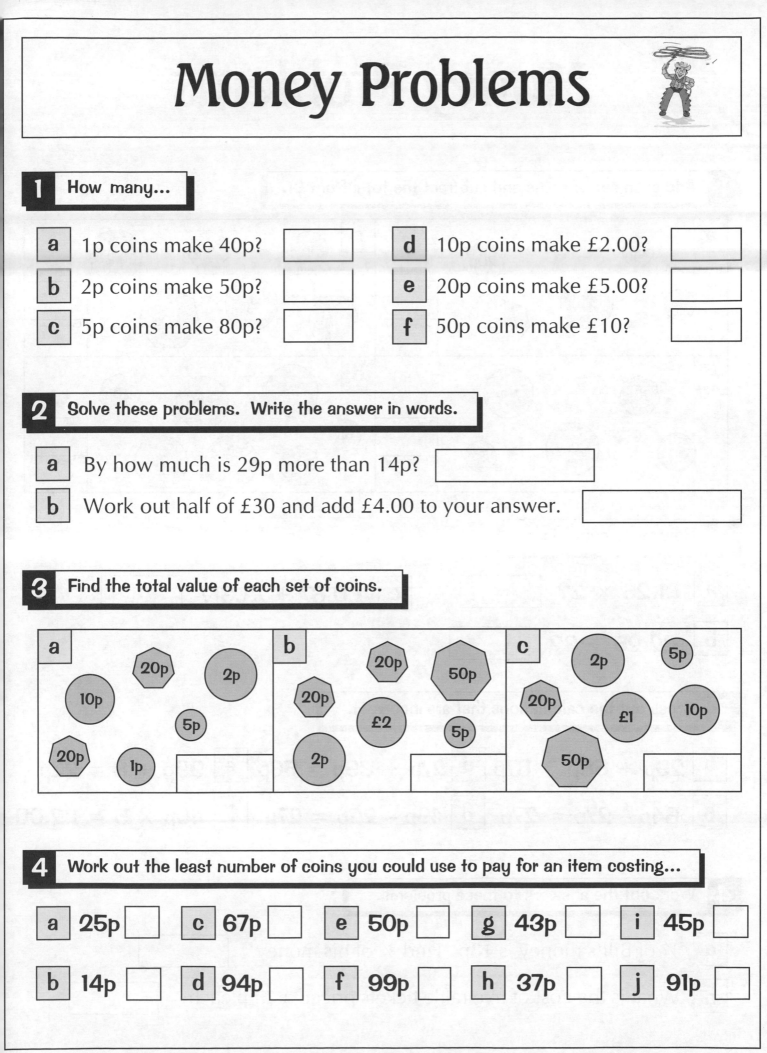

a 20p 2p 10p 5p 20p 1p

b 20p 50p 20p £2 5p 2p

c 2p 5p 20p £1 10p 50p

4 Work out the least number of coins you could use to pay for an item costing...

a 25p ⬜   **c** 67p ⬜   **e** 50p ⬜   **g** 43p ⬜   **i** 45p ⬜

b 14p ⬜   **d** 94p ⬜   **f** 99p ⬜   **h** 37p ⬜   **j** 91p ⬜

27

Money Problems

1 — Add each set of coins and subtract the total from £1.

a
5p, 20p, 5p, 2p, 20p

Total

Change from £1

c
1p, 20p, 2p, 2p, 10p, 50p

Total

Change from £1

b
20p, 10p, 1p, 2p, 5p

Total

Change from £1

d
2p, 2p, 20p, 5p, 20p, 2p, 2p

Total

Change from £1

2 — How many pence is...

a £1.25 × 2? _____

c £0.67 + £1.31? _____

b £2.25 ÷ 3? _____

3 — Cross out the calculations that are incorrect.

a 29p + 58p = 87p   **c** 27p + 39p = 56p   **e** 99p ÷ 3 = 22p

b 64p – 27p = 27p   **d** 49p – 22p = 27p   **f** 40p × 5 = £2.00

4 — Work out the answers to these problems.

a ¼ of Bill's money is 18p. Find ¾ of his money. _____

b What is the cost of five raffle tickets priced at 55p each? _____

Measuring Problems

Measure each line and write your answer in centimetres.

a ——— [ ]   d ————————— [ ]

b ——————— [ ]   e ———— [ ]

c ————————— [ ]

2 **How many centimetres in these metre lengths?**

a 5m [ ]   c 6m [ ]   e 10m [ ]   g $4\frac{1}{2}$m [ ]

b $3\frac{1}{2}$m [ ]   d $9\frac{1}{2}$m [ ]   f 8m [ ]   h $8\frac{3}{4}$m [ ]

3 **Solve these problems.**

a The length of a footpath is 3km. How many metres is that? [ ]

b One side of a square measures 16cm.
What is the sum of the other 3 sides? [ ]

c Susan has a pace of 50cm. How many paces measure 3m 50cm? [ ]

4 **Put these lengths in order starting with the longest.**

10mm   110cm   101cm   110km   101m   10m   1 mile

[   ]

29

Measuring Problems

1 How many grams in the following kilogram amounts?

a 3kg [ ]   c 9kg [ ]   e 8kg [ ]

b 7kg [ ]   d 5kg [ ]   f 10kg [ ]

2 Name the objects listed in the box in order of mass, starting with the heaviest.

1 [ ]   4 [ ]   bookcase   pencil

2 [ ]   5 [ ]   motorcycle   chair

3 [ ]   6 [ ]   minibus   scissors

3 Find the total mass in kg of the animals listed in each question.

A — 14½ kg   B — 3½ kg   C — 16½ kg   D — 6½ kg

a A and C [ ]   c C and D [ ]   e A and B [ ]

b D and B [ ]   d B and C [ ]   f D and A [ ]

4 Change these amounts into kilograms and grams.

a 4556g [ ]   c 5229g [ ]   e 3741g [ ]

b 8873g [ ]   d 6401g [ ]   f 2030g [ ]

Measuring Problems

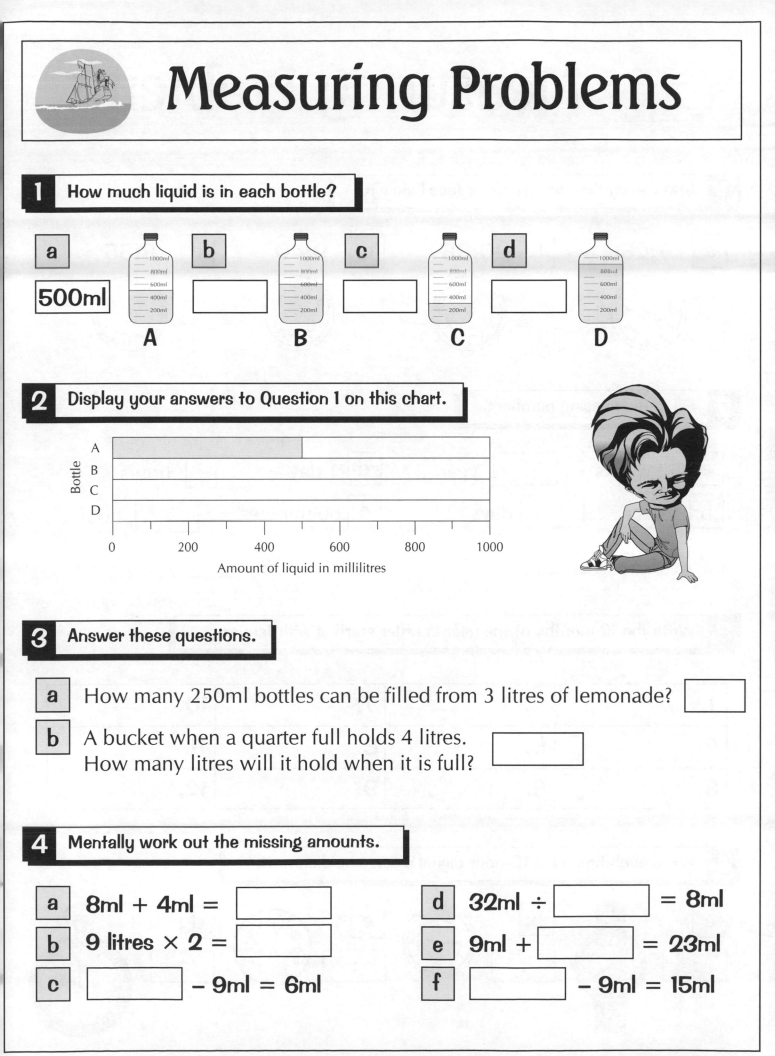

1 How much liquid is in each bottle?

a 500ml **A**

b [ ] **B**

c [ ] **C**

d [ ] **D**

2 Display your answers to Question 1 on this chart.

Bottle: A B C D

0   200   400   600   800   1000

Amount of liquid in millilitres

3 Answer these questions.

a How many 250ml bottles can be filled from 3 litres of lemonade? [ ]

b A bucket when a quarter full holds 4 litres.
How many litres will it hold when it is full? [ ]

4 Mentally work out the missing amounts.

a 8ml + 4ml = [ ]

b 9 litres × 2 = [ ]

c [ ] – 9ml = 6ml

d 32ml ÷ [ ] = 8ml

e 9ml + [ ] = 23ml

f [ ] – 9ml = 15ml

31

Measuring Problems

1 Show each time on the clock face below it.

a 7:25

b 10:05

c 9:40

d 3:55

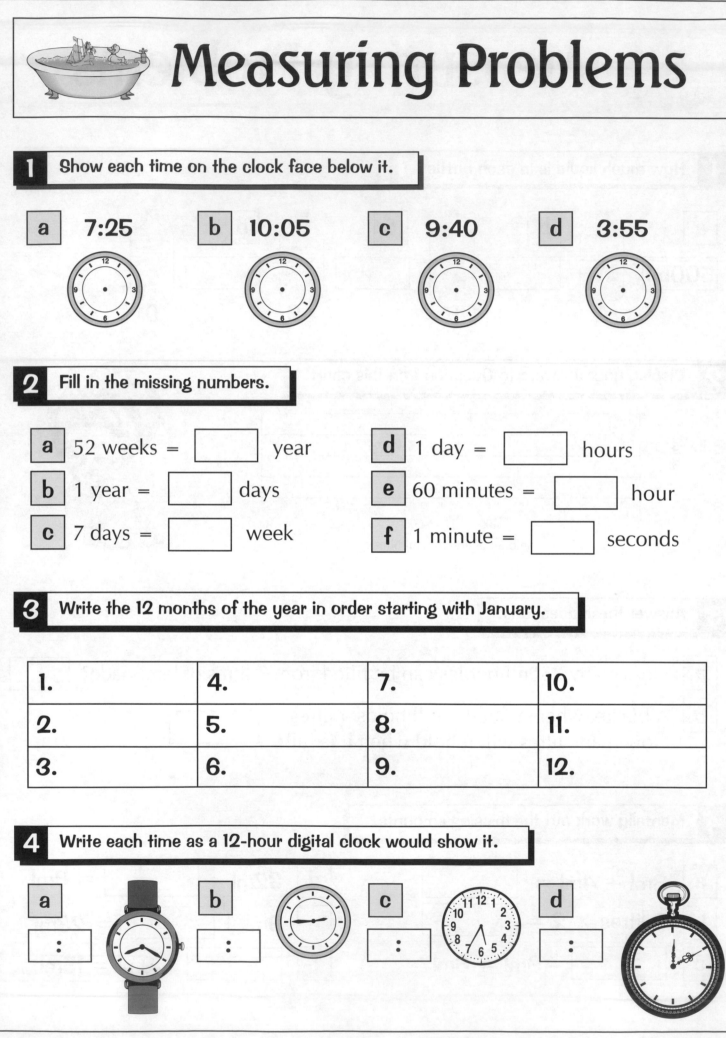

2 Fill in the missing numbers.

a 52 weeks = ☐ year

b 1 year = ☐ days

c 7 days = ☐ week

d 1 day = ☐ hours

e 60 minutes = ☐ hour

f 1 minute = ☐ seconds

3 Write the 12 months of the year in order starting with January.

1.	4.	7.	10.
2.	5.	8.	11.
3.	6.	9.	12.

4 Write each time as a 12-hour digital clock would show it.

a ☐ : ☐

b ☐ : ☐

c ☐ : ☐

d ☐ : ☐

Handling Data

1 The tally marks show the different kinds of pets kept by a group of children. Total each set of marks.

fish | Total [ ]   cat | Total [ ]   dog | Total [ ]   hamster | Total [ ]

||||| | ||||| |||| ||||| ||||| || |||

2 Complete the frequency table using the information given in Question 1.

pet	tally	frequency
fish		
		12
hamster		

3 Name the 2 pairs of animals that each make up half of the total number of pets.

[ ] [ ]   [ ] [ ]

4 Use the information in Question 1 and the frequency table in Question 2 when answering these questions.

a Which pet was 4 times as popular as the hamster? [ ]

b Which pet was the least popular? [ ]

c Which pet was twice as popular as the fish? [ ]

d Which pet was three times as popular as the hamster? [ ]

33

Handling Data

1 The graph shows how Henry spent his pocket money. Look at it and then answer the questions.

a Which item cost twice as much as the eraser?

b Which item cost 15p more than the pencil?

c How much more did the ruler cost than the eraser?

d How much less than the pen was the pencil?

e How much did Henry spend altogether?

Give your answer using the £ sign.

35p					
30p					
25p					
20p					
15p	Pencil	Eraser	Ruler	Notepad	Pen
10p					

Cost of item

Name of item

2 Answer the questions about the month of May.

a How many days are there in May?

b On what day is the 18th of May?

c Give the dates of all the Fridays shown on the calendar page.

d On what day of the week is the 1st of June going to be?

e On what day of the week was the 30th of April?

		May			
Mon		6	13	20	27
Tue		7	14	21	28
Wed	1	8	15	22	29
Thur	2	9	16	23	30
Fri	3	10	17	24	31
Sat	4	11	18	25	
Sun	5	12	19	26	

Handling Data

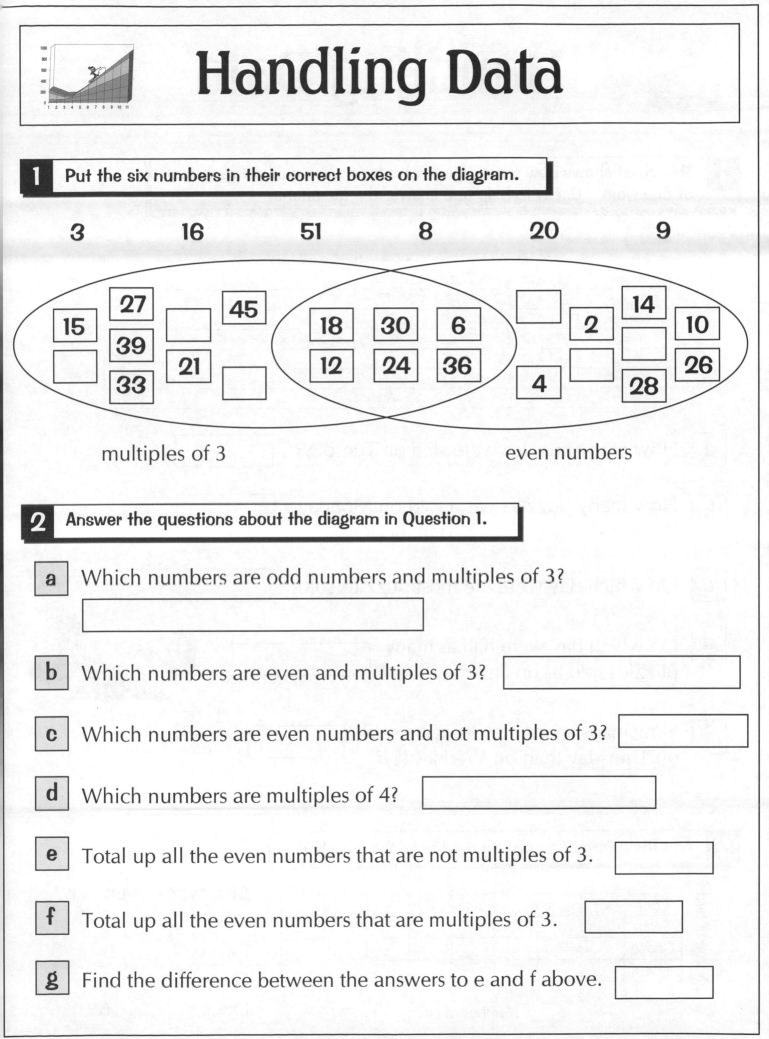

1 | Put the six numbers in their correct boxes on the diagram.

3   16   51   8   20   9

multiples of 3   even numbers

2 | Answer the questions about the diagram in Question 1.

a Which numbers are odd numbers and multiples of 3?

b Which numbers are even and multiples of 3?

c Which numbers are even numbers and not multiples of 3?

d Which numbers are multiples of 4?

e Total up all the even numbers that are not multiples of 3.

f Total up all the even numbers that are multiples of 3.

g Find the difference between the answers to e and f above.

Handling Data

1 This chart shows how many jigsaw puzzles a shop sold on each day of one week. Use it to help you answer the questions.

Key: 🧩 = 2 puzzles

	Number of jigsaw puzzles sold
Monday	🧩 🧩 🧩 🧩 🧩 🧩
Tuesday	🧩 🧩 🧩 🧩 🧩 🧩 🧩 🧩 🧩
Wednesday	🧩 🧩 🧩 🧩
Thursday	🧩 🧩 🧩 🧩 🧩 🧩 🧩 🧩 🧩 🧩 🧩 🧩 🧩
Friday	🧩 🧩 🧩 🧩 🧩
Saturday	🧩 🧩 🧩 🧩 🧩 🧩 🧩 🧩 🧩 🧩 🧩 🧩 🧩 🧩 🧩 🧩
Sunday	🧩 🧩 🧩 🧩 🧩 🧩 🧩 🧩

a How many puzzles were sold on Tuesday?

b How many puzzles were sold on Monday, Wednesday and Friday combined?

c On which day were the most puzzles sold?

d On which day were half as many puzzles sold as on Saturday?

e How many more puzzles were sold on Thursday than on Wednesday?

2 Add the information on the right onto the bar chart.

Name of bird

Coot								
Swan								
Goose								
Duck								

0   2   4   6   8   10   12   14   16
Number of birds

Bird type	Number
Coot	11
Swan	8
Goose	5
Duck	16

Shape

1 **Write the name of each shape in the correct column on the chart.**

cube   rectangle

triangle   prism

sphere   octagon

cylinder   cone

square   circle

pyramid   hexagon

2D shape	3D shape

2 **How many sides has a...**

a square? ☐

b octagon? ☐

c pentagon? ☐

d rectangle? ☐

e triangle? ☐

f circle? ☐

3 **Circle the vertices on these shapes.**

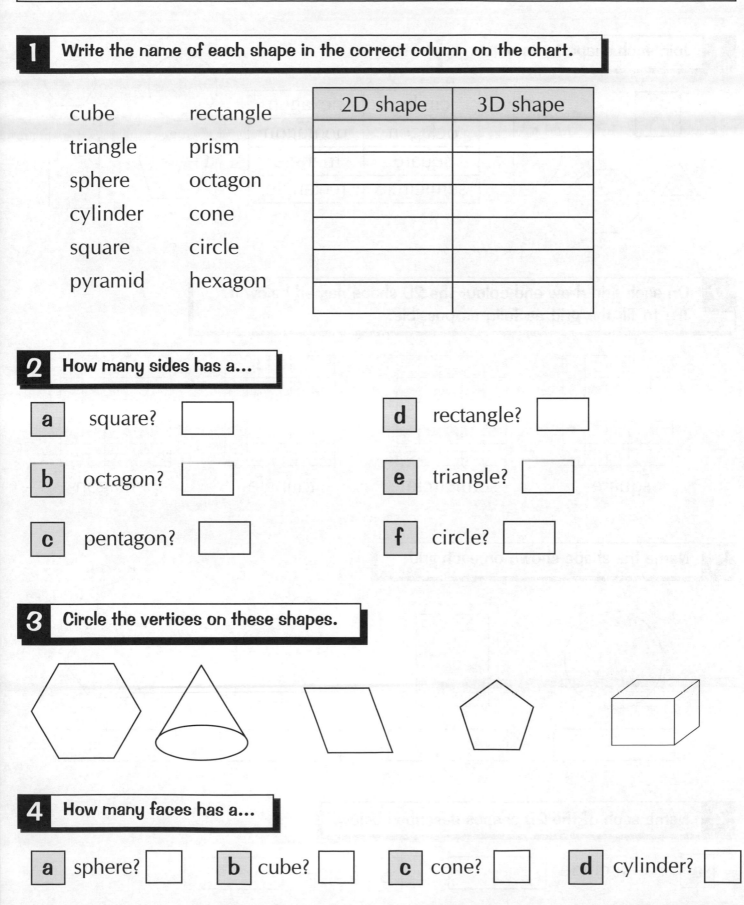

4 **How many faces has a...**

a sphere? ☐   **b** cube? ☐   **c** cone? ☐   **d** cylinder? ☐

Shape

1 Join each shape to its name.

circle	hexagon
octagon	pentagon
square	triangle
semicircle	rectangle

2 On each grid draw and colour the 2D shape named below it. Try to fill the grid as fully as possible.

square   semicircle   triangle   pentagon

3 Name the shape shown on each grid.

4 Name each of the 2D shapes described below.

a half a circle   b 8 sides

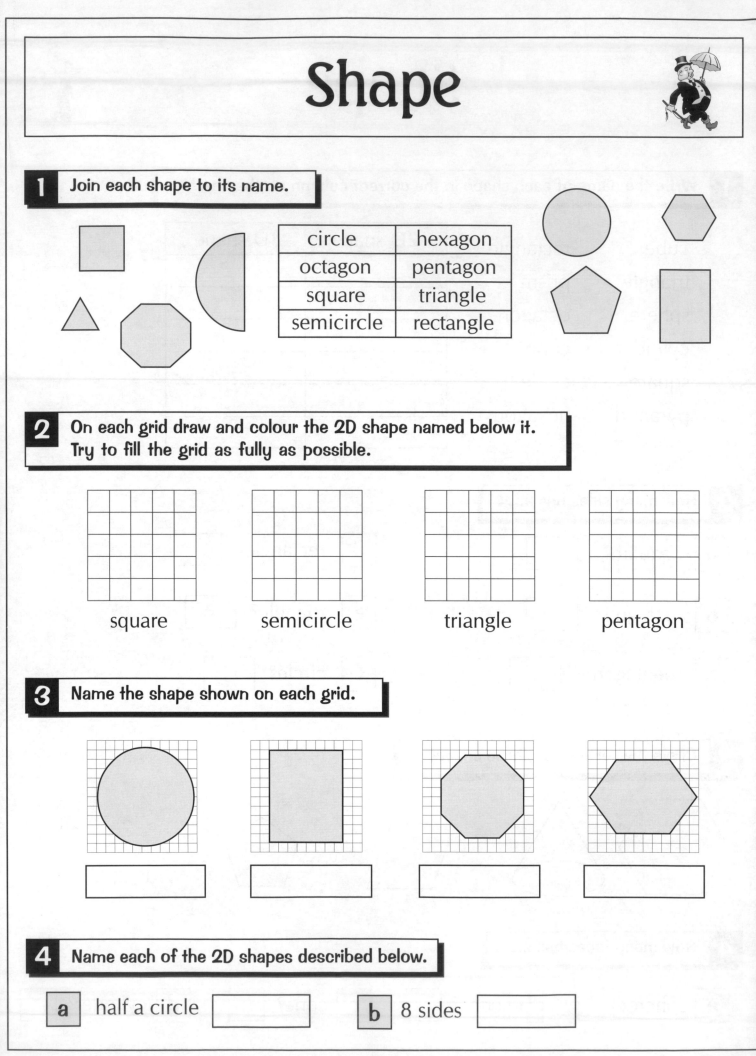

Shape

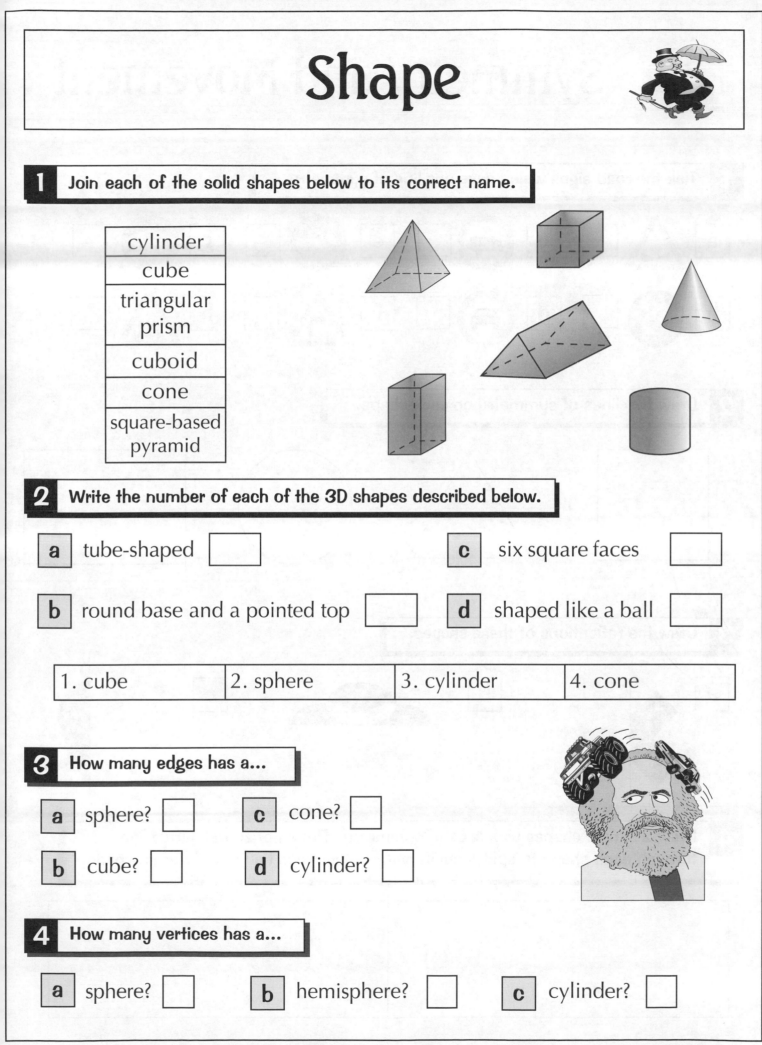

1 Join each of the solid shapes below to its correct name.

cylinder
cube
triangular prism
cuboid
cone
square-based pyramid

2 Write the number of each of the 3D shapes described below.

a tube-shaped ☐   **c** six square faces ☐

b round base and a pointed top ☐   **d** shaped like a ball ☐

1. cube	2. sphere	3. cylinder	4. cone

3 How many edges has a...

a sphere? ☐   **c** cone? ☐

b cube? ☐   **d** cylinder? ☐

4 How many vertices has a...

a sphere? ☐   **b** hemisphere? ☐   **c** cylinder? ☐

39

Symmetry and Movement

1 Tick the road signs which have one line of symmetry.

a   □   c   □   e   □   g   □

b   □   d   □   f   □   h   □

2 Draw two lines of symmetry on each shape.

3 Draw the reflections of these shapes.

a   b   c

4 Draw 2 simple shapes with lines of symmetry. Put a horizontal mirror line through each shape to split them in half. Colour each half in a different shade.

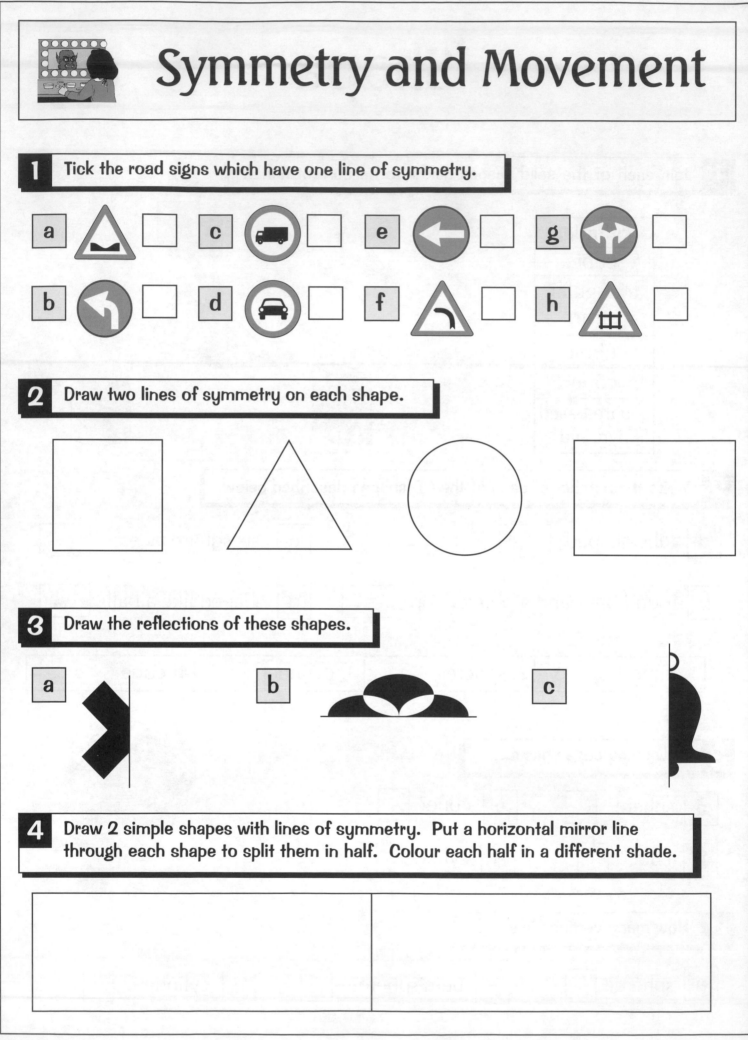

Answers — Pages 1 to 12

PAGE 1

Q1. a) forty-seven b) seventy-three
    c) sixty-nine d) eighty-two
    e) fifty-one f) thirty-four
    g) ninety-five h) twenty-six

Q2. a) 360 b) 502 c) 850 d) 1000

Q3. 498, 499, 500, 501, 502, (503),
    504, 505, 506, 507, 508

Q4. a) 6, 21 b) 55, 70 c) 34, 49
    d) 82, 97 e) 18, 33 f) 97, 112

PAGE 2

Q1. a) (45), 55, 65, 75, 85, 95, 105,
    115, 125, 135, 145
    b) (376), 386, 396, 406, 416,
    426, 436, 446, 456, 466, 476

Q2. 29, 39, 49, 59, 69, 79, 89, 99,
    109, 119, (129)

Q3. - (43), 45, 47, 49, 51, 53
    - (38), 43, 48, 53, 58, 63
    - 42, 45, 48, 51, 54, (57)
    - 75, 79, 83, 87, 91, (95)

Q4. a) 7 b) 6 c) 12

PAGE 3

Q1. Circled - 74, 424, 568, 724, 268,
    144, 32, 96, 392, 882, 88, 806
    Boxed - 39, 253, 61, 141, 97, 45,
    725, 537

Q2. a) 26, 52, (34), 70, 48,
    40, 66, 48, 84, (62)
    b) 40, 28, 64, 52, (66),
    48, (36), 72, 60, 74

Q3. a) odd crossed out.
    b) odd crossed out.

Q4. a) 62 b) 52 c) 88 d) 106 e) 72
    f) 46 g) 94 h) 38

    All the answers are even numbers.

PAGE 4

Q1. a) 625 b) 704 c) 193 d) 580

Q2. a) 400 b) 4 c) 40 d) 4000

Q3.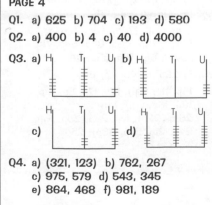

Q4. a) (321, 123) b) 762, 267
    c) 975, 579 d) 543, 345
    e) 864, 468 f) 981, 189

PAGE 5

Q1. a) 462, 482 b) 388, 408
    c) 649, 669 d) 500, 520
    e) 690, 710 f) 793, 813

Q2. a) 971 b) 716

Q3. a) 227 b) 0

Q4. a) 1000, 400
    b) 628, 735
    c) 196, 147

PAGE 6

Q1. 102, 123, 131, 201, 213, 231, 302,
    312, 321

Q2. a) Check that suitable numbers have
    been chosen.
    b) Check that suitable numbers have
    been chosen.

Q3. a) 6 b) 50 c) 104, 106, 108

Q4. 654, 645, 605, 564, 546, 506,
    465, 456, 405

PAGE 7

Q1. a) D b) A

Q2. Any reasonable answer.

Q3. The 16 metre length should be
    ticked.

Q4. 20, 40, 50, 70

PAGE 8

Q1. a) not enough b) too few
    c) approximately

Q2. a) 220 or 221
    b) any number more than 657 but
    less than 701.
    c) any number more than 399 but
    less than 405.
    d) 450
    e) 999
    f) any number more than 609 but
    less than 906.

Q3. a) 1000 b) 150

Q4. Accept answers between the
    following ranges:
    a) 20 to 24 b) 13 to 17
    c) 23 to 27 d) 45 to 50

PAGE 9

Q1. a) 60 b) 60 c) 70 d) 50
    e) 800 f) 300 g) 500 h) 800

Q2. (36 – 9 = 27 — 30)
    19 + 19 = 38 — 40
    48 ÷ 2 = 24 — 20
    60 – 7 = 53 — 50
    2 x 31 = 62 — 60
    50 + 26 = 76 — 80

Q3. a) 40 circled b) 200 circled
    c) 300 circled

Q4. a) 130, 100 b) 110, 100
    c) 180, 200 d) 590, 600

PAGE 10

Q1. $\frac{1}{10}$, $\frac{1}{8}$, $\frac{1}{5}$, $\frac{1}{4}$, $\frac{1}{3}$, $\frac{1}{2}$

Q2. a) 4 boxes shaded
    b) 3 boxes shaded
    c) 2 boxes shaded

Q3. a) 60 b) 4 c) 50

Q4. a) 4 b) 8 c) 6 d) 9 e) 50 f) 70
    g) 20 h) 100

PAGE 11

Q1. a) $\frac{3}{5}$ b) $\frac{9}{10}$ c) $\frac{5}{6}$ d) $\frac{5}{8}$

Q2. a) 4 b) 1 c) 3

Q3. a) $\frac{1}{3}$ (accept $\frac{4}{12}$ or $\frac{2}{6}$)
    b) $\frac{3}{4}$ (accept $\frac{12}{16}$ or $\frac{6}{8}$)

Q4. a) 5 b) 8 c) 3 d) 7 e) 60 f) 90
    g) 40 h) 100

PAGE 12

Q1. Shape C should be circled

Q2. a) 2 b) 4 c) 6 d) 4 e) 3 f) 1

Q3. a) 4 b) 6 c) 5

Q4. a) 3 b) 7 c) 20 d) 60

41

Answers — Pages 13 to 25

PAGE 13

Q1. These pairs of numbers in any order:
10+1, 9+2, 8+3, 7+4, 6+5

Q2. a) 14 b) 18 c) 30 d) 32
e) 36 f) 38 g) 26 h) 24

Q3. a) 10 b) 7 c) 15

Q4. a) 400 b) 700 c) 800 d) 100

PAGE 14

Q1. a) 30 b) 29 c) 26 d) 26 e) 29
f) 31

Q2. Any eight addition sums using all the numbers from the central grid

Q3. a) seventy b) eighty-eight

Q4. a) 20 b) 23 c) 27

PAGE 15

Q1. a) 47 b) 87 c) 72 d) 91 e) 82

Q2. a) (54), 66, 77
60, (72), 83
68, 80, (91)
b) 111, 124, (137)
119, (132), 145
(125), 138, 151

Q3. a) 873 b) 985 c) 693 d) 624

Q4. a) 92 b) 250 c) 92 d) 153

PAGE 16

Q1. a) 8 b) 15 c) 7 d) 5 e) 9
f) 8 g) 9 h) 11

Q2. a) 17 b) 42 c) 45 d) 34 e) 26
f) 23 g) 59 h) 31

Q3. a) 6 b) 7 c) 8

Q4. a) 1000 b) 200

PAGE 17

Q1. a) 5 b) 33 c) 36 d) 9

Q2. Any eight subtraction sums using all the numbers from the central grid

Q3. a) fifty b) sixty-three

Q4. a) 20 b) 33 c) 41

PAGE 18

Q1. a) 34 b) 41 c) 39 d) 27 e) 36

Q2. a) (28), 42, 56
16, (30), 44
3, 17, (31)
b) 26, 46, (66)
38, (58), 78
(64), 84, 104

Q3. a) 445 b) 418 c) 178 d) 86

Q4. a) 72 b) 80 c) 88 d) 98

PAGE 19

Q1. 8, 18, 2, (12), 0, 10, 6, 16, (20), 4, 14
(20), 45, 5, 30, 0, 25, 15, 40, 50, 10, (35)

Q2. 11 — 22, 12 — 24, 13 — 26,
14 — 28, 15 — 30, 16 — 32,
17 — 34, 18 — 36, 19 — 38,
20 — 40

Q3. Shaded - 30, 12, 21, 6, 24, 9, 18, 36, 15

Q4. 8 x 4 = 32

PAGE 20

Q1. a) 96 b) 68 c) 95 d) 39 e) 48
f) 60 g) 70 h) 84

Q2. a) 76 b) 90 c) 90 d) 84 e) 65
f) 72

Q3. 28 — 280, 37 — 370, 46 — 460,
54 — 540, 55 — 550, 63 — 630,
72 — 720, 81 — 810, 90 — 900

Q4. a) 600 b) 850 c) 650 d) 950
e) 750 f) 900

PAGE 21

Q1. a) 21 b) 16 c) 15 d) 35 e) 32
f) 45

Q2. 9, 30, (18), 3, 15, 6, 27, 21, 0,
(12), 24
12, (40), 24, 4, 20, 8, 36, (28), 0
16, 32

Q3. a) twenty-seven
b) one hundred and sixty
c) twelve

Q4. Shaded - 25, 30, 45, 15, 40, 60
90, 35, 75

PAGE 22

Q1. 3, 6, 0, (1), 8, 10, 4, 2, (7), 9, 5

Q2. 2 — 1, 4 — 2, 6 — 3, 8 — 4,
10 — 5, 12 — 6, 14 — 7, 16 — 8,
18 — 9, 20 — 10

Q3. Shaded - 40, 16, 8, 36, 24, 28,
12, 32, 20

Q4. Circled - 12 ÷ 2, 24 ÷ 4, 30 ÷ 5,
60 ÷ 10

PAGE 23

Q1. a) 16 b) 40 c) 3 d) 2 e) 7 f) 9

Q2. a) 9 b) 7 c) 6 d) 6 e) 8 f) 5

Q3. 100 — 10, 200 — 20, 300 — 30,
400 — 40, 500 — 50, 600 — 60,
700 — 70, 800 — 80, 900 — 90

Q4. 8, 3, 10, (1), 6, 4, 0, (9), 2, 7, 5

PAGE 24

Q1. a) 13 b) 27 c) 13 d) 14 e) 15
f) 18 g) 25 h) 17 i) 30 j) 22
k) 40 l) 18

Q2. 5, 0, (9), 2, 6, 4, 1, 10, 8, 3, (7)
10, 0, (18), 4, 12, 8, 2, 20, 16, 6,
(14)

Q3. a) 3 r 1 b) 8 r 1 c) 4 r 1
d) 7 r 1 e) 10 r 2 f) 5 r 2

Q4. a) Circled - 60 ÷ 2
b) Circled - 100 ÷ 2
c) Circled - 140 ÷ 2

PAGE 25

Q1. a) 31p b) 17p c) 23p d) 8p
e) 5p f) 22p g) 16p h) 34p

Q2. 47p, (58p), 78p, 49p, 38p, 56p,
69p, 36p, (76p), 67p, 79p
(62p), 73p, 93p, 64p, 53p, 71p,
(84p), 51p, 91p, 82p, 94p

Q3. a) 26p b) 45p c) 110p

Q4. 15p, 11p, (6p), 12p, 17p, 5p, 13p,
10p, 16p, (7p), 14p
26p, (22p), 17p, 23p, 28p, 16p,
24p, 21p, 27p, (18p), 25p

PAGE 26

Q1. a) 20 b) 96p c) 40p

Q2. a) 21p b) 5 c) 84p d) 16p
    e) 5 f) 42p

Q3. a) 18p, 27p, (21p), 24p
       24p, (00p), 20p, 32p
       (30p), 15p, 35p, 40p
    b) 20p, (40p), 30p, 50p
       8p, 16p, (12p), 20p
       4p, 8p, 6p, (10p)

Q4. a) (6p, 3p) b) 30p, 15p
    c) 60p, 30p d) 150p (£1.50), 75p
    e) £3, £1.50 f) £6, £3

PAGE 27

Q1. a) 40 b) 25 c) 16
    d) 20 e) 25 f) 20

Q2. a) fifteen pence b) nineteen pounds

Q3. a) 58p b) £2.97 c) £1.87

Q4. a) 2 b) 3 c) 4 d) 5 e) 1
    f) 6 g) 4 h) 4 i) 3 j) 4

PAGE 28

Q1. a) 52p, 48p b) 38p, 62p
    c) 85p, 15p d) 53p, 47p

Q2. a) 250p b) 75p c) 198p

Q3. The following number statements
    should be crossed out: b), c) and e)

Q4. a) 54p b) £2.75

PAGE 29

Q1. a) 2cm b) 4cm c) 12cm d) 5cm
    e) 3cm

Q2. a) 500 b) 350 c) 600 d) 950
    e) 1000 f) 800 g) 450 h) 875

Q3. a) 3000m b) 48cm c) 7

Q4. 110km, 1 mile, 101m, 10m, 110cm,
    101cm, 10mm

PAGE 30

Q1. a) 3000g b) 7000g c) 9000g
    d) 5000g e) 8000g f) 10000g

Q2. 1. minibus 2. motorcycle
    3. bookcase 4. chair 5. scissors
    6. pencil

Q3. a) 01kg b) 10kg c) 23kg d) 20kg
    e) 18kg f) 21kg

Q4. a) 4kg 556g b) 8kg 873g
    c) 5kg 229g d) 6kg 401g
    e) 3kg 741g f) 2kg 30g

PAGE 31

Q1. a) (500ml) b) 600ml c) 300ml
    d) 900ml

Q2.

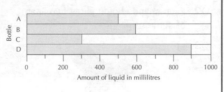

Amount of liquid in millilitres

Q3. a) 12 b) 16 litres

Q4. a) 12ml b) 18 litres c) 15ml d) 4
    e) 14ml f) 24ml

PAGE 32

Q1. a)   b)   c)   d)

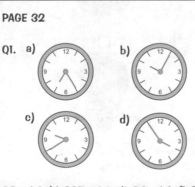

Q2. a) 1 b) 365 c) 1 d) 24 e) 1 f) 60

Q3. 1. January 2. February 3. March
    4. April 5. May 6. June 7. July
    8. August 9. September
    10. October 11. November
    12. December

Q4. a) 8:20 b) 2:45 c) 5:35 d) 12:10

PAGE 33

cat	(丗 IIII)	9
dog	丗 丗 II	(12)
(hamster)	III	3

Q3. fish/cat, dog/hamster

Q4. a) dog b) hamster c) dog d) cat

PAGE 34

Q1. a) pen b) notepad c) 10p d) 10p
    e) £1.25

Q2. a) 31 b) Saturday
    c) 3, 10, 17, 24, 31 d) Saturday
    e) Tuesday

PAGE 35

Q1. 3, 51 and 9 should be in the
    'multiples of 3' section
    16, 8 and 20 should be in the
    'even numbers' section

Q2. a) 3, 9, 15, 21, 27, 33, 39, 45, 51
    b) 6, 12, 18, 24, 30, 36
    c) 2, 4, 8, 10, 14, 16, 20, 26, 28
    d) 4, 8, 16, 20, 24, 28, 36
    e) 128 f) 126 g) 2

PAGE 36

Q1. a) 20 b) 30 c) Saturday
    d) Sunday e) 18

Q2.

Name of bird								
Coot								
Swan								
Goose								
Duck								

Number of birds

2D shape - triangle, square, rectangle, octagon, circle, hexagon
3D shape - cube, sphere, cylinder, pyramid, prism, cone

Q2. a) 4 b) 8 c) 5 d) 4 e) 3 f) 1

Q3.

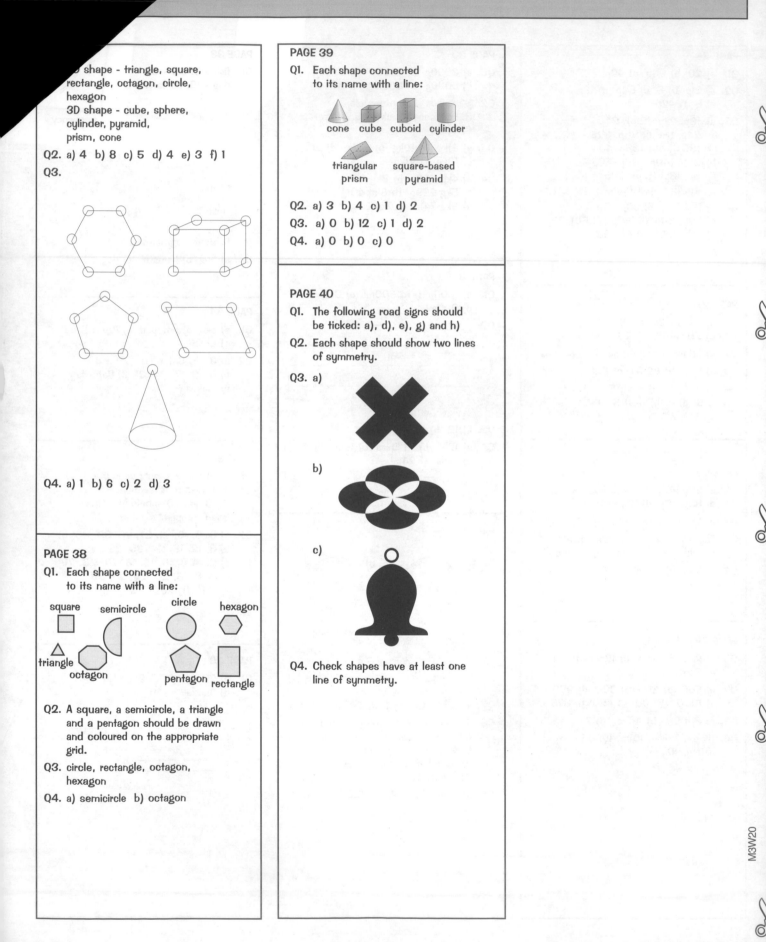

Q4. a) 1 b) 6 c) 2 d) 3

PAGE 38

Q1. Each shape connected to its name with a line:

square   semicircle   circle   hexagon

triangle   octagon   pentagon   rectangle

Q2. A square, a semicircle, a triangle and a pentagon should be drawn and coloured on the appropriate grid.

Q3. circle, rectangle, octagon, hexagon

Q4. a) semicircle b) octagon

PAGE 39

Q1. Each shape connected to its name with a line:

cone   cube   cuboid   cylinder

triangular prism   square-based pyramid

Q2. a) 3 b) 4 c) 1 d) 2

Q3. a) 0 b) 12 c) 1 d) 2

Q4. a) 0 b) 0 c) 0

PAGE 40

Q1. The following road signs should be ticked: a), d), e), g) and h)

Q2. Each shape should show two lines of symmetry.

Q3. a)

b)

c)

Q4. Check shapes have at least one line of symmetry.

M3W20

Let's face it, you want <u>CGP</u> Revision Books — not other people's dreary stuff.

Everyone else just gives you dreary revision books with only the boring stuff in and no entertainment. Boo. Hiss. We're different — we always try and make sure you're gonna enjoy using our books.

What you *really* need is a ***Free Catalogue*** showing the full range of CGP Revision Books. That way you can be sure you're not missing out on a brilliant book that ***might just save your life***.

At CGP we ***work our socks off*** to despatch your stuff really quickly.
If you get your order to us before 5.00pm (Mon-Fri) you should get it next day — most of the time, anyway.

(Obviously, if you order on Saturday night on a bank holiday weekend then you won't get it 'til Wednesday morning at the very earliest — no matter how hard we try!)

FIVE ways to get your Free Catalogue really quickly

- Phone: 0870 750 1252   (Mon-Fri, 8.30am to 5.30pm)
- Fax: 0870 750 1292
- E-mail: orders@cgpbooks.co.uk
- Post: CGP, Kirkby-in-Furness, Cumbria, LA17 7WZ
- Website: www.cgpbooks.co.uk

CGP books — available in all the best bookshops

CGP

Key Stage 2

Maths — Year Three

Workout

Everything in moderation (except chips)

ISBN 978 1 84146 069 7

9 781841 460697

M3W20

CGP

CGP
— books
like no others!

www.cgpbooks.co.uk

Setting up the programme

The programme is the list of what is happening at the event and the order in which it is happening. It guides the organisation of the event and will be used by **attendees**. The programme's quality and content will help to guide people's interest as well as give them an outline of what is going to happen during the day. The programme will also give details of any special guests, speeches, entertainment, prize-giving or free gifts that might be part of the event. Sometimes a guest speaker may encourage more people to attend and this will need to be highlighted in the programme.

There are a variety of different types of programme that may be used for an event. These may include programmes that have various activities that attendees can select from or programmes where everyone is following the same structure for the event.

The length of time for the event will also influence the programme. All-day events need more time for people to travel to the event and for coffee and lunch breaks. Events that take place over a few days may require arrangements for accommodation including breakfast.

Activity: Taylor Made Computer Solutions

Taylor Made Computer Solutions holds free events to help local businesses understand different aspects of information technology at work. Go to their website (www.tmcs.co.uk) and find out more about them. Then answer the questions below.

1. Why do you think Taylor Made Computer Solutions holds free events for local businesses?

2. What are the advantages of holding free events? Are there any potential disadvantages?

3. Carry out research on the Internet to find free events that are happening in your area. In small groups, consider why these organisations are holding these events.

Functional skills

Researching the role of an event organiser as part of this activity will help you to develop your **ICT** skills.

Preparing and distributing supporting documents

Most events require some form of hard copy or **soft copy** that can be distributed. For environmental and cost reasons, soft copies are often preferred. Sometimes documents may be supplied on a USB stick or in a free wallet or bag that is given out by the event organiser. Often promotional items include advertising material for the organiser to give them maximum publicity and raise awareness of the organisation.

The main documents that might be needed for an event are listed in Table 18.2 (see page 48). A number of different documents may be needed to support an event. These may be more traditional paper documents or other methods that organisations are increasingly using such as websites with a secure username and password, email or social networking websites to distribute information about events.

Key terms

Attendee – a person who is going to attend an event.

Soft copy – a version of a document, such as a pdf, that can be emailed or uploaded to a website.

There are also a number of other documents that may be produced that are not given out to attendees. These are used by the organisation to monitor and track the progress of the event, for example, a risk assessment or a budget plan. These are discussed in more detail on pages 67 and 56.

Organisational procedures

Organisations will usually have a set of procedures that they follow for events, and these procedures will change depending on the size of the organisation, the type of event that is taking place and who is involved.

Did you know?

To request a member of the Royal Family to attend an event, you need to invite them about a year in advance so that security arrangements can be made.

Table 18.2: Main documents needed for an event

Document	What is included
Background to the event	The event's purpose The target audience The cost of attending the event and any discounts that might be available Details of how much and where tickets can be purchased if required Who to contact for further information
The agenda or schedule	Information about what is happening and the times involved May also include the deadline for submitting any papers or items that people want to put forward for discussion at the event
Event papers	Minutes of previous meetings Biographies of previous speakers Information about organisations involved with the event
Information about travel arrangements	How to get to the event by train, car or even by plane
Information about accommodation	Arrangements for hotels that are close to where the event is being held
Information about additional arrangements required	Highlight particular adjustments that attendees may request Arrangements for people with disabilities or those who have special dietary needs

A business meeting may only require an employee to let their line manager know that it is taking place as part of the organisation's procedures. A business conference may need to be agreed by the chief executive or managing director. Procedures for signing off events will depend on the purpose of the event and the potential effect of the event on the organisation's reputation. If there are a number of expenses involved, the finance manager or director may need to authorise the event and confirm that there is money available for this purpose.

As the organiser of the event, you will need to know who must give authority for any event and the forms that need to be completed. You should follow the procedures for the organisation or you may get into serious trouble, especially if something goes wrong.

Current legal requirements

There are a number of important legal requirements that need to be considered when organising an event. These include contractual, health and safety and age requirements.

Most legal requirements are covered by a contractual agreement that will be agreed either verbally or in writing. The contract sets out the offer and prices for the individual elements of the event including:

- venue
- catering
- insurance
- advertising/promotion.

Separate agreements can be made with outside suppliers and may include those used for booking a hotel venue or hiring equipment.

The Supply of Goods and Services Act 1982 ensures that the event organiser is supplied with goods and services as part of a contract; it also protects suppliers and customers. The Act sets out requirements for ticketing that protect both the event organiser and attendees, and also protects consumers from faulty equipment. There is more information about contracts, agreements and consumer protection in Unit 21 on pages 93–105.

There are stringent health and safety requirements for events. Risk assessments will highlight any issues found whilst organising an event and help the organiser take steps to reduce the likelihood of anything untoward happening. More specific requirements for health and safety can be found on page 66 of this unit.

Finally, any event that is organised needs to meet age requirements. For example, at a music event or festival, it must be ensured that young people are aged 18 or over if they are going to buy any alcohol or tobacco products that are on sale. Remember that any event must take place within the law and steps must be taken to avoid any problems.

Limits of the role

An event organiser must consider the levels of **authority** that come with the role. Knowing what you can and cannot do is very important. For example, at some events the event organiser may not have the authority to sign a contract for services or they may not have the authority to make the final decision as these decisions may ultimately be the duty of their line manager. An event organiser may also work with other individuals or groups who need to make decisions about the event, which means that any decisions have to be shared by the group rather than be taken by a single person.

1.2 Skills

To understand the role of the event organiser you must be aware of the skills that are required to perform the role effectively. These are shown in Figure 18.2.

Figure 18.2: Skills needed for the role of event organiser

Communication and interpersonal skills

Communication skills are extremely important for an event organiser if an event is going to succeed, whether this communication is about the size of a venue, queries from potential attendees or how many to cater for. Organising a large event can be challenging and **interpersonal skills** can have a huge influence on how successful an event will be.

Some of the key ways that communication can support or damage an event are shown in Table 18.3.

Table 18.3: Interpersonal skills

Communication style	The benefit or damage to event planning
Making assumptions about what is happening	This may lead to mistakes – it is important as an event planner to check and then double-check arrangements so you are in control rather than out of control.
Communicating positively	People are more likely to want to work with you if you are positive, and this should lead to your event being successful.
Communicating regularly and often	If people know what is happening they are less likely to be anxious and will put all of their energy into the event.
Listening to what others are telling you	If someone more experienced is able to give good advice or recommendations, make sure you give it serious consideration. They may be able to help you think of something that you may not have thought of yourself.
Asking others for help when you need it	Communicating that you need some help means you are more likely to be successful than if you try to do everything on your own.

Key terms

Authority – the power a person has in their role.

Interpersonal skills – skills that are used to deal with other people, such as dealing with their feelings through body language or tone of voice.

Time management

The role of an event organiser involves **multi-tasking** which means that good time management is an important quality for the job. Good time management means that you focus on what is important and keep everything on track. The most common time management mistakes made are:

- wasting time doing activities that are not relevant to the event, such as checking personal emails
- waiting for someone else to do something before being able to progress on another aspect of the event
- not being organised, e.g. spending time looking for paperwork or going over tasks that you have done before.

Activity: Time management

In small groups, think of all the different activities you do to avoid doing something. Then do the following.

1. Produce a three-table column. In the first column, list the different activities you came up with.
2. In the second column, write the consequences of wasting time on these activities.
3. In the third column, write suggestions on how to avoid wasting time for each activity.

PLTS

Collaborating with others to produce this table will help you to develop your skills as a **team worker**.

Problem solving

There are few events that do not have any problems at all. To help the event run smoothly the organiser will need to have already thought about what possible problems might occur and have made **contingency plans**. For example, if the event is to include computer presentations or DVDs the organiser may want to check the services provided at the venue and also take along their own lap top and projector as a back-up. Some problems cannot be anticipated; therefore quick

Key terms

Multi-tasking – carry out a number of different tasks at the same time.

Contingency plan – a back-up plan in case the original plan goes wrong.

thinking is necessary and good event organisers have this quality and are able to sort out solutions.

Negotiating

Negotiating skills are essential for any event organiser. Negotiating, unlike other types of communication, is not about making demands or threatening people, it is about trying to get to what is known as a 'win win' situation where both parties are happy with the outcome. It may be necessary to negotiate prices on contracts to try to get the best possible deal, which is particularly important if the event is being done on a budget. Negotiating may also be used to ask for something that is not usually possible, for example, a particular type of catering or entertainment that may be more difficult to provide than usual.

Planning

The main role of an event organiser is to ensure that everything goes to plan so that the event is a success. Planning does not just include the event itself, it also needs to take into account other events that are happening around the same time. Too many similar events happening in the same week may result in poor attendance at your event.

The time of year will also influence the planning of an event. When planning an event, the organiser needs to think about the following.

- Whether the event needs to be inside or outside. It is usually more appropriate to run outside events in the summer.
- Whether the event is linked to a particular festival or tradition. If so, it will need to happen at the same time.
- Whether the event depends on other factors such as supplies that are only available at certain times of year or are cheaper in a particular month to save costs.

Resource management

Resources include any physical items, expenses or other costs needed to run an event. This may include

Activity: Ice Creations

Ice Creations produces ice sculptures that can be used at corporate events to enhance the look of the event.

In pairs, go to the Ice Creations website (www.icecreations.co.uk). Choose one of the events they provide ice sculptures for and then discuss the following.

1. What type of planning would be required to have an ice sculpture at this event?

2. What would some of the problems be in having an ice sculpture at an event?

3. Now think of any other unusual resources that could be used at your event. Do some research on the Internet and find out how much such items would cost.

PLTS

Generating ideas for different resources at an event will help you to develop your skills as a **creative thinker**.

the buildings, ICT equipment, the catering team or even a special feature of entertainment or display that is brought in for the event.

Resources are normally finite and some can be expensive, so a good event organiser will make the most of their resources. It is possible to measure how effectively resources have been used – this is known as resource utilisation.

Monitoring

An event organiser needs to continually keep track of how the event is progressing. They need to ensure that everything is checked and double-checked. Monitoring takes many different forms and involves checking many things such as:

- bookings
- deliveries
- advertising and publicity
- staffing
- security.

Monitoring may also involve taking into account aspects of the event outside of the organiser's control. This may be done on a daily, monthly or annual basis depending on the type of event. Some monitoring takes place during the planning stage of the event, whilst further monitoring will take place during the event to ensure that everything runs smoothly. A good event organiser will need to be able to monitor many different things at the same time to ensure that all the parts come together to make a successful business event.

Evaluating

Any organiser will become very involved in a business event but the true skill of an organiser is to recognise not only what they have done well but also when they have not done as well or could have done better. Being able to evaluate events is an important skill. An event organiser should be able to make judgements about the event in order to make improvements for the next time. When evaluating the event, the organiser needs to be as **objective** as possible.

Key term

Objective – making a judgement without having feelings attached to it.

Assessment activity 18.1

P1 P2 M1 M2 BTEC

1. Think back to a business event that you have attended or one that you have learnt about in this chapter. Put together a short presentation which:
   - describes the skills required of an event organiser **P1**
   - explains the role of the event organiser. **P2**
2. Using the event chosen for P1 and P2, assess the importance of meeting organisational and legal requirements when planning this event. **M1**
3. Analyse the arrangements made by the event organiser to plan the business event. **M2**

Grading tips

1. You must demonstrate that you have gained understanding of the role of a business event organiser. Remember to include all the different skills that are needed for event organisation, including time management, problem solving and evaluating. When you explain the role of the event organiser you need to include as many different examples as possible drawn from a specific event or bring in other examples of events that you have been to yourself. **P1 P2**

2. You will need to show you understand the organisational and legal procedures for planning the event, including procedures for organising supplies and the importance of supplier contracts and agreements. **M1**

3. You should build on your answer to P2 and explain the key planning activities needed to be done for the event. **M2**

PLTS

Exploring the role of the event organiser will help you to develop your skills as an **independent enquirer**.

2   Be able to plan a business event

As an event organiser, you need to be able to organise an event, run the event and then make judgements and recommendations for improvement. It is very important that you choose the right event in the first place and do the planning stages effectively so that you can run the best event possible.

2.1 Types of event

There are many different types of event that can be called a business event. These fall into different categories and are described below.

Routine and non-routine

A routine event happens at a given time every year. It may be annual event such as a spring fair or January sale. If an event is a routine one, the organiser will need to consider its impact on the business. For example, if it is known that every year a company will have big reductions on products or services in January, customers may decide to wait until that time to purchase from the business. Some routine events, such as an annual ball, may also be linked to charitable causes.

Did you know?

In July 2009, Carnival UK, the UK's biggest cruise ship operator, opened its new headquarters Carnival House in Southampton. The event that celebrated the opening raised £5,000 for Naomi House, a local charity.

Non-routine events are those that do not happen regularly; they may happen once for a particular reason or an event. Such events include the opening of a building, the launch of a new product or a new service. Sometimes the event may also be part of a campaign to ask for permission to do something such as an event to discuss a planning application in a residential area or a public consultation on something that is happening in the local area.

Activity: Arsenal Football Club annual charity ball

Every year Arsenal Football Club hosts a charity ball that raises a significant amount for charity. Each year the charity changes – in 2009 the ball, which was hosted by Matt Lucas, raised around £200,000 for the Teenage Cancer Trust.

1. In small groups go to the Arsenal FC website (www.arsenal.com). Use their search engine and find out more about the charity ball.

   - What time of the year does it happen?
   - What is the significance of this time of year?

2. Search the Internet and find out about annual charitable events that are organised by businesses and organisations in your area.

   - Produce a table showing how much money they have raised and for which charities.
   - Discuss which ideas seem to generate the most money for charities and which generate the most publicity for the businesses or organisations themselves.

Formal or informal

Business events are divided into **formal** or **informal** occasions. Both types of events are similar in that speakers may need to be booked and facilities need to be made available.

A formal business event could involve a meeting where information can be shared with other interested groups known as stakeholders. Formal meetings will normally be minuted and be led by a chairperson. Another type of formal event is a black-tie ball. In either case, formal events have certain rules and etiquette that need to be followed.

Informal business events are much more relaxed than formal ones. There are many different types of informal events including the following.

- Speed networking – business people get together to share business tips and find ways to work together.
- Business breakfasts, lunches or dinners – business people get together to meet and talk informally about their businesses.
- Business clubs – business people get together with a special focus such as groups of women, older business people or business people who are from individual ethnic minority groups.

Did you know?

The Women's Business Club (www.thewomensbusinessclubs.com) organises events all over the country aimed specifically at helping women in business.

Activity: Associated British Ports

Since 2004, Associated British Ports (ABP) has been in consultation with the local public and other stakeholders, including shipping companies and the government, about plans for the development of the Port of Southampton.

1. Using the ABP website (www.abports.co.uk) and other sources from the Internet, find out how many business events have been held by ABP in order to work with stakeholders on the development of the Port of Southampton.

2. How many of these events have been formal? How many have been informal?

Key terms

Formal – an event that is carried out in a more serious and structured way.

Informal – an event where speech and dress are much more relaxed and the rules or procedures are not as strict.

Another type of informal business event is a staff training session. Some businesses will have regular weekly training events; others will have days each year when the whole staff receive training. Staff training sessions are especially common in schools and colleges.

Activity: Team building event

Some organisations use staff training sessions as team building events. They can take a variety of different forms, for example, activities such as a day of chocolate making or a day of off-road driving.

1. Find out about the different business events that are on offer for team building on the following two websites.

   - www.teambuilding.co.uk
   - www.southernpursuits.co.uk

2. Compare the activities and discuss their similarities.

Exhibitions

Exhibitions can be used to highlight the different services or products that a business offers or to publicise changes that a business wishes to make in the local area. An exhibition could also be an event that appears to have no direct link with the company, for example, a company will host or sponsor a local art society's exhibition as a way to generate publicity.

Did you know?

Beaulieu Motor Museum in the New Forest hosts car exhibitions each year to show the history and latest developments in car technology.

Receptions

Receptions give businesses the chance to host an event or launch a new service. The type will depend on the organisation being promoted. Sometimes a reception may be more formal, such as a champagne reception, and include drinks or canapés as part of the evening. Other receptions might be less formal and therefore more relaxed.

Activity: Air Southwest

In November 2009, Air Southwest (www.airsouthwest.com) held a reception in the airport lounge. Do some research on the Internet and answer the following questions.

- Why did Air Southwest hold this reception?
- Who attended?
- Was the reception informal or formal?

Do some more research and find out about receptions that have been held in your local area. Answer the above questions about the receptions you find, then give a five-minute presentation to your class about your findings.

Functional skills

Researching and gathering information for this activity will help you to develop your **English** skills in reading.

Conferences

Conferences are popular events for businesses. Different sectors will have conferences that provide an opportunity for similar businesses to get together and share ideas. Some conferences are now very large and have to be held in hotels, convention centres or other large venues or locations. Conferences usually have a programme which lasts anywhere from one day to one week. Important speakers are usually invited to give presentations on different topics within their sector. There may also be meetings, dinners and activities that are organised as part of the conference events.

The style of a conference will depend on the people that are expected to attend and also the fees they are prepared to pay. Conferences are usually routine, with most occurring annually or bi-annually. For example the Career Development Organisation (CRAC) organises annual conferences to support teachers and careers advisers. Each year the conference is held over three days at a different university allowing participants to learn more about the institution and its facilities.

Trade fair stands

For many businesses, holding a conference and inviting businesses to come and visit the organisation may either be too difficult to organise or even dangerous due to the type of work that the organisation carries out. Trade fair stands may be a good alternative. This type of event gives the business a chance to meet other business people whilst also promoting their business.

Case study: Business2Business shows

JobServe Events Ltd organises annual business shows in different parts of the country. Business South 2010 took place at the Rose Bowl near Southampton in March 2010.

Local businesses were invited to buy stands to promote their products and services. The JobServe Events Team also offered exhibitors a free half-day workshop on exhibitor training to give them the chance to learn how to run their stands more effectively.

The cost of having a stand at this show depended on the size of the stand. Stands were available from £290 per square metre.

1. Why do you think JobServe Events offers free training workshops to small businesses who buy stands for their events? What are the benefits of doing this?

2. Why might a business decide to attend one of these events rather than organising its own conference and what are the advantages of doing this?

3. Carry out research into business conferences that are happening in your area. Find out the types of stands that are available and their costs. Produce a short guide with the information you have found.

2.2 Prior arrangements

In order to hold a successful business event, an event organiser will need to make various arrangements before the event.

Clarifying the purpose

There are a huge number of business events held every day of the year. Each event has to have a very clear purpose. The people invited need to be clear about why they should attend and have information to help them to decide what they will get out of the event. Therefore, clarifying the purpose of the event is extremely important for any organiser who wants to cover their costs.

The event brief

Many organisations use an 'event brief' to collect data and information that is critical to the planning of the event. The brief is a way of summarising information about the type of event, its size, target audience, number of people attending and the responsibilities and procedures for everyone involved. You will learn about the importance of each of these elements and how they could relate to the business event that you will be planning as part of your assessment for this chapter.

Type of event

You have already learned about the different types of event that will need planning including routine and non-routine and formal or informal events. The prior arrangements for the type of event significantly influence all other arrangements. Arrangements will be adapted for each and every event depending on why it is being held and who is involved.

Size

The size of the event must be decided during the early stages of making arrangements. Size may refer to the venue or to the number of potential attendees. Sometimes it is best to start out with a smaller event and see how successful it can be before moving on to a larger one. Many very successful events have been running for a number of years and people keep returning because they are happy with the information that they receive at those events.

Did you know?

BETT organises the world's largest educational IT event each year. It attracts over 600 suppliers and 29,000 visitors. In 2010 it was held in January at Olympia in London over four days.

Target audience

The target audience refers to the people who will be attending the event. There are a variety of potential people who could be targeted to attend a business event including:

- the public
- previous customers
- students
- charities
- businesses
- suppliers.

When considering a target audience, you should think about any celebrities or special guests that might help to attract people to come to the event. Celebrities may charge a fee to appear at an event or sometimes if it is for charity they may appear at a reduced fee or for free.

Numbers

The number of people to be invited to an event needs to be decided early on. Estimating the number of attendees may be one of the most difficult aspects to predict but is essential if the event is to be a success. Too many people may mean the event is unsafe; not enough people may mean that it cannot cover its costs and therefore be loss making.

Responsibilities

Responsibilities of the different organisations and groups need to be worked out well in advance of any event with the organiser. Often business events will be run by a team with each member taking responsibility for different aspects of the event planning such as advertising, catering, and so on. This means that each team member can ensure that they make the event a success. Some of the roles that have specific responsibilities include:

- media and marketing
- customer service
- health and safety.
- administration
- finance

Procedures

Having procedures in place ensures that everything runs properly and that the right decisions are made. There needs to be a set of procedures to follow, including who will authorise invoices and who has authority to make decisions. For some events, the whole team may need to agree every aspect of the arrangements. For other events, authority may be delegated to different members of the team.

Budget and cost analysis

It is important that events **break even** at a minimum. All business events should have a budget which needs to be analysed so that the most appropriate event can be organised with the money available. For example, a business breakfast with training may only cost a few hundred pounds to organise compared to a large conference in a prestigious venue that might cost thousands. The type of event and finances of the business will influence which type of budget will be needed.

There are various ways to budget. One way is zero budgeting, where the event organiser is asked to work out how much they think that an event will cost and then put in a proposal for the money needed. Alternatively, event organisers might be given a specific allocated budget; therefore they know exactly how much they can spend. Either way, a good way to budget for an event is by producing a spreadsheet.

Key term

Break even – when costs are equal to income so there is no profit or loss.

Once a budget is set, it can be used to work out any income that may come in for the event. For example, Table 18.4 shows the budget for a business breakfast event. For this breakfast, if 60 people attend and they all pay £35, the event will receive £2,100 income. By calculating the differences between the costs and the income we will come up with the event's profit: £2,100 − £1,850 = £250. To break even, the number of people needed to attend the event will be £1,850 ÷ 35 = 53 people.

Table 18.4: Budget for business breakfast event

Cost	£
Food	300
Hotel conference room	350
Visiting speaker	500
Advertising	500
Administration	200
Total	1,850

Sometimes businesses run events in which they do not expect to break even as there are other benefits such as making new customer contacts or publicity.

Distribution of supporting documents/files

Sending out documents prior to a business event is an important step. A formal business meeting will need to send out an agenda in advance so that people attending know what will be discussed. Some agendas are regularly published on the Internet so that people who may be interested can see what is being discussed.

Did you know?

The Mayor of London organises a consultation each year for Young Londoners in which young people are able to put questions to a panel of experts about the way forward for London. The agenda is published in advance and the full transcript of the meeting can be viewed online at www.london.gov.uk.

Relevant meeting papers

Sometimes it is important to send out other paperwork before the event so that participants can be prepared. The types of papers depend on the audience and the level of discussion. Many organisations will publish biographies of people who are speaking at the event. Larger events, such as conferences, usually publish a list of all the abstracts of submitted papers and distribute this before the event. Another type of meeting paper that might be published and sent out prior to the event would be a list of the different workshops available.

Consultation and planning

Consultation and planning are also key to a successful event. The organiser will need to find out if people are likely to want to attend, and consultation before the event will help to highlight any issues that may affect the quality and success of the business event. For example, if the event is organised at the same time as another similar event, attendance may be poor. Planning ahead will help to solve this problem. Consultation may also generate ideas for a very different event.

Consulting the different groups that are likely to be interested in the event may also lead to further ideas or extra items being added to an agenda. During the planning stages of a formal meeting, there is usually an opportunity for prospective participants to add items or issues they would like to cover to the agenda.

When planning a business event, such as staff training or team building, the organiser needs to ask the following questions.

- What do the staff expect to get out of the event? What would they like to do?
- How much time do staff have available for the event?
- When would it be best to hold this event so it does not affect the business' operations?

Clear and accurate communication

Information on the business event includes the time the event starts, the cost of attendance, the specific programme of the event and how to get there. The event organiser must be able to communicate this information in a clear and accurate manner. Many organisations use websites to communicate this information easily and cheaply. Other **communication**

Key term

Communication channel – the method that is used to communicate.

channels include email, posters, advertising in magazines or newspapers, flyers or letters. Some organisations now also use social media to advertise and promote events and this may be done using text or video on different social and business networking sites. Individuals are asked to pass on the information to their friends and families or other business associates to increase numbers.

Once people have signed up for the event the organiser will need to send them joining instructions and, if necessary, notify them of any alterations to the arrangements. Sometimes, for various reasons, events have to be changed. This may be because the event is becoming too large for the chosen venue or the event cannot take place, because of illness, changes in the weather, lack of funding or even lack of interest. It is very important that records of all participants or ticket-holders are kept so information or changes can be communicated. It is also useful to make contingency arrangements so that if a time or location change needs to be made, the event will still be able to take place.

Organising appropriate venues

Organising an appropriate venue is one of the most important prior arrangements an event organiser has to arrange. It is critical to make the right decision about the venue during the early planning stages and then use the venue to influence other event decisions. Make sure that you have booked a venue well in advance; some places require booking a year in advance. More information about venues is found in the following section.

2.3 Venue

The venue is central to any business event because it influences the **ambience**. Choosing the right venue can make the difference between an event being a success or not.

Location

The location of a venue will influence the success of a business event. The target market should influence the location. For example, if the event is trying to sell upmarket products, it needs to be held in an upmarket area.

The location can also be influenced by the type of participants, local business people or for example, the public. For local participants, the event organiser needs to think of the best location in a local area. If the event is planned with regional participation in mind, the organiser needs to pick a location based on geography so that people attending the event all travel approximately the same distance to get there.

Knowing a bit about the type of people that will be attending and the theme of the event will also influence the suitability of a location. For example, if the event is focusing on green issues it should be at a location with easy access to public transport rather than a venue that can only be reached by car. If the event is linked to an activity that requires specific facilities, such as water for a boat trade show, then the location needs have those facilities.

> **Key term**
>
> **Ambience** – the atmosphere of the event.

Case study: British International Motor Show 2010

The Society of Motor Manufacturers and Traders (SMMT) cancelled the 2010 British International Motor Show for the first time in its history because of concerns about poor attendance. The SMMT communicated the cancellation by email, through press releases and the information was also published on the show's website (www.britishshow.co.uk).

In pairs, discuss the following.

1. Why do you think the British International Motor Show 2010 was cancelled?

2. Do you think the SMMT communicated this cancellation effectively? What could they have done differently?

3. Using the Internet, books or corporate magazines, find out about other events that have been cancelled and how the decision to cancel was communicated.

Some business events are organised at a location such as a tourist destination, so event participants can combine visiting the business event with the attractions. Event organisers may even plan afternoon excursions for participants.

Did you know?

The Southampton Boat Show is held each year in Mayflower Park, Southampton because it has access to the sea. This means that boats can be taken out and customers can actually experience sailing during the event.

Activity: Marwell Wildlife Park

Marwell Wildlife Park, located in Hampshire, offers facilities for business events including meetings and conferences. They have a range of facilities available, including the Seymour Library, the Woodlock Room and the Long Room, each of which can hold different numbers. Every **delegate** who attends a business event also receives free entry to the park.

Go to the Marwell Wildlife Park website (www.marwell.org.uk) and do some research on the different costs and packages for business events. Then answer these questions.

1. What are the different packages available? What is the minimum number of people who could attend an event at Marwell Wildlife? What is the maximum?

2. What are the advantages of using this location? What would the disadvantages be?

3. What kind of business event would be suitable for this location?

Key term

Delegate – the name given to a person who is attending an event. This term is used particularly with conferences.

Size

The size of the location will have a big influence on the event. A large location will be able to accommodate larger numbers of people and may have a greater range of facilities such as restaurants and leisure facilities. However, smaller locations may have the advantage of being able to offer a more relaxed and friendly atmosphere if fewer people are in attendance. Some locations, like hotels, have a number of different meeting room options that can accommodate from two to 1000 people. Other locations are specifically designed to have thousands of people, such as conference or convention centres.

Layout

The layout of a venue for a business event needs careful consideration. Venues can be open plan, such as a conference hall, or divided into different sized rooms, such as a hotel. Some event venues may cover large areas and include different buildings (see Figure 18.3). The most appropriate layout shape should be chosen to ensure that the look of the event is right.

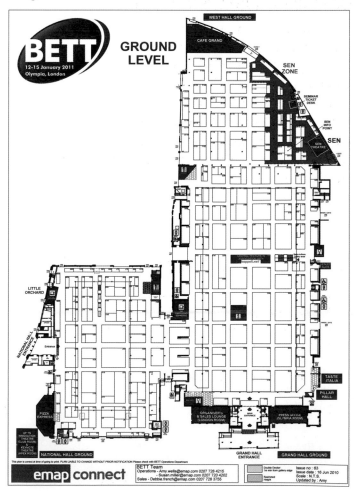

Figure 18.3: Layout of BETT, the world's largest education technology event held at Olympia, London

Time for advance notice or bookings

Some venues are extremely popular and bookings need to be made well in advance, sometimes as much as a year ahead. Other locations might be able to offer something at much shorter notice. The availability of a location will depend on the type of event that is being held and the number of people that will be attending.

The timing that is needed for advance notice or booking will often depend on the popularity of the location and the date of that event. It is very important to choose the right date for your event and ensure that it does not clash with other events, as this may affect its popularity. Different days, different seasons or even different conference rooms do have an influence on the costs of an event. The more flexible that an event organiser can be, the easier it may be to keep down costs and enable the event to break even or even make a profit.

Did you know?

The NEC in Birmingham (www.thenec.co.uk) is a huge location that hosts many exhibitions, conferences and other events during the year, including DFS Crufts and the Clothes Show.

Facilities assessment

All venues must have basic facilities that are required by law, for example, toilets and washing facilities. Some locations offer additional equipment and packs that may be used during the business event and these may be offered with or without charge. The event organiser will need to assess the facilities that will be needed for the event and then check that the venue has the required facilities. It is essential that good facilities are on offer to support delegates.

Facilities at an event will be influenced by the type of event and the number of attendees. Business events that involve staff team building might need outdoor facilities or access to specialist equipment. Weekend networking conferences might need to have access to leisure facilities such as swimming pools or spas. If an overnight stay is essential for the event, then hotel accommodation must be available. If it is not essential, it may be better to avoid offering hotel accommodation as this can be complex.

The facilities at the location will also determine how easy the event will be to manage. An exhibition will need to have access for suppliers and caterers and easy access for exhibitors. It is also important to consider the parking at any venue. It will then be possible to work out whether people may drive to the event or if it is more appropriate for them to use public transport to get there.

Activity: Facilities

There are a range of different venues that can be used for business events, each with different facilities, including restaurants, photocopying services, phones and audiovisual equipment.

Do some research on the Internet and find three different venues in your area. Then answer the following questions for each of the venues.

1. What type of venue is it (hotel, activity centre, etc.)?
2. What type of facilities are available? Is there an extra charge for their use?
3. Which kind of business events would be suitable for this venue?

If you were planning a team building event for 30 participants, which of the venues would you choose? Why?

Number and type of delegates

The number of delegates will help to establish whether or not the venue is suitable. If the venue is too large for the number of delegates, the attendees will be lost in the middle of a room. Conversely, if the venue is too small, the event will become overcrowded and potentially unpleasant or even dangerous for the delegates.

Delegates will want to feel relaxed and happy during the event, so the venue must be suitable for the type of delegate who is attending. An event staged for a group on a team building exercise will need a different venue from an event for a business group who want to discuss market trends.

Furthermore, some delegates may want to arrive and stay the night before so a hotel venue would be a good option. The type of entertainment may need to be considered for the evening, and the event organiser will need to decide whether the delegates will want to stay in their rooms or if they would like to socialise with other delegates during the evening. This means that the event organiser may need to host a dinner, so a venue with restaurant facilities will be essential.

Special requirements

Delegates at a business event must have all their needs met. This includes making sure that any special requirements are catered for. The type of delegate attending will influence whether or not special adjustments need to be made. For example, the venue should be able to offer wheelchair and disability access; some venues have additional facilities such as hearing loops for delegates with hearing disabilities. Special dietary needs may need to be provided if people are on special diets for health or religious reasons. Some venues may also be able to offer rooms or spaces for prayer or reflection.

Travel to and from the event may be another special requirement to be organised for delegates. Some locations will be able to receive guests who have arrived by plane or even helicopter. Others will be accessible by taxi.

Venue checklist

The event organiser will need to have a venue checklist for planning the event. This checklist is used to compare venues and make a judgement about which one is the most appropriate.

There are many different checklist templates that can be used. Figure 18.4 is an example, which you can use for your event planning. This template will give you a very general idea to get you thinking about your own checklist.

Event checklist			
Transport method	**Distance to transport method (e.g. station)**	**Time to venue using this method**	**Cost**
Airport			
Train			
Taxi			
Car			
Hotel rooms (if applicable)	**No. required**	**Cost**	**Availability**
Single			
Double			
Triple suite			
Quadruple suite			
Facilities	**No. required**	**Cost**	**Availability**
Toilets			
Room layouts			
Leisure e.g. swimming pool			
Conference rooms			
Projectors			
Pens/paper			
Restaurants			
Tea and coffee making facilities			
Wireless Internet points			
Other information	**Covered? Y/N**	**Cost**	**Availability**
Public liability insurance			
Use of credit cards			
Insurance for cancellation			

Figure 18.4: Venue checklist template. Remember, this is a standard template and will need to be amended for your event to ensure everything runs smoothly

Activity: Venue checklist

Using Figure 18.4 as your template, put together your own venue checklist.

1. Design a set of questions that would help you compare different locations.

2. Turn these into your venue checklist.

3. Use your checklist to compare three different venue locations. Have you thought of everything that needs to be covered?

2.4 Resources

Room

There are a lot of different possible room sizes and layouts. These are influenced by the size and layout of the venue's location. The physical shape of a room and how it can be laid out may also influence its suitability for an event and the number of people who can attend it. Rooms or facilities may be square or rectangular and they can be organised in a variety of layouts.

Activity: Room layouts

1. Look up the meaning of each of the different room layouts below and find out what they mean:
   - boardroom
   - U-shaped
   - classroom based
   - V-shaped
   - herringbone
   - theatre
   - horseshoe.

2. Draw a diagram of each layout.

3. In pairs, decide what type of event would work best for each layout.

Equipment

A venue used for a business event has to have the right resource equipment. With any type of equipment, the event organiser will need to consider what is necessary for the event to run smoothly and create the most appropriate atmosphere. Common items that

are required for any business event may include an overhead projector and an electronic whiteboard that is able to show DVD clips, web conferencing or even presentation software slides.

Flip charts are also still very popular for events. Having paper available for notes is useful to ensure that delegates can write down important information. If the event needs the use of ICT, it is important that good quality ICT equipment is provided, including fast broadband Internet access.

Many events will also need display stands so that extra literature can be presented as professionally as possible.

Refreshments

Refreshments are an important element of any business event. Even short meetings will often have tea, coffee and water available. If the event is for a whole morning or afternoon it may also be appropriate to offer small pastries or cakes to delegates. All-day events usually have lunch, which may be a buffet where delegates can help themselves or a sit-down lunch with silver service. The type of food will depend on the delegates attending and whether the event is a formal or informal occasion. Often multi-day conferences will include dinner, bed and breakfast as part of the accommodation deal. Delegates are then able to network with each other overnight to make contacts that can help them in the workplace.

Delivery of materials

Most business events require packs of materials or equipment to be delivered to the venue before it starts. Boxes of information or products may need to be dropped off and stored at the venue until the day of the event. The event organiser will need to check that the venue is able to offer this storage service.

2.5 Scheduling

Scheduling is another key part of organising a business event. Keeping people up to date and resolving any changes that are needed is very important and an essential part of business event planning. Scheduling is also used to keep an event on track.

Software

There is a variety of scheduling software available to help event organisers, for example, Microsoft Outlook, which includes a planner and scheduler. Email updates

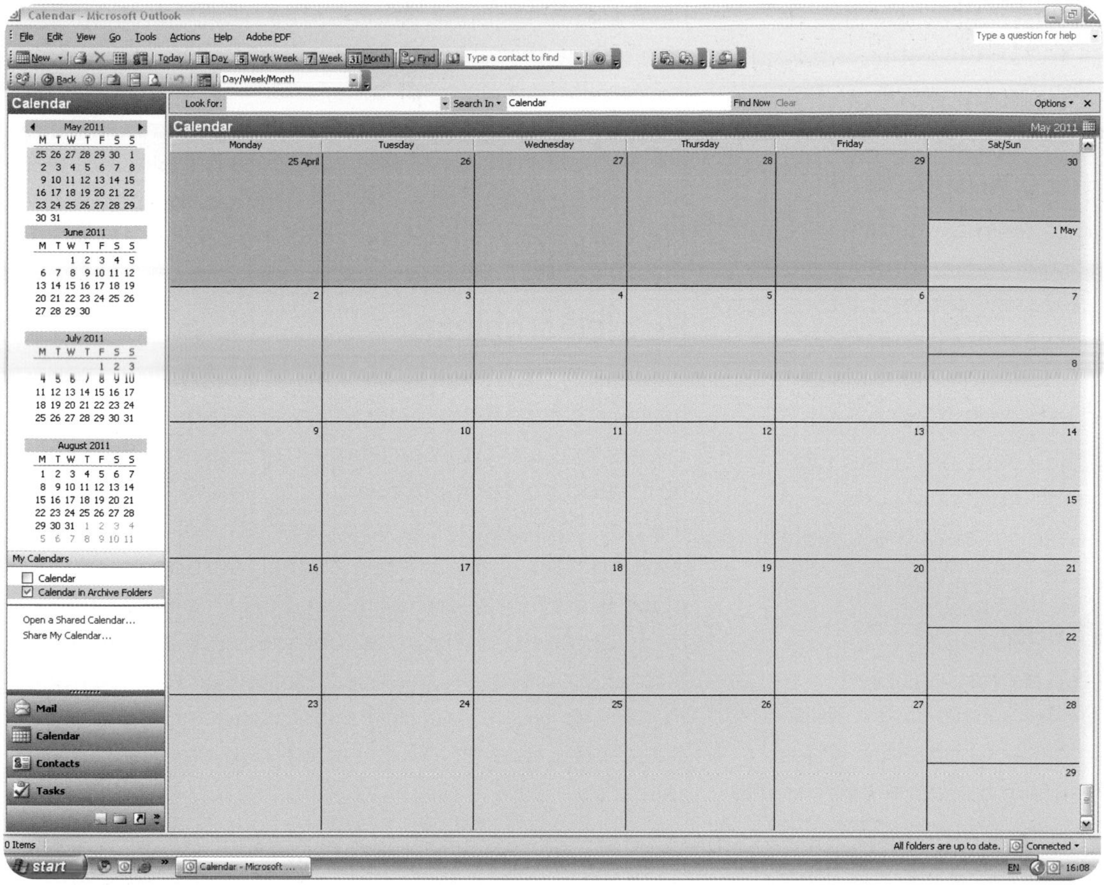

Figure 18.5: Microsoft Outlook has a scheduler to help with event planning

can be sent to delegates, making event planning easier to control.

Liaising with participants

The event organiser has a key role in keeping everything to schedule. They will need to liaise with the participants to ensure they are aware of what and when things are happening. If a meeting needs to be arranged or if it has to be changed, the event organiser will be the person responsible for updating diaries.

The event organiser will also need to resolve any problems of availability to ensure that the event goes ahead. For example, if the hotel to be used for the event is already booked, it is the responsibility of the organiser to search for another appropriate location.

Care and experience in allocating times

All events usually have an itinerary or programme to guide the day(s). Different business events will have different timings, and it is the job of the event organiser to get them right. The organiser will need to think about these timings and make sure that if the event is going to run smoothly that time has been

allowed for travel, rest and preparation. There should be time allocated for morning and afternoon breaks as well as for lunch and perhaps an evening meal. There should also be preparation time allocated in both the morning for set up, and in the evening for clear up and/or restock.

Organisational policies

It is important for event organisers to know the various organisational policies, for example, booking travel. Sometimes businesses will only allow their employees to travel by second-class rail travel or pay a certain amount of money per mile for car travel. There may also be policy guidance on the amount of money that can be spent on an evening meal or whether or not it is permissible for employees to consume alcohol whilst they are on a conference. Event organisers should be aware of these policies to avoid any conflict at the event.

Confirming plans in good time

With any business event, plans must be made in good time, especially for travel and accommodation arrangements. Confirming plans well in advance will enable both organisers and participants to get the travel options of their choice. Transport is often cheaper if booked a long time in advance.

Booking flights and accommodation

Part of an event organiser's duties may involve scheduling for participants, such as booking flights and accommodation. Flights are usually cheaper if they are booked well in advance. Most airlines offer incentives to book early and there may be further incentives if accommodation is booked at the same time.

For large business events, the event organiser will often negotiate a special price with a hotel for accommodation or flights as this makes the travel to the business event even more attractive.

Checking return journeys

The event organiser may also be responsible for planning the return journeys for participants. This may be done in advance in order to obtain the best possible option. They must make sure that participants

have a smooth journey home. The organiser should also review these arrangements just before the event in case of road works or other changes in travel arrangements. For some events it may be more appropriate for everyone to return to the place of work or other location before they then travel home; this will depend on the organisation and the people involved.

Related problems

There may be other problems that arise which are related to scheduling, including language issues. Events that attract international delegates may require translated packs or interpreters to be available during the day. Language may also be an issue if the event is being held abroad. International locations may make the event seem more exciting and interesting to delegates and might encourage more people to attend. However, as the event organiser you will need to have an awareness of the language and cultural differences so that you can make sure the event is a success.

Activity: British Airways

British Airways offers a special service for groups of ten or more called Group Travel. Go to BA's website (www.ba.com) and find out more about this service.

1. What does the Group Travel service entail?
2. What are the different group travel options that are available?

3. Why would an event organiser use this service? What are the advantages of using it? What are the disadvantages?
4. Do some research on the Internet and find other airlines that offer a similar service. Compare the different services that are on offer and make a judgement about which you think is best.

3 Be able to run a business event

Now that you have learned about the way to plan a business event, we will look at the actual running of the event, taking into account all aspects including health and safety requirements.

3.1 Types of activity

Presentations

Often conferences and meetings involve presentations. This may be done using PowerPoint or other software. Presentations need to be planned and timed. It is also

important to make sure that any information does not overlap with other speakers. The **biographies** of the speakers are also useful information to help delegates understand their background and appreciate the context of the speaker's presentation.

Key term

Biography – the life story of a person written by someone else.

Group activities or workshops

Business events should have a variety of different activities. These will depend on the type of event. Group activities such as idea storming or problem-solving sessions can help to make the event more interactive. As an event organiser, you may think it is appropriate to run parallel workshops so that delegates have a choice of what to attend. This will enable the participants to get the most out of the event, which will benefit their needs. A variety of workshops or activities included in the programme takes more planning, but the results can be very interesting and rewarding for the delegates involved.

Manning stands

If the business event is an exhibition or a conference, you will be expected to have some sort of manned stand, which means that it should never be left unattended to avoid the business missing out on discussions with potential supporters or gaining sales from customers.

Displays

Displays are another form of activity that can be undertaken as part of a business event. They may be used to highlight a business idea or sell products in a prominent location. Having a display of what is on offer can help to increase sales.

Displays which advertise the business event can sometimes be placed in other locations. Some local libraries allow displays from small businesses to be placed in their foyer. Other places that may allow such a display, with permission, include shopping centres and places of worship.

Activity: Displays

Think about your local area and where products or information about services could be displayed. In pairs, discuss the following.

1. Would any of these areas be good for displaying information about a business event?

2. Choose one of the places and find out:
   - if there is a charge for a display
   - how long a display could be put there
   - if there is any potential for the organisation hosting the display to sell products or services on another organisation's behalf.

Stands at large business events may need several staff to provide advice and information to potential customers

Screenings

With advances in digital technology it is now possible to play DVDs or videos of work or projects undertaken by the organisation on a big screen. Such an event can generate income for a charity or could be used at the start or end of an event to highlight the success of projects carried out by the business.

Minute/note taking

Formal meetings usually require minutes to be taken so that everything that has been agreed at the meeting can be shared with other interested parties. Other events may only require notes to be taken. It is a good idea to have note-taking facilities at any event to help delegates to write down key information that they may otherwise forget. Offering a service activity that does this for them may really impress delegates and gives them a chance to concentrate on listening.

3.2 Health, safety and security

Matters relating to health, safety and security need to be considered during the planning and running of the event because they are very important and are required by both civil and criminal law.

Venue emergency procedures

The event organisers must be aware of the emergency procedures that are used by the venue where the event is being held. They will need to talk to the venue's manager or co-ordinator to find out what happens in an emergency, where the nearest fire exits are and what kind of sound indicates that there is an emergency. This information will need to be made available to delegates and other attendees to the business event.

Under the Health and Safety at Work Act 1974, it is the event organiser's responsibility to ensure that their employees are looked after. The event organiser has a duty of care to any other people who might be attending the event. Many different aspects need to be considered, including arrangements for first aid, insurance and food hygiene. If anything goes wrong at the business event including if someone is injured or even dies, there could be serious consequences for the employer and individual under criminal law. It is possible to be prosecuted for corporate manslaughter and go to prison if found guilty. Venues must have public liability insurance, which is insurance that is paid

out in the event that a member of the public has an accident in that venue.

Case study: St Michael's Hospice

St Michael's Hospice in Hastings (www.stmichaelshospice.org) used to run an annual fundraiser on 1 January. The New Year Dip involved participants jumping into the cold sea to raise funds for the hospice. In November 2009, the Hospice announced that it was going to cancel the 1 January 2010 dip for health and safety reasons. It was unable to supply enough lifeguards or other volunteers to help run the event. The Hospice announced instead that it was changing the event so that the lives of fundraisers were not put at risk.

1. Do you agree with the Hospice's decision to cancel the event?

2. What do you think could have been done to save the event?

3. Find other events in your area that have been cancelled for health and safety reasons. Consider the reasons and any measures that could have been put in place to avoid the event being cancelled.

To make sure all the risks are assessed correctly and steps are put in place to minimise risk, the event organiser should carry out a risk assessment for the event. There are lots of different ways of doing risk assessments but an example of how a hazard can be identified and then controls be put in place is given in Table 18.5.

Activity: Risk assessment

Think of a business event you would like to plan. Take into account the venue you would use and the people who would come. Then, using the risk assessment template from Table 18.5 or one supplied by your tutor, carry out a risk assessment for this event. Remember to think of all the possible hazards and come up with controls for how the risks of these hazards may be reduced.

Table 18.5: Risk assessment for an indoor business fair event

Hazard identified	People at risk	Likelihood	Severity	Controls	Further action
Trip or fall on the steps in the entrance	Visitors Exhibitors Employees	Low	Low	Keep the steps clear during the event	Not needed
Too many people attending the event	Visitors Exhibitors Employees	Low	Low	Make sure that visitor numbers are controlled at the entrance	Not needed
Trailing wires from stands may cause a trip	Visitors Exhibitors Employees	Low	Low	Wires should be taped to the floor	Not needed

Case study: Birmingham City Council

In November 2009, Birmingham City Council organised a free concert event to mark the switching on of the city's Christmas lights. Pop band JLS were asked to sing at the concert. While the band was performing, the crowd surged forward and a security barrier failed, leaving dozens of people injured. The Council had been through the planning of the event and had considered all the health and safety issues but could not have accurately predicted the number of people who decided to attend, which was significantly more than expected.

1. What type of risk assessment do you think would have been performed before the event?

2. Who was at fault for this accident?

3. Do some research and find out more about this case and the actions that followed it.

Housekeeping arrangements

Housekeeping arrangements are those arrangements that relate to the facilities that are on offer. Part of an event organiser's role will be to make sure delegates understand access arrangements for wash rooms and toilets, where smoking areas are and what time coffee breaks and lunch are available. It is important to give this information to delegates at the beginning of the day so that they are comfortable and their needs are met.

Security of materials and equipment

Materials and equipment must be kept secure before, during and after the event, from the time it is placed in the venue until it has been picked up. Some equipment is extremely expensive and would be costly to replace so it must be secured, monitored and returned to its owners at the end of the event. For some events and venues, it may be possible to have a security officer or guard who takes charge of looking after high value items.

Confidentiality of information and communication

An event organiser must follow the law relating to how information about delegates and suppliers is stored. All information storage that relates to individuals is covered by the Data Protection Act 1998. This Act requires event organisers to keep information secure and give access to delegates and suppliers if they wish to see records kept about them. Any forms or paperwork that are sent to suppliers or delegates should ask them to agree to their details being recorded for data protection purposes.

Assessment activity 18.2

P3 **P4** **BTEC**

Under your tutor's guidance decide on a business event you would like to organise. Once you have decided on the type of event you will need to do the following.

1. Prepare a plan for this business event. **P3**
2. Arrange and organise a venue for this event, ensuring health and safety requirements are met. **P4**

Grading tips

1. You must produce a written plan for the event

that includes type of event, arrangements, resources and scheduling. Use graphs and charts to help illustrate your points and do not forget to reference any ideas that you find in books or on the Internet to avoid plagiarism. **P3**

2. Make sure you keep an accurate record of the activities you carried out to organise the event and venue; you should include a risk assessment to help you. **P4**

PLTS

Planning a business event, working towards goals and organising time and resources will help you to develop your skills as **self-manager**.

3.3 Event support

During the event, there will be support requirements to make sure that everything runs smoothly.

Note taking

It is usual for a person or persons to be appointed to take notes. This service may be arranged by the event organiser or volunteers might be asked to do this during the event. The extent to which note taking is required will depend on the type of business event. For formal meetings, a secretary is usually appointed to take notes and then write them up into formal minutes.

Papers

It is the job of the event organiser to make sure delegates receive the correct papers for the business event. The type and number of papers will depend on the event itself. Formal governing body meetings such as those at a school, college or university may have a large number of different papers that must be read in advance of the meeting. For conferences or less formal meetings there may be a pack of information that is given out to delegates at the event. Some conference organisers, for example CRAC (www.crac.org.uk), give delegates online access to all the papers from its conferences so they can use them after the event.

Location of rooms and facilities

At any event, delegates may get lost. There should be support available to help them find their way. In large hotels, a key point of contact is often the reception staff. In other event locations, there may be a sign-in table that is constantly staffed; delegates can use this to ask additional questions about room locations and facilities. It may be an idea to set out a location map of the venue and facilities at these tables.

Recording attendance and cancellations

Recording attendance must be done for any business event. Not only is this important for health and safety reasons, but it also provides proof for an employer or trainer that the person actually attended the event. Often the record of attendance will include extra information such as telephone numbers or email addresses so that the delegates may be contacted again after the event. This is particularly important if names are not given in advance.

Monitoring cancellations is also very important. Some organisers offering free events now only charge if an organisation does not turn up rather than if they do. In some instances, there is a £50 charge for non-attendance; this helps to ensure that people do go when they have booked a place. If an organisation keeps cancelling places, the event organiser may decide not to offer them a place in the future.

3.4 Trouble shooting

Trouble-shooting covers any issues that the event organiser may become aware of during the event.

An event organiser must try to resolve such issues so that there is a positive outcome for everyone.

Liaison with delegates

During the event, the organiser should have frequent interaction and liaise with the delegates regularly. In doing so the event organiser will ensure that the delegates feel that they are being well looked after and that, if there are any issues, these can be resolved before they turn into a complaint. Liaison may be possible when delegates arrive at the venue, through formal introductions at different times during the event or during refreshment breaks such as coffee or lunch.

Delegates must be told who they should go to in the event that there is an issue or problem. During the event, it may also be appropriate to get feedback directly from the delegates through surveys or questionnaires. Any issues raised at that time can then be dealt with straight away. Whether or not it is possible to gain such feedback during the day will depend on the type of event, the delegates involved and any technology that may be necessary to do this. For example, at the entrance to the event, it may be possible to have an event feedback form that is available online throughout the event and is checked regularly.

Potential revision/rearrangements of event outcomes

Even the best events may have things that go wrong and require rearrangements. There are a number of reasons why an event may need to change its outcomes. How an issue is dealt with depends on the type of issue, for example, if a speaker is delayed, it may be possible to rearrange the time that they were due to talk by moving another speaker to an earlier point in the day.

If something has happened with the location, the event may be able to move to another location. Sometimes there will be problems that cannot be overcome so it may be necessary to cancel the event or postpone it until another time. The event organiser will need to have access to the right people and funds to get additional resources if this is necessary. This may involve having an amount of cash or a debit/credit card available for the event organiser's use.

Arising issues

Arising issues are anything or everything that happens which were not expected. These issues may happen at the beginning, middle or even towards the end of the event. Issues may be categorised into two types: those that can be controlled by the event organiser and those that cannot (see Table 18.6). The most important aspects of dealing with arising issues is to make sure that there is good communication. If delegates do not know what is happening, they are more likely to be unhappy; if they are kept informed, they can make decisions about what to do next.

Even if something cannot be controlled by the organiser, it is important to consider how the impact of that issue could be minimised. For example, if there is extreme weather on the day of the event, the organiser can just accept that there is a problem or make a back-up arrangement to move the event to a different location or provide other facilities. Of course, any event that takes place should already have had a risk assessment so that any possible hazards and steps to avoid those hazards should have been assessed.

Did you know?

The annual two-day Narberth Food Festival in 2009 had so many visitors on the first day that many of the 40 stallholders ran out of supplies. Many of them either made or transported more stock to the event so that they could have a successful second day.

Table 18.6: Examples of issues that can or cannot be controlled by the event organiser

Issues that can be controlled by the event organiser	Issues that cannot be controlled by the event organiser directly
Facilities available in the venue Resources available in the venue Catering arrangements Schedules Non-attendance of delegates	Bad weather Transport issues such as problems on motorways or public transport A major incident such as a fire in the area around the venue Fraud promotion or selling associated with the event, e.g. scam ticket sales Publishing of event details incorrectly by a third party Worldwide issues such as the Icelandic volcanic ash crisis in April 2010 which grounded all UK flights

Last minute photocopying

Sometimes during a meeting, delegates will request a copy of an article or piece of information that they do not have. Knowing where to get this copying done is very useful and can help the event to run smoothly. Therefore, it is a good idea for the event organiser to find out where the nearest facilities are for last-minute photocopying.

Inadequate room or facilities

It is good practice, if possible, to visit the room or facilities several days or weeks before the business event will take place. This should help avoid any significant issues arising. However, sometimes this type of visit is not possible if the event location is far away or there is not time to visit. If the rooms are inadequate, the equipment is insufficient or the facilities are out of order or broken, it is the role of the event organiser to find out what can be done. Sometimes there will be an instant solution and the organiser will be able to source other suppliers. For example, if during a business meeting with lunch you realise that lunch is not going to be arriving due to a catering problem, it is sensible to go out and purchase lunch from another supplier locally.

If there is equipment missing, the venue should be able to source alternatives or you can make a call to a colleague and ask them to help you by urgently bringing equipment to the location.

Non-delivery of resources

There may be times when resources such as stands or display boards may not be delivered. As the event organiser, you will need to be able to solve this problem. You should have access to a mobile phone with Internet facilities so that you are able to look up other suppliers at short notice.

Planning deliveries in advance and then checking that resources arrive well in advance of the event will also give you more time to make alternative arrangements. Some resources may not be able to be used after the event; therefore the event organiser will need to put this information in the contract or agreement that is made with the supplier in case there is a dispute over payment for non-delivered resources. These resources may also include those that are delivered directly to the delegates such as agendas, event packs or entrance tickets. Having a back-up list of people arriving will help to avoid this being a problem.

4   Be able to follow up after a business event

An event organiser will need to plan the ending of the event as carefully as they planned and supported it while it was happening. When the event itself actually finishes this is not the end of your job as event organiser. There is still a lot of work to do. This is to make sure that you leave a good impression with the people who own the venue and other users who might use it after you leave. You will also need to make judgements about the event immediately after it has finished so that you can make recommendations to improve it for next time.

4.1 After the event

Vacating the venue

At the time of booking the venue, you will have been told the time at which you can arrive and also the time when you must leave. Some venues are very busy so it is important that you work out how long you will have to remove any resources or equipment that you have

brought. Venues will have different arrangements for how the owners want them to be left. Usually leaving the location tidy is the absolute minimum.

When you are leaving the event, as the organiser, you should make sure that you help delegates by considering transport away from the location, for example, some delegates will need taxis. You should also try to minimise the level of noise and disturbance in the area around the event as delegates are leaving, including any potential traffic issues.

Sometimes venues will ask you to clean when the event has finished. Make sure you take equipment for this purpose including any materials such as cloths, cleaning sprays and bags to collect any rubbish.

If you are not required to clean the venue yourself, it is likely that you will have paid for this service in the cost of the use of the venue. Make sure that you find out the requirements for how the venue should be left before the event starts so that you have made the right arrangements.

London Canal Museum

The London Canal Museum offers itself as a venue. As part of the conditions of its hire agreement, the museum asks that event organisers do the following in terms of cleaning and refuse:

'Under the hire agreement clients are responsible for taking away what they bring in. However we are generally willing to deal with a reasonable amount of refuse arising from the event. We do require that glass bottles are separated from all other rubbish and are stored in cardboard boxes – generally the ones they came in. Please don't let the boxes get wet, or break up empty boxes in usable condition. This enables us to load boxes of empty bottles to be taken for recycling. Other rubbish should be bagged. We don't expect clients to do any cleaning. However please note that you should clear everything from all tables at the end of the event. Rubbish can be left for us but everything else should be taken off the premises, or, if a storage facility has been booked, placed in the storage location. We will put away the "basic furniture" but you should arrange for your caterer to put any hired furniture, including our banqueting furniture if hired from us, back in the store room after use, unless we have agreed to do this, possibly at an additional charge.'

Think about it!

1. Is there anything you find unusual in this agreement?

2. What other aspects of using the London Canal Museum as a venue would you need to think about after the event?

3. Now research other venues and produce a checklist of things that you should remember for your event. Is there anything you missed?

Returning or securing equipment

Any equipment that was borrowed for the event will need to be returned and checked to see if it is still working. It is far better to make the owner of the equipment aware if there has been a problem with it during the event as this will avoid it being used by another event organiser at a later date.

Make sure you think about the packing and removal of equipment or any other resources. You will need to think about wrapping, bags and boxes to do this. Food may need to be thrown away immediately if it has been out of chilled conditions for a while, but other resources such as brochures or leaflets should be taken away and reused or recycled. Some venues will allow you to leave a limited amount of publicity material around after the event so it is important to ask the venue owner if this is possible.

Reconciliation of accounts to budget

Another very important task that must be completed at the end of the event is the reconciliation of the accounts to the budget. This means that every item of expenditure that you budgeted for is checked against the actual amounts that were spent. You should make sure that every time someone has bought something that the receipt or invoice has been correctly stored. Any receipts of income will also need to be checked against the sales budget.

When the checks have been made and the accounts have been finalised it is then possible to check whether the event has made a surplus/profit, broken even or made a loss. If there is a surplus/profit, then it is important to consider how this money will be used. It may be re-invested in the organisation, shared amongst the investors or even given to a charitable cause. Breaking even means money is neither lost nor made but costs are covered. If the event is loss making this will be a problem unless there is another reason for holding it that is not financial, for example, a consultation or awareness of a particular organisational issue in a local community.

Assessment activity 18.3 **P5 P6 P7** BTEC

1. Under your tutor's guidance choose a business event at which you can provide support. Provide support during the running of the event and produce a written account of what you did. **P5**
2. Produce written guidelines for dealing with problems at a business event. **P6**
3. Produce a written report describing how you carry out follow-up activities after a business event. **P7**

Grading tips

1. You will need to show how you provided support at the event. Your tutor may assess you on the running of the actual event and provide observation statements, or you will be asked to give a written account of what happened. **P5**

2. You should also describe in a written report the problems that you could have as well as those that you actually had at the event you supported and how they should be dealt with. **P6**

3. You will need to describe the processes that you followed at the end of the event including the circulation of any materials and the reconciliation of the budget. **P7**

PLTS

Producing guidelines for dealing with problems using reasoned arguments will help you to develop your skills as an **independent enquirer**.

4.2 Evaluation

Evaluating an event is a very important stage of running a business event that is sometimes not completed in as much detail as other elements of the event. This often happens because at the end of the event organisers may be relieved that the event has finished or immediately start thinking about their next event. Event planning can be very hard work. However, it is critical that an event evaluation is made so that the event can be improved if it was held again. Notes or minutes of this meeting should be kept and filed so that they may be referred to.

Debrief

Debriefing of the event may take place at a meeting or may be written down on a debrief form. At a debriefing meeting, all the people who were involved with the event need to get together to look at what has worked well and what has not worked well and how the event could be improved for the next time. Alternatively, an event debrief form can be filled out by a nominated person.

Delegate questionnaire

It is also possible to ask delegates to complete a short questionnaire asking them to give feedback on their thoughts about the event and any ways that they think it should be improved. Figure 18.7 shows a sample questionnaire that may be used or adapted.

Event problems and solutions

After the event, any problems that arose should be investigated and the source of the problems identified. For example, if too many or too few delegates turned up, the event organiser will need to consider which factors contributed to this.

Activity: Debrief form

Use either the sample debrief form from Figure 18.6, a form you have received from your tutor or one you have produced yourself.

1. Complete a debrief form for the event you supported for your Assessment activity 18.3.
2. Consider how well the activity went and how it could be improved next time.
3. Share your results with other members of your class or with your teacher and discuss your findings.

EVENT DEBRIEF FORM
Name of the event
Date, time and location
Event organiser
How did the event run overall, including what was particularly good about it (if anything)?
Were there any accidents/emergencies/major issues?
Was anything missing on the risk assessment?
Were there any problems with the venue or facilities, including catering if applicable?
Any other issues or notes from the event that other event organisers should be aware of?
Would you recommend using this venue again?

Figure 18.6: Debrief form

DELEGATE FEEDBACK QUESTIONNAIRE

Name of delegate

Delegate's email address

Name of event

Date and location

Please rate the event using the scales provided (1 being very good; 4 being very poor). *Please circle.*

How useful was the pre-event information?	1	2	3	4
How easy was the location to find?	1	2	3	4
How good was the registration process?	1	2	3	4
What did you think of the refreshments?	1	2	3	4
What did you think of the facilities on offer?	1	2	3	4
How did you find the equipment provided ?	1	2	3	4
How did you find the presentations given?	1	2	3	4
How good was the event overall?	1	2	3	4

General comments about the event

Suggestions for other events or ways to further enhance the event

Would you recommend this event to a colleague or friend?	Yes	No
Can we contact you about future events?	Yes	No

Figure 18.7: Delegate questionnaire

Identifying the problems will help the organiser to consider possible solutions and thus avoid problems next time. A few of the most common problems that organisers may have when organising their event for the first time are shown in Table 18.7.

Activity: Problem and solution table

Using ICT, type up the problem and solution table shown in Table 18.7. Add further problems that you have encountered or others that you have heard of and their solutions.

Lessons learned

After any event, a good organiser will make a note of lessons learned. This should be for all outcomes, whether they are positive or negative. If something has worked really well you will need to remember it, but if it has not worked well you will need to try to ensure that it does not happen again.

4.3 Circulation of materials after the event

Bringing all the materials together after the event allows the findings of the event to be shared with others and kept on record.

Table 18.7: Common event problems

Problem	Possible solution
Not enough people turn up	Increase publicity, including advertising and other methods of promotion. Check if other similar events are happening at the same time to avoid any clashes. Check whether or not the event was aimed at a particular target group or was so general that no particular group was interested. If tickets were sold, check that the right price was suggested and that the places where the tickets were promoted were appropriate.
Too many people turn up	Expect larger numbers next time. Increase the ticket price (if applicable) to reduce demand. For health and safety reasons continue to allow only a safe number of delegates to attend.
Poor catering or refreshments	Change venue. Change catering supplier. Consider the budgeted cost of catering to be realistic with what is being asked for compared to the cost of producing it.

Minutes of meeting

Meetings often have formal minutes attached to them or, at the very least, have notes. Minutes record what happened in the meeting and any actions that need to be taken before the next meeting. Minutes need to be shared with attendees at the meeting as soon as possible so that they can look through them, check that they are accurate and carry out any actions if this is applicable.

Evaluation forms/questionnaires

Any forms, such as the debrief form or the delegate questionnaires, should be pulled together and the results analysed. Any conclusions or recommendations about the event should be shared with the event organising team and the organisation that was responsible for sponsoring the event. If the event was viewed positively this will help the reputation of the organisation, but if it is viewed negatively it may be necessary to think of ways to improve the reputation after the event.

The event organiser should also review comments by other people about the event on evaluation websites or those of the local or national media.

Other evaluations about the event may be drawn together in a written paper, which is then passed to the organising committee.

Post-event papers

For large conferences or exhibitions it is common to issue post-event papers that may contain details of the presentations or of the exhibitors who were at the event. It is also becoming increasingly common to share post-event papers in other ways such as through websites, podcasts, blogs or even through social or business networking sites.

Circulation lists

Circulation lists are a way of distributing information to delegates who have attended the event and can be a very useful way of encouraging delegates to attend future events that you hold. It is becoming more common to have e-lists, or email lists, that are used to send information to the delegates. Other ways that event organisers can put together circulation lists is through a website with password access for previous delegates. Some event organisers have social or business networking sites that keep their delegates up to date with information and events in their local area.

Assessment activity 18.4   P8 M3 D1 D2   BTEC

You have just run a business event. Now produce a presentation and full written report to provide a detailed review by covering the following performance criteria.

1. Review the success of the business event. **P8**
2. Evaluate how a business event can inform future planning. **M3**
3. Evaluate the management of a business event making recommendations for future improvements. **D1**
4. Evaluate feedback from delegates participating in the event. **D2**

Grading tips

1. You should look at how successful the event was in terms of meeting its objectives, how well it was organised and how any issues were solved to keep the activity running smoothly. **P8**

2. You should identify different methods of evaluation, such as a delegate questionnaire or a debrief form. You should explain how these methods contribute to identifying problems and providing solutions for future events. **M3**

3. For D1 and D2, you will need to make judgements about the management of the business event as well as consider feedback from delegates participating in the event. Build on your work for P8 and M3 to develop your thoughts and understanding. Include references to other events and information from books, websites and journals where you can. Remember to put those references in your bibliography. **D1 D2**

Just checking

1. Name two different roles of an event organiser.
2. Why might a business event need an agenda?
3. Which law covers the sale of tickets for an event?
4. Why is negotiation important in business event planning?
5. Name two different types of business event that could be organised.
6. What is the difference between a formal and informal business event?
7. What does 'target audience' mean in the context of an event?
8. Give one reason why there might be a change to event arrangements.
9. Why is the location of an event critical to any business event?
10. Name two special requirements that delegates may have when they attend a business event.
11. Which activities need to take place immediately after a business event has finished.
12. Why might the type of catering affect where you hold an event?
13. What is the purpose of an event programme?
14. Who are attendees at an event?
15. How can you send a soft copy document?
16. How does the Supply of Goods and Services Act protect event organisers?
17. What is corporate manslaughter?
18. When should a risk assessment be completed for an event?
19. Why is it important to have clear levels of authority when planning an event?
20. What does multi-tasking mean?

edexcel

Assignment tips

1. Make sure you include the paperwork that you have used for researching your work. Include these in your appendices and reference information, using a bibliography.

2. Carry out research into as many different business events as you possibly can. Find out which ones worked well and which ones did not work well. Try to learn from any errors that were made by other event organisers.

3. Make sure you get a lot of advice from your tutor as you work through this unit; it is important that you check that you have the authority to make decisions, especially those that include spending money.

21 Aspects of contract and business law

Contracts exist in every aspect of the business world. From buying a sandwich or newspaper to creating multi-million pound deals, contracts are the essential business requirement. The whole basis of business has been underpinned by agreements made between traders and individuals. Whether you are a sole trader selling apples from a market stall or a tycoon like Sir Richard Branson or Lord Sugar securing contracts worth millions of pounds, the essential elements of the contract will be the same with the same rules and ideas of fairness between the parties.

In this unit, you will learn about the key elements of a valid contract and factors which might invalidate them and apply these points to business situations. Whilst many contracts are concerned with agreements between businesses, there are many contracts made between a business and a member of the public. You will also learn how statutory consumer protection law will protect the parties in such contracts by looking at the following law. When contracts go wrong, parties will want to know that there is the opportunity to gain compensation. In the final part of this unit, you will look at the remedies available to help the injured party.

Learning outcomes

After completing this unit, you should:

1. understand the legal requirements for a valid contract
2. understand the meaning and effect of terms in a standard form contract
3. understand the impact of statutory consumer protection on the parties to a contract
4. know the remedies available to the parties to a contract.

Assessment and grading criteria

This table shows you what you must do in order to achieve a **pass**, **merit** or **distinction** grade, and where you can find activities in this book to help you.

To achieve a **pass** grade the evidence must show that the learner is able to:	To achieve a **merit** grade the evidence must show that, in addition to the pass criteria, the learner is able to:	To achieve a **distinction** grade the evidence must show that, in addition to the pass and merit criteria, the learner is able to:
P1 identify the legal criteria for offer and acceptance in a valid contract **See Assessment activity 21.1, page 93**	**M1** analyse the impact of the requirements for a valid contract in a given situation **See Assessment activity 21.1, page 93**	
P2 explain the law in relation to the formation of a contract in a given situation **See Assessment activity 21.1, page 93**		
P3 describe the law with respect to misrepresentation in a given situation **See Assessment activity 21.1, page 93**		
P4 describe the meaning of terms in a standard form contract **See Assessment activity 21.2, page 99**		**D1** evaluate the effectiveness of terms in a given contract **See Assessment activity 21.2, page 99**
P5 explain the effect of terms in a contract **See Assessment activity 21.2, page 99**		
P6 explain the law with respect to consumer protection in given situations **See Assessment activity 21.3, page 106**	**M2** analyse how consumers are protected in the event of breach of contract for the supply/sale of goods or services **See Assessment activity 21.3, page 106**	**D2** evaluate the statutory protection given to a consumer in their dealings with a business and the remedies available **See Assessment activity 21.4, page 111**
P7 describe the remedies available for breach of contract **See Assessment activity 21.4, page 111**	**M3** analyse the remedies available to a business provider in the event of breach of contract for the supply of goods or services **See Assessment activity 21.4, page 111**	

How you will be assessed

This unit will be assessed by an internal assignment that will be designed and marked by the staff at your centre. The assignment is designed to allow you to show your understanding of the unit outcomes. These relate to what you should be able to do after completing this unit.

Your assessment will be in the form of:

- presentations
- case studies
- practical tasks
- written assignments.

Fran, 25, part-time BTEC National student

I own a small business selling computer spares and accessories for the gaming world. I have been doing this for three years. The business has grown from my dealing with a few items per week to owning two shops and a warehouse. I had to take the BTEC Business course to learn about contract and business law.

I've learned about how contracts can be created through offer and acceptance, which has really helped me in my business. When I first started the business, I used to deal with people who would only use verbal contracts, but whilst studying this unit, I realised that contract law can help and protect business people like me. I'm glad I studied this unit! I am now much more confident in dealing with contractual issues and I know how important it is to have excellent contract writing skills. The business world is ever changing and I want to start to sell online and have developed a website to do this. Again, this area is covered by contract law and this unit has helped me understand this.

The unit has taught me how vital contracts for business are and the importance of contract terms like price, description and delivery. Contract law is quite complicated, so my advice to anyone studying it is to spend quality time looking at the case studies and principles that make this subject so fascinating. I found it useful to try to put some of the older contract cases into a more modern context.

1. When do you think a contract is formed?
2. How useful would it be to know when a valid contract exists?
3. How do you think studying this unit will help you to understand contract law?

1 Understand the legal requirements for a valid contract

Life without contract

When an organisation agrees to provide a service to an individual, the parties will usually sign a contract which explains what services the organisation will provide to the individual, and will set out the terms of this service. For example, a contract for a domestic broadband connection may say there are no limits on downloads, so long as it is within reasonable use.

1. Using the example, if an individual started to use their broadband connection for commercial purposes and their usage was constantly well above average levels, would they have broken the contract?

2. Now, imagine a business world without contract law. What might be the consequences of business agreements not being formally recognised?

1.1 Contracts

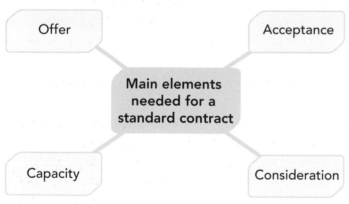

Figure 21.1: The main elements needed for a valid contract

In order to run a business, an owner will require premises, staff, plant or machinery to produce goods and, of course, buyers or users of the product or service the business provides. At the heart of these business dealings is the **contract**. Contract law will allow the business to secure premises, hire staff, buy equipment and allow it to trade legally.

The key elements of a contract that will need to be applied are an offer, followed by an acceptance, together with consideration and capacity.

Definition

A contract is an agreement or set of promises, enforceable by law, made between two or more persons to do or refrain from doing something. In the business world, it is more than a mere promise; there must be an intention to create a legally binding agreement between the parties and they must intend to give something of value as consideration to add value to the set of promises. The starting point for an enforceable contract is the offer and its acceptance.

Types

Contracts can be found in everyday transactions such as buying a newspaper or sandwich to more complex transactions such as buying a mobile phone. In the business world, the range of contractual agreements can be vast from buying photocopier paper to placing orders for multi-million pound contracts. These contracts can take a variety of forms.

Key term

Contract – an enforceable agreement made between two or more parties.

Verbal

A verbal contract is when two parties agree through the spoken word and are therefore bound by a verbal agreement. This is often done between friends or business people who know each other well enough to agree to be bound legally on a spoken word or a handshake.

Written

In the business world it is more common for parties to be bound by the terms of a written contract, where the details of the contract are included in a document signed by each party. These can range from relatively simple agreements to much more formal contracts signed by the parties.

Some contracts that must be written and signed by all parties include:

- the sale of land – the law requires that the contract must be written together by all parties, with all terms agreed, signed and dated by them

Why are written contracts so common in the business world?

- regulated credit and hire agreements – under the Consumer Credit Act 1974 all agreements of this type must be in writing

- employment – it is a requirement of employment legislation that all employees are given, within two months of commencing work, a contract showing the terms and conditions of employment.

Legally, the effects of verbal and written contracts are exactly the same and all the parties agree to be bound by the contract. However, there are many benefits of having the contract in writing, some of which are as follows.

- A well-written, clear, concise contract can avoid, or at least lessen, customer disputes and complaints. It should, if the parties are clear as to their respective rights and obligations, minimise litigation, which can be extremely expensive and time consuming.

- The subject matter may be easier to understand in a written contract. Disputes can be avoided if the specifications of the product are carefully and accurately described, or if the services being provided are set out in full.

- Written contracts can specify delivery times and/or deadlines for performance of service(s).

- Remedies for defective products or inadequate performance should clearly be stated on a written contract.

- It is easier to put down the payment terms in a written document.

- A written contract can provide alternative methods for the settlement of certain disputes, such as arbitration or a system of 'alternative dispute resolution' (ADR). For some types of dispute, such a method may be quicker and cheaper than going through the courts.

Standard form contracts

Companies may use their own **standard form contracts**, which often contain terms that amount to custom-made offers and acceptances that fit individual business needs. So it is quite possible for one company to make an offer on its own standard form

> ### Key term
>
> **Standard form contract** – a contract made between parties using their standard set of terms.

contract and the other company to accept it on their own standard form contract.

Benefits of using standard form contracts include:

- cost reduction
- avoiding the need for individual negotiation
- regular parties such as producers and suppliers, who are contracted frequently, become familiar with their rights and obligations.

Where one party is an individual and not acting in the course of business, the terms must be written in plain intelligible language so that all sides can understand the contract. For a larger business, this can be considered a disadvantage. There are other disadvantages of using standard form contracts.

- They can appear one-sided and heavy-handed, particularly when one of the contracting parties is an individual not acting in the course of a business and the other has a stronger bargaining position.
- There are certain statutory controls regulating standard form contracts, and some terms will be subject to a reasonableness test. Also, where one of the parties is a private individual, in general, terms must be 'fair', otherwise, they will be declared invalid and unenforceable by the business.
- A business may come to rely too much on its standard terms, and not bother to negotiate individual contracts for customers.
- Any standard terms must clearly form part of the business arrangement, so that the other party is given notice of the terms before the contract is entered into so that they can be accepted or rejected.

Offers

An **offer** is a definite promise from one of the parties to the agreement made. They make this promise with the intention that it shall become binding or legally enforceable as soon as it is accepted by the person receiving the offer.

Invitations to treat

There is a difference between an offer and an **invitation to treat**. An invitation to treat is an indication that a person is prepared to receive offers from another person. In this sense, 'treat' means 'trade' or 'to do business'. The person who is available to receive an invitation to treat can accept or reject

the offer until the final moment of acceptance. An invitation to treat can exist in many ways, such as:

- goods displayed, with a price ticket attached, in a shop window or supermarket; the customer can make an offer to buy that can be accepted or rejected by the seller at any time until it is accepted
- products advertised in catalogues, brochures and the Internet, even if the word 'Offer' is used by sellers to promote their goods
- the company prospectus issued when a company is selling its shares, as potential investors offer to buy the shares at a price that the directors can accept (through allocation) or reject.

Invitations to treat can sometimes cause confusion and embarrassment when mistakes have been made about product information (usually on price). This has resulted in businesses having to tell disappointed customers that their products strangely are 'not for sale'. This is because information classed as an invitation to treat does not have to be sold at all.

At an early stage in any negotiation the parties must decide whether they are intending to form a contract (by making a definite offer) or whether they are merely making enquiries about the possibility of making a contract in the future (for example, an invitation to treat). One way to do this is to look at the intention of the parties and from their actions decide whether a definite offer had been made or whether the parties are still merely negotiating. This can be very difficult to establish and it is normally up to the person relying on the offer to prove that a contractual intention was to be formed.

Counter-offers

The principle of acceptance is that the offer must be accepted on the same terms as it was made. One factor that indicates the offer has not been accepted is the existence of a **counter-offer**. The effect of a counter-offer is to terminate or end the original

Key terms

Offer – a promise that is intended to be followed.

Invitation to treat – indication that a person might be open to receive an offer; this is not legally binding.

Counter-offer – an offer that invalidates the original offer.

Case study: Stevenson Jacques & Co. v McLean [1880]

An offer was made to sell a quantity of iron by Mr McLean. The offer was accepted by Mr Stevenson, but he wanted to know if delivery of the iron could be done in stages as he was unable to accept all of the iron at once. Mr Stevenson, having heard nothing, then sent a formal letter of acceptance. Mr McLean, however, based on the enquiry about delivery methods, believed that the contract was ended and had sold the iron to a third party.

Mr Stevenson successfully sued for breach of contract.

The defendant's argument that there had been a counter-offer failed. The Court held that the enquiry was not a counter-offer.

1. Explain why the Court was able to maintain that the claimant's enquiry was not a counter-offer.

2. Why is it important that the acceptance is the same as the offer?

3. Evaluate the effect of a counter-offer on an original offer.

offer. However, mere enquiries about the variation of contract terms at the negotiating stage will not amount to a counter-offer although it may appear to be one.

Communication of offers

An offer must be communicated to the other party, usually in writing although verbal communication will still be valid. The offer must also be certain and not too vague or it will be invalid. A person embarking upon entering into contract negotiations must know what it is that they are agreeing to in certain terms.

There is, however, an exception to this rule. In certain situations, known as 'reward cases', an offer to make a contract can be made to many people, or even in theory the whole world. The term has come from the idea that if you were to lose your dog and then offer a reward for its safe return, you would be making a universal offer to any person in particular who might accept the challenge and begin to look for the dog.

Acceptance

A valid offer must be accepted by the **offeree** to the contract. Several important factors should be considered when looking at **acceptance**.

- In normal circumstances, acceptance of the offer must be communicated to the person making the offer, the **offeror**.

- Acceptance of an offer must be in the form (if any) specified in the offer. If no form is specified, written or oral acceptance will suffice.

- Acceptance need not necessarily be in the specified form as laid down in the offer as long as the method of acceptance used satisfies the offer and the offeror is not prejudiced in any way.

Key terms

Offeree – the person receiving an offer.

Acceptance – the formal agreement to accept an offer.

Offeror – the person making the offer.

Case study: Carlill v Carbolic Smoke Ball Company [1892]

The Carbolic Smoke Ball Company placed advertisements in various newspapers advertising its new flu remedy. The advertisement stated that it would pay £100 to any person who used their smoke balls for 14 days and still caught flu. Mrs Carlill used the remedy but unfortunately still caught the flu and made a claim against the company for the money.

The Smoke Ball Company refused to pay the money, so she took legal action to recover the money. Amongst many arguments put forward by the company was that the advertisement was an attempt to make an offer to the whole world which

communication of it was impossible. Finding in favour of Mrs Carlill, the Court of Appeal stated that the company had made an offer to the whole world which was capable of being accepted by anyone coming forward to perform the required conditions of the offer.

1. Explain how an offer was made in this case. How is this case a reward case?

2. Give examples of other types of reward cases.

3. Why would businesses create such offers?

Case study: Household Fire & Carriage Accident Insurance Co. v Grant [1879]

Mr Grant made an offer to purchase some shares in the Household Fire Insurance Company. The company posted their acceptance, but Mr Grant never received it.

Shortly afterwards, the company got into financial difficulty and went into liquidation. Mr. Grant claimed that as he had not received the acceptance, he was not a shareholder. The Court, however, held that there was valid acceptance of

his offer even though he never received it.

1. Describe the normal rules of acceptance and evaluate why they were valid in this case.

2. Describe the postal acceptance rules.

3. In today's world of instant electronic communication, would the outcome of this case have been different?

- Acceptance of an offer must be absolute, unqualified and without condition. The effect of a change in acceptance will have the effect of cancelling the original offer as it creates a counter offer.

Acceptance by post is an exception to the rule that acceptance must be communicated to the person making the offer. When posted, acceptance is considered to be effective as soon as a correctly addressed, stamped envelope is posted in a letterbox. Acceptance will be valid even if the letter is delayed or never reaches its destination. Proof of postage will be required to show the acceptance was posted. It is not acceptable to hand the letter to the postie.

With the increased use of technology in the business world, there have been problems associated with offers and acceptances sent using forms of communication such as email or fax. The general position had been

that the postal rules still apply here. However, the Electronics Commerce Regulations (EC Directive) 2002 stated that contracts created and sent by electronic means, such as via the Internet, will only be formed when the offeror has acknowledged receipt of the offeree's acceptance.

The parties in a contract can get around the postal rules by either:

- always asking for proof of postage and receipt
- stipulating in the contract that acceptance is upon confirmation.

The battle of the forms

Particular difficulties have arisen in business law when companies deal with one another using standard form contracts (see Standard form contracts, page 81). When businesses go into contract with each other they each may make an offer and acceptance on their own forms. These standard form contracts often contain terms that are in conflict with each other.

As businesses increasingly rely on standard form contracts, inevitable disputes arise. It is not an easy thing to decide and it may be very difficult to determine whose terms have prevailed. Sometimes there may not be a valid contract at all, due to the conflict. The modern approach of the courts is to take the most recent counter-offer as being accepted by the offeror, which means the contract will be concluded on those terms.

No turning back; the contract is formed

Case study: Butler Machine Tool Company Ltd v Ex-Cell-O Corp. (Eng) Ltd [1979]

The Butler Machine Tool Company offered to supply machinery to the Ex-Cell-O Corporation for £75,535. The quotation included a term in a standard form contract called a variation clause that allowed the seller to increase the price of the quotation. The Ex-Cell-O Corporation accepted the offer on their own standard form contract that was silent as to variation clauses.

An agreement was made and on delivery, the price had been increased by £2,892. The defendant refused to pay this.

The Court of Appeal decided that the defendant's form had been accepted by the claimant so the defendant's terms governed the agreement. Therefore, the claim to recover the extra money failed.

1. How do you think the Court decided which standard form contract should be used in this case?

2. Explain why businesses use standard form contracts.

3. Can you propose a better way of dealing with such disputes?

Consideration

Under contract law, the agreement between the parties will not in itself create a legally binding contract. There must be some degree of **consideration** between the parties for a valid contract. Consideration would be something of value given, promised or done in exchange by each party to the agreement.

Something already completed by a party can never be deemed consideration, since, by its very nature, a consideration is a promise for something to happen. Consideration can take two forms:

- **executed consideration** – an act in exchange for a promise, such as a reward case where the person making the offer promises to pay the reward upon the act of the task being completed

- **executory consideration** – the parties exchange promises to perform acts in the future; most contracts begin in this way. For example, a seller promises to deliver to a buyer as a result of the buyer's promise to buy at the agreed price.

Consideration from the buyer is the promise to pay the price on completion.

Consideration must not be illegal. A contract will not be valid if the consideration involved is illegal or considered immoral. Furthermore, consideration cannot be one-sided; it must always move from the **promisee** to the **promisor** which emphasises the idea that there must be consideration in form from both parties to a contract. Therefore, if Person X makes a promise to Person Y, Person Y must also show consideration for that promise.

Key terms

Consideration – the value attached to the promises on a contract.

Executed consideration – an act in exchange for a promise.

Executory consideration – a promise yet to be fulfilled.

Promisee – the person receiving the promise.

Promisor – the person making the promise.

Case study: McArdle [1951]

When Mr McArdle died, he left his wife a life interest in their house, after which it was to be given to their children.

The widow and her three grown children all moved into the house. The wife of one of the sons made voluntary improvements to the house valued at £488. The other siblings agreed to reimburse their brother for the work done. Later, however, a dispute arose and they refused to pay.

The Court held that the promise to pay was not legally binding since it was made after the work had been done.

1. Why was consideration not valid in this case?

2. Explain what consideration means.

3. What could have been done to satisfy the requirements of consideration in this case?

Case study: Chappell & Co. Ltd v Nestlé Co. Ltd [1960]

As part of a promotional campaign, Nestlé offered to send a record to consumers who sent in a postal order for one shilling and sixpence plus three wrappers from Nestlé Six Penny Bars. A copyright dispute arose between Nestlé and the owners of the record who claimed Nestlé was selling the record for money, which would require a separate agreement. Nestlé claimed it was not selling the record for money. It argued that the wrappers had no value and, under the Copyright Act 1956, all it was required to do was give the owners notice and 6.25 per cent of the retail-selling price as payment.

The House of Lords disagreed and held that the wrappers were consideration in the transaction as the offer by Nestlé was to supply the record in return for cash *plus* the wrappers.

1. Explain what consideration was given in this case.
2. Do you think the consideration was sufficient?
3. Can you think of any other similar types of promotion today? What are the types of consideration provided?

Did you know?

Many manufacturers and businesses offer promotional voucher and money-saving schemes. Often these coupons will have monetary value of less than 1p to satisfy the rules of consideration.

In all valid contracts, consideration must have some value but there is no requirement for that value. It is agreed by the parties and the Court will not side with parties who agree on considerations and then complain of making a bad bargain.

Privity of contract

In contract law, the traditional position regarding contract formation has been that the contract only created rights between the parties. This meant that a third party could not acquire rights under the contract. The relationship between third parties and the main parties to a contract is known as **privity of contract**.

Key term

Privity of contract – the relationship between third parties to a contract. It is a legal concept denying third parties the right to sue on a contract.

A simple example of this would be Person A promising Person B that he will pay a sum of money to Person C. In this case, the contract is between Person A and Person B; therefore, Person C cannot sue Person A for the money.

Privity of contract is firmly linked with consideration. This is one of the most important ways a third party can either become liable or gain rights on a contract.

Contracts (Rights of Third Parties) Act 1999

The Contracts (Rights of Third Parties) Act 1999 created the law that allows third parties to have rights in a contract that affects them, thus becoming a statutory exception to the idea of privity of contract.

The third party rights, under the Act, are limited by the terms and conditions in the contract. The parties must limit and define what rights they want to give the third

Did you know?

In the 1975 case, Jackson v Horizon Holidays, Lord Denning ruled that the claimant could recover damages for himself as well as for the family members who went on holiday with him (yet had not paid for the holiday themselves).

Case study: Price v Easton [1833]

This case involved a three-way agreement between Easton and X. Easton had agreed with X that if they completed work for him, Easton would pay Price. X completed the work and Price expected to be paid; however, Easton refused to pay Price who sued him for the money. Price's action failed.

1. Who was Price in relationship to the contract?
2. Why was Easton able to refuse to pay Price, and then win the case?
3. Do you think privity of contract is a fair rule?

Case study: Tweddle v Atkinson [1861]

Before Mr Tweddle was to marry, his father and future father-in-law, Mr Atkinson exchanged promises in which the father-in-law would pay Mr Tweddle a sum of money in consideration of his intent to marry.

The marriage went ahead and unfortunately, the father-in-law died without making a payment, Mr Tweddle sued the executors of Mr Atkinson's estate.

The claimant's action was unsuccessful in the courts.

1. What might the consideration have been in this case?
2. Why did the case fail?
3. Should agreements like these form valid contracts at all? Justify your answer.

Case study: Nisshin Shipping Co. Ltd v Cleaves & Co. Ltd [2004]

Cleaves & Co. Ltd were brokers who, in this case, had negotiated contracts between Nisshin Shipping Co. Ltd, a ship owner, and companies who wished to hire vessels. In the contract, there was reference to a payment that should be made to Cleaves & Co.

Nisshin Shipping Co. refused to pay the commission to the broker, who then sued for damages. The broker won the case.

1. What consideration had the broker provided in the case
2. Why was the broker able to receive compensation in this case?
3. How well do you think the Contracts (Rights of Third Parties) Act 1999 has solved the problems caused by privity of contract?

party at the negotiation stage. Furthermore, to gain rights under the Act, the third party must be clearly identified by name, class or description but need not (in the case of a company) be in existence yet so long as it is clearly identified. With this, all remedies will be available to a third party as if they were part of the contract made between the original parties.

Capacity as applied to business situations

Having looked at offer, acceptance and consideration, we should also consider whether a person has legal **capacity** to enter into an agreement. This is vital if a contract is to exist between the parties. Capacity relates to whether or not a person has the legal power to enter into a contract.

There are certain classes of person that only have limited capacity to enter into legal agreements.

Minors

Legal rules have been developed to protect **minors** from contractual liability and to allow them to also enter into agreements in limited circumstances. There are two types of contract that will bind a minor when dealing with adults: those for the supply of necessary goods and those for employment.

What are you going to spend your pocket money on?

'I wish I was older!'

Key terms

Capacity – the legal power to enter into a contract.

Minors – people who are under 18. They are generally unable to make contracts.

Under the Sales of Goods Act 1979, contracts for the supply of necessary goods and services and beneficial contracts of service are binding on the minor. Under this Act, necessities are defined as:

'goods suitable to the condition in life of the minor and to his actual requirements at the time of sale and delivery'.

In the courts, necessities will be looked at in context of the social and financial background of the minor involved. Luxury goods are generally excluded as are items or services that the minor already has since these are not seen to be necessities of life.

Activity: Minors and legally binding contracts

In small groups, discuss which of the following would be legally binding, if a minor were to make contracts to purchase them:

- a set of golf clubs
- a motorcycle
- a copy of an exam revision guide
- a quantity of music downloads
- a pair of shoes
- a train ticket to London to attend an interview for a job
- a holiday to Florida
- cosmetic surgery.

Functional skills

Discussing the different aspects of legally binding contracts for minors will help you to develop your **English** skills in speaking and listening.

PLTS

Working in groups to discuss these issues will help you to develop your skills as a **team worker**.

A minor is also bound by contracts of employment, apprenticeship and education as long as the whole contract is for the benefit of the minor. This also includes contractual matters such as football apprenticeships and music scholarships.

A minor who sets himself up in business will not be bound by his trading contracts, even if they are

Did you know?

In September 2006, a three-year-old boy used his parent's home computer to successfully bid £9,000 for a pink Nissan Figaro car on the Internet site eBay. Having received the confirmation message from eBay the boy's parents believed that they were about to receive the new pink car! As soon as the seller was told what had happened he immediately rejected the boy's offer and put the car back up for sale.

deemed to be for his benefit. So a minor will not be liable to repay the price of goods if he fails to deliver them! If the contract was created fraudulently, however, it will be binding upon the minor.

Incapacitated persons

People suffering from a medically diagnosed mental health condition cannot enter into a valid contract as it is believed they do not have sufficient mental capacity to understand what they are doing. However, under the Mental Health Act 1983 the court may enter into valid contracts on a patient's behalf. Furthermore, the courts can continue contracts that were entered into before the person became ill.

If a person is suffering from temporary insanity, or a drink- or drug-related problem, any contract made by that person can be voidable providing they can prove that at the time of negotiation, they had no understanding of what was going on and the other party to the agreement knew this or should have known this.

Organisations

Organisations can enter into contracts, so it is necessary to consider the contractual position of various types of organisations.

Registered companies

Companies created by registration under the Companies Act 1985 (as amended) and, according to the law, have legal identities of their own and can sue and be sued on contracts made in their name. Under this Act, the company's power or capacity to contract is limited and defined to those powers in the **Memorandum of Association** in its Objects clause.

Key term

Memorandum of Association – the document which sets out the purpose of the company.

Case study: Kelner v Baxter [1866]

Kelner was the promoter of a proposed hotel and agreed to buy a stock of wine on its behalf from Baxter. At the time of the agreement, the company was not incorporated. After the company was incorporated it tried to enforce the contract in the name of the company, but a dispute arose and Baxter did not deliver the wine. The Court had to decide whether a contract existed at all, and if so, between whom.

1. What do you think was the outcome of this case?

2. Evaluate who you think was liable for the contract before the company was incorporated.

3. Find this case by doing some research on the Internet. Were you correct?

The Companies Act 1989 amended the 1985 Act, allowing a company to change its Objects clause by Special Resolution so that it can carry on any trade or business whatsoever. However, a company has no legal power before it is formed to enter into binding contracts. Any person acting on behalf of the company before the **date of incorporation** will be personally liable on the contract.

Unincorporated associations

These are groups of people joined to further a common interest, such as a sporting, social or political group. In general terms these groups are not considered legal entities and capacity to contract belongs to members jointly and not with the group or association in its own right.

Partnerships

Many partnerships are in fact associations formed for business purposes and are governed by the Partnership Act 1890. Under this Act, each partner has a capacity to contract on behalf of all the partners. Each partner is jointly liable on any contract entered into on behalf of the partnership. Here, it is not the partnership that has legal capacity but the individual partners themselves.

Local authorities

Local authorities are separate legal entities and have capacity to contract in their own right and have power from both the Royal Charter and the Local Government Act 1972. Local authorities are subject to the **ultra vires** rule and can be found to have acted beyond their powers.

1.2 Factors which invalidate or vitiate contracts

We have already seen that a binding agreement between two or more parties forms a valid contract. A binding contract will only be formed when there is consent between the parties and the contract was entered into voluntarily and freely. There are however a number of factors that will invalidate or vitiate (corrupt) an agreement.

Misrepresentation

Contracts are often preceded by a series of negotiations made between the parties. These negotiations are a series of representations forming the basis of the contract itself. If these representations are, in fact, **misrepresentations**, then the contractual position between the parties is in doubt.

A misrepresentation is a false statement of fact (not law) made by one party to the other party before the contract is made with a view to inducing the other to enter it. It must be shown that the statement has induced the person to whom it was made to enter into the contract. If it is a false statement, it can be a misrepresentation but if the person to whom the

Functional skills

Obtaining web-based information to find the results in this case study will help you to develop your **ICT** skills.

Key terms

Date of incorporation – the date a company comes into existence.

Ultra vires – to act outside of one's powers.

Misrepresentation – a set of untrue facts made by one party which are relied on by the other party when entering into the contract.

Activity: Car dealer

You are a second-hand car dealer and need to check that the information on your cars is correct so that you do not misrepresent the facts to customers. How would you do that? Copy and then complete the table below.

Representation	How could you check this?
Colour of car	
Age of car	
Number of previous owners	
Engine size	
Whether it had been stolen	
Whether it had been involved in an accident	
Mileage	

Functional skills

Filling out the table in the car dealer activity will help you to develop your **English** skills in writing.

statement was made attempts to check the truth of what has been said to him, then clearly they have not relied on that statement and the statement cannot be a misrepresentation.

Generally, for the law for misrepresentation to exist a positive statement must be made by a party making the representation. There is no general duty to disclose facts and silence will not normally amount to a misrepresentation. But gestures, smiles or a course of conduct may amount to a misrepresentation.

There is a duty to disclose relevant information in full. This information includes:

- contracts of insurance
- contracts for the sale of land
- contracts of family arrangement
- contracts to purchase shares.

The misrepresentation must involve a statement of fact not a statement of law or intention. However, if a person misrepresents what they intend to do in the future they may be liable for misrepresentation.

Case study: Spice Girls Ltd v Aprilia World Service BV [2000]

Spice Girls Ltd (SGL) was formed to promote the band the Spice Girls. At the beginning of May 1998 SGL entered into a contract with Aprilia World Service BV, an Italian company which manufactures motorcycles and scooters. The Spice Girls agreed to take part in a TV commercial promoting the scooters.

The contract was signed at the beginning of May and Geri Halliwell left the group at the end of May. A month before the contract was signed Geri had told the group that she would be leaving the band. The group did not disclose this information to Aprilia World Services BC and the contract was signed.

The Spice Girls went ahead with the shoot even though they knew Geri would have left by the time the commercial was due on air. This misrepresentation, according to the defendants meant that the commercial showing the five girls was of little value.

1. **What representations did the Spice Girls make to the defendant?**

2. **How was it claimed that the representations were broken?**

3. **Critically assess how far a person is under a duty to disclose the facts in a contract.**

A statement of opinion will not normally be considered a misrepresentation because a statement of belief is not capable of proof. There may be occasions when a statement of opinion may become a representation of fact when it can be proved that the person was in the position to know facts on which the opinion was based.

There are various types of misrepresentation, each resulting in a voidable contract.

Fraudulent misrepresentation

A person will be liable for fraud if they make a statement which they know to be false or they have no belief in its truth or they are reckless or careless whether it is true or false. In such a case, an injured party may reject the contract and also sue for damages for the tort of deceit. Furthermore, the person committing fraudulent misrepresentation may also be prosecuted in the criminal courts for fraud.

Always check what you have ordered when it arrives

> ## Did you know?
>
> In 2008, a new winter attraction was launched in the New Forest, Hampshire, called *Lapland New Forest*. A website was produced showing fantastic winter scenes. Unfortunately, the photos on the website were not taken at the park and customers were hugely disappointed at their experience; many demanded their money back. In 2009 the owners of the park appeared in court charged with fraudulent misrepresentation.

Negligent misrepresentation

A person can be liable for negligence when they make a false statement and have no reasonable ground for believing the statement to be true.

There is now statutory negligent misrepresentation under **S2(1)** of the Misrepresentation Act 1967. Under this Act, the burden of proof is on the defendant to show they are not liable and to show that they had a reasonable belief in the accuracy of their statement. Negligent misstatement will entitle the other party to rescission, whereby the injured party refuses to carry out the contract and the parties then return to their pre-contract prosition, or damages or both.

Innocent misrepresentation

An innocent misrepresentation is a false statement made by a person who had reasonable grounds to believe that it was true, not only when it was made but also when the contract was entered into.

There are various remedies for misrepresentation, including rescission. The injured party also has the right to claim damages for the misrepresentation.

Case study: Hedley Byrne & Co. Ltd v Heller & Partners [1963]

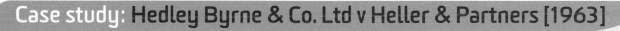

Hedley Byrne & Co., an advertising agency, needed financial advice on a particular company's standing and approached the company's bankers, Heller & Partners, for credit information. The defendants stated that the company was financially sound. A short time later, the company went into liquidation.

The Court ruled that the defendants were in principle liable as they had a duty of care to the claimants.

1. Describe how a duty of care existed in this case.
2. What type of misrepresentation existed here?
3. What could Heller & Partners have done differently?

Mistake

There is a rule of common law that **mistakes** with regard to the agreement will not affect the validity of the contract. The common law principle applied here is the maxim of *caveat emptor* or 'let the buyer beware'. This means that it is in reality up to the parties to accept the contract even if there had been a mistake. For example, if a person agrees to pay £500 for a second-hand car when in reality it is only worth £100, a valid contract for £500 can be created. The buyer must be aware of such factors as they will suffer any loss incurred.

There are circumstances however when a mistake will invalidate a contract. These instances include:

- where the parties make a mistake about the subject matter of the contract
- where there is a mistake as to the identity of the parties
- where a document has been signed in error.

Duress

As already stated, the parties must enter into a contract freely. If one of the parties has been forced into the contract due to violence or threats of violence to themselves or their family, the contract may be invalid. In such circumstances, the affected party can void the contract on the grounds of **duress**. This has now been extended to include threats of economic harm.

Undue influence

Undue influence occurs when one party to a contract has a dominant position over the other. Where such a relationship exists, there is a presumption that the more dominant party will have used undue influence and the weaker party may avoid the contract due to this influence.

Activity: Duress

Read the following cases. Then work with a partner to compare and contrast the different types of duress shown.

Barton v Armstrong [1976]

Mr Armstrong was the chairman of a company and Mr Barton was the managing director. Armstrong threatened to have Barton killed unless he signed an agreement buying Armstrong's share in the company at a highly inflated price. The claimant signed the contract but the Court decided that this contract could be voided by the claimant due to duress.

D&C Builders Ltd v Rees [1965]

D&C Builders completed some work valued at £482 for Mrs Rees. The company was in severe financial difficulties and continually chased Mrs Rees for payment. Rees, who got to know of the company's troubles, offered them £300 in full settlement, which was reluctantly accepted. D&C Builders subsequently sued for the balance. Rees tried to argue that she should owe nothing since the company agreed to the settlement. The Court disagreed and said Mrs Rees had held the company to ransom.

PLTS

Discussing the cases will help you to develop your skills as an **effective participator**.

Key terms

Mistake – when a person enters into a contract after getting the facts in the negotiation wrong.

Duress – when a person enters into a contract against their will.

Undue influence – when a party exerts pressure on another to enter into a contract due to the nature of their relationship or position.

Assessment activity 21.1

P1 P2 P3 M1 **BTEC**

1. Prepare a report that describes the essential elements of a contract in an area of your choice, such as mobile phone contract, a credit card or a new car. In your report:

   - identify the legal criteria for offer and acceptance of the contract **P1**

   - explain the law in relation to the formation of the contract. **P2**

2. Discuss possible examples of misrepresentation in the contract you have chosen and explain how the misrepresentation will affect that contract. **P3**

3. Prepare a presentation and information sheet analysing the impact of the requirements of the contract you have chosen. **M1**

   ### Grading tips

   1. Make sure you include both when and how a contract would come into existence. You should include a description of:

      - invitations to treat

   - how the contract comes into existence

   - the offer, acceptance and counter-offers. **P1 P2**

2. Ensure that you explain what misrepresentation is and the effect it has on contracts. **P3**

3. You should consider the strengths and weaknesses of the formation of a contract including relevant problems such as:

   - what is good or weak about the offer

   - implications of pricing through the invitation to treat

   - clarity of communication and capacity for acceptance

   - likelihood of counter-offers and their effect.

   You may wish to work as part of a group, but remember to write up your own ideas and presentations individually. **M1**

PLTS

Researching the contract law for this assessment activity will help you to develop your skills as an **independent enquirer**.

2 Understand the meaning and effect of terms in a standard form contract

A contract is a set of mutually agreed promises made between the parties with the intention of creating a legally binding agreement. It is important to analyse exactly what it is that the parties are agreeing to do.

2.1 Types of term

The statements made by the parties under negotiation that are not meant to form part of the contract are called representations, whilst the things that the parties are bound to perform under the contract are called the **terms** of the contract.

There are two types of term which can be found in a contract:

- the express term
- the implied term.

Key term

Terms – the parts of the contract agreed to by the parties.

Express

Express terms are statements made by the parties either by word of mouth or in writing and the parties intend that these terms will create the fundamental part of the contract. Express terms can be either **conditions** or **warranties**.

Conditions

A condition is a fundamental part of the agreement and is something which forms the root of the contract. For example, when buying a new car, a condition of the contract would be the dealer supplying the new car. If the parties agree to buy and sell a brand new car and the actual item supplied is a motorbike, then there is a clear breach of contract. A breach of condition will entitle the injured party to **repudiate** and claim damages.

Warranties

A warranty is a less important term that does not go to the root of the contract. A breach of a warranty will only give the injured party the right to claim damages; the contract itself cannot be rejected. For example, consider the issue of buying a new car. You agree with the supplier that it will be fitted with a particular model of DVD player. The car arrives, so the supplier has completed the main condition of the contract the supply of the car, but it has been fitted with the wrong type of DVD player. The DVD player is not the vital part of the contract and will be seen as a warranty. This failure although annoying for the person buying the car will not mean the contract can be automatically voided.

It is common in business contracts to not only have express terms relating to conditions and warranties but also to have common express key terms included in the contract These might include:

- exclusion clauses limiting the parties' responsibilities under the contract
- terms relating to the amount of damages that the parties might receive if things go wrong
- terms allowing parties to vary the contract price, known as a price variation clause.

Implied

Implied terms are not actually stated in a contract but are introduced into the contract by statute, custom and common law.

Key terms

Express terms – clauses in the agreement that are agreed to by the parties.

Conditions – essential parts of the contract.

Warranties – important terms of the contract, but not as important as to be classed as essential.

Repudiate – treat the contract as if it is over and invalid.

Implied term – part of the contract not necessarily included by the parties but automatically included by law to protect the parties.

Terms implied by statute

To protect parties, terms are implied into a contract by virtue of legislation. The best example is the Sale of Goods Act 1979 which is implied by statute into contracts for the sale of goods. According to this Act, in every contract for the sale of goods there will be the following terms implied.

- Every seller has the right to sell goods.
- Where there is a sale of goods by description there is an implied condition that the goods will correspond with that description.
- Goods sold are of a satisfactory condition and that they are fit for the particular purpose stated.
- In sample sales, there is an implied condition that the bulk order will correspond with the sample.

Terms implied by custom

An agreement may be subject to customary terms not actually specified by the parties. These could be historical; therefore, a person making a contract should try to find if any such terms are in existence. It should be noted, however, that such a custom will be overruled by any express clause to the contrary.

Terms implied by the common law

The courts will be prepared to imply a term into the contract in order to validate the obvious intentions of the parties. This may be a point that has been overlooked or may not have been clearly stated by the parties. In such circumstances, the court will imply such a term in the interests of 'business fairness' so that the contract makes commercial common sense.

The distinction between express and implied terms

Express terms will be those terms in the contract that the parties have negotiated and expressly agreed.

Parties can strike these terms out and re-negotiate until all terms have been agreed. The parties have total control over the type of express term their contract contains.

On the other hand, implied terms are those terms that the law insists are included in the contract. Here the parties have no say in the matter and if they wish to do business with each other must follow these implied terms precisely.

2.2 Impact of contractual terms

When the parties create a contract, its terms are expected to be followed by both sides. Probably the most important terms of the contract are the terms relating to the seller's delivery of the goods and the buyer's payment of these goods. Other important terms would be the quality of the goods delivered, issues relating to **title** or ownership and those terms describing how the parties can avoid or exclude responsibility on the contract.

Time for performance and rejection of goods

Usually the parties will have agreed on a date for delivery of the goods. This is known as a fixed delivery date and failure to deliver on time will allow the other person to repudiate the contract and sue for damages. Where there is no such fixed date the law implies into the contract that the delivery will take place within a reasonable time.

Price variation

Many businesses will include in their contracts a term that is known as a price variation clause. This is included to protect the parties from uncontrollable variations. The price first agreed when the parties negotiated may have changed due to unforeseen rises in perhaps inflation, fuel costs and production costs. Understandably, a business will not want to lose out financially and will cover such a rise with this term that allows them to increase the contract price.

Payment terms

The payment for goods delivered by the seller is a very important part of the contract. The payment terms will normally be agreed between the parties when the contract is negotiated. It will be usual to expect payment on delivery, payment by instalments or payment by any method agreed by the parties.

Quality and quantity of goods delivered

When the goods are delivered, it is expected that what was agreed to be delivered will in fact be delivered. The goods will be expected to match in terms of quality and quantity.

In terms of quality, the law implies into contracts that the goods delivered are fit for the purpose that they were intended, that they should be free from minor defects in terms of finish and appearance and that they should be safe and lasting. The buyer will have time to examine the goods upon delivery before deciding to accept them or to reject them if they fail to meet the required standard (see page 102 for more details).

If the wrong quantity is delivered, then the buyer has various options available regardless of what was agreed between the parties. If the seller delivers a smaller amount than was expected, the buyer can either reject the entire delivery or accept the smaller quantity for which full payment will be expected.

If the seller sends a larger quantity, the buyer can:

- accept the quantity expected and reject the rest
- reject the entire delivery
- accept the entire delivery at a new contract price.

If, however, the difference in quantity is so slight that it would make no difference to the contract then the buyer will be prohibited from rejecting the delivery.

Reservation of title

It is not unusual for a seller, wishing to protect themselves, to insert a clause into the contract that ownership of the goods is not to pass to the buyer until the seller has been paid. This is known as a **reservation of title** clause.

Key terms

Title – the legal right of ownership.

Reservation of title – retaining ownership of the goods until the contract is completed.

Activity: Key terms of a contract

You run a linen company and have secured a contract to deliver 10,000 bath towels to a national hotel chain.

What key terms would you include in the contract? Why?

Exclusion clauses

An **exclusion clause** is a term in a contract that tries to exempt or limit the liability of a party who is in breach of that agreement. The Unfair Contract Terms Act 1977 came into effect as a parliamentary control over the law relating to exclusion clauses. It was intended to be used primarily for contracts of sales by commercial organisations and businesses and not by individuals. Although this Act is a vitally important piece of legislation, there are some contracts where the Act does not apply. These are contracts for land, insurance, company promotions, shares and debentures and patents or copyrights.

Under the Act, exclusion clauses are regulated in one of two ways.

- They are rendered void and ineffective automatically because they are unfair.

- They are made subject to a test of reasonableness; should they fail the test, they will be deemed unfair.

If there is a dispute, the reasonableness of an exclusion clause will be a matter for the court to decide. They will do so in light of all of the circumstances of the case, such as the relative strength of the parties concerned.

Standard form contracts

Businesses will almost certainly try to limit their liability should things go wrong when they do business

---

STANDARD TERMS OF ENGAGEMENT

PLEASE NOTE: These Standard Terms of Engagement form part of the contract between the Surveyor and the Client. A modified form of the Homebuyer Survey & Valuation Service applies in Scotland.

PART 1: GENERAL

1 The Service. The standard HOMEBUYER Survey & Valuation Service ("the Service") which is described in Part 2 of these Terms ("the Description") applies unless an addition to the Service is agreed in writing before the Inspection. (An example of such an addition is reporting upon parts which are not normally inspected, such as the opening of all windows.)

2 The Surveyor who provides the Service will be a Chartered Surveyor who is competent to survey, value and report upon the Property which is the subject of these Terms.

3 Before the Inspection. The Client will inform the Surveyor of the agreed price for the Property and of any particular concerns (such as plans for extension) which he or she may have about the Property.

4 Terms of payment. The Client agrees to pay the fee and any other charges agreed in writing.

5 Cancellation. The Client will be entitled to cancel this contract by notifying the Surveyor's office at any time before the day of the Inspection. The Surveyor will be entitled not to proceed with the provision of the Service (and will so report promptly to the Client) if, after arriving at the Property, he or she concludes:

a) that it is of a type of construction of which he or she has insufficient specialist knowledge to be able to provide the Service satisfactorily; or

b) that it would be in the typical Client's best interests to be provided with a Building Survey, plus valuation, rather than the HOMEBUYER Service.

In case of cancellation, the Surveyor will refund any money paid by the Client for the Service, except for expenses reasonably incurred. In the case of cancellation by the Surveyor, the reason will be explained to the Client.

6 Liability. The Report provided is solely for the use of the Client and the Client's professional advisers and no liability to anyone else is accepted. Should the Client not act upon specific, reasonable advice contained in the Report, no responsibility is accepted for the consequences.

Figure 21.2: An extract from a typical standard form contract. Can you see how the surveyor excludes their liability?

---

with consumers by using their standard form (pre-written) contracts. To be effective the clauses in the standard form or term contract must be deemed to be reasonable.

2.3 Impact of statutes on common contractual terms

Generally, in the past businesses were free to create contracts on whatever terms they wished. The law never stepped in to protect parties who signed into bad bargains. However as businesses have become

---

> ### Key term
>
> **Exclusion clause** – a term in a contract that tries to exempt or limit the liability of a party who is in breach of contract.

Case study: RW Green Ltd v Cade Brothers Farm [1978]

RW Green, a farmer, bought seed potatoes from Cade Brothers Farm. An exclusion clause in the supplier's standard form contract stated that any complaint had to be brought within three days of delivery of the product.

After the seeds were planted, it was apparent that they were not of the correct quality and carried a virus. RW Green complained but the supplier tried to rely on the exemption clause in the contract. The Court ruled

in Green's favour, agreeing that three days was an unreasonably short period of time to find out if the seeds carried a virus.

1. Explain how an exclusion clause worked in this case.

2. How did the Cade Brothers Farm try to limit its liability?

3. How far do you think this clause was reasonable?

Proceed at your own risk

CONDITIONS OF PARKING
THE ROYAL HIGHLAND CENTRE
DOES NOT ACCEPT RESPONSIBILITY/
LIABILITY FOR DAMAGE OR THEFT
HOWSOEVER CAUSED TO ANY
VEHICLES OR PROPERTY ON
THE PREMISES

more powerful, with stronger bargaining positions, Parliament has passed more laws that have had an impact on business contracts.

Unfair Contract Terms Act 1977

The Unfair Contract Terms Act 1977 (UCTA) is a vitally important piece of legislation intended to protect innocent parties from unfair exclusion clauses such as:

- 'The management accepts no responsibility for loss or damage.'
- 'Cars parked at owners' risk.'

With these kinds of examples, the Act ensures that such clauses satisfy the test of reasonableness by making sure that those who are relying on them for protection display such signs adequately so users know of their existence.

There are some contracts where the Act does not apply, which include those for:

- land
- insurance
- company promotions, shares and debentures
- patents or copyrights.

Exclusion clauses under the Act are regulated in two ways.

- They are rendered void and ineffective.
- They are made subject to a test of reasonableness.

The reasonableness of an exclusion clause will be a matter for the court to decide. It will do so in light of all of the circumstances of the case. But the Act does lay down some interpretation guidelines for judges when deciding this question. These are:

- reasonableness will be judged in light of all the circumstances of the case
- it is up to the person claiming reasonableness of the term to prove it is reasonable
- there should be resources available to cover liability such as insurance
- the relative strengths of the parties should be looked at
- any inducements offered must be reviewed
- whether the customer should have known about the term
- practical considerations should be looked at, such as time factors
- any special circumstances requiring special terms should be evaluated.

The Act itself lays down some very important rules relating to exclusion clauses as noted below.

S2 states that a clause restricting liability for death or personal injury is void. Furthermore, liability for any other types of damage caused by negligence is subject to the reasonableness test.

S3 excludes liability in standard form contracts as well as **consumer contracts**. Consumer for the purpose of the Act means a person who makes the contract other than in a course of a business. With this definition, the other party makes the contract in the course of a business and the goods that pass under the contract are the type of goods that are usually supplied for private use or consumption.

S4 excludes liability for **indemnity clauses**. Exclusion clauses restricting liability must satisfy the reasonableness test.

Key terms

Consumer contract – a contract made between businesses and members of the public for consumer goods such as food, clothes and furniture.

Indemnity clause – a term in a contract between two parties, in which one of the parties agrees to protect the other party against liabilities such as damages, loss or injury, in respect of a third party.

S5 deals with guarantees of consumer goods. A manufacturer or distributor cannot restrict their liability in negligence for losses arising from defective goods. They are not allowed to restrict liability by means of a term in a guarantee.

S6 and **S7** both deal with implied terms in contracts of sale and hire purchase, whilst **S8** deals with exemption of liability for misrepresentation. It states that any clause that excludes or restricts liability for misrepresentation will be ineffective unless it satisfies the reasonableness test.

The Unfair Terms in Consumer Contract Regulations 1999

The Unfair Terms in Consumer Contracts Regulations 1999 was created to deal with exclusion clauses. The regulations apply only to consumer contracts and with them, the court can strike out any term in a contract that it deems to be unfair. The idea of unfairness looks at whether all of the parties have acted in good faith

Activity: The small print

In September 2006 the world's largest computer maker, Dell Inc., in response to a request by the Office of Fair Trading (OFT), made some changes to the small print in its contracts relating to faulty goods. The OFT discussed a number of terms with the company which it considered to be inconsistent with the Unfair Contract Term Act 1977 and the Unfair Terms in Consumer Contracts Regulations 1999.

Go to the Office of Fair Trading's website (www.oft.gov.uk) and find out more information on the changes Dell Inc. made to its contracts.

- What terms did OFT wish Dell Inc. to change?
- Why did OFT ask Dell Inc. to make these changes?
- Do you think that the changes made are enough?

Functional skills

Obtaining more information about Dell Inc.'s contract changes by doing web-based research will help you to develop your **ICT** skills.

and a judgment that will be made on the basis of the strength of the parties, whether any inducements were offered to make the consumer agree to the contract and whether the seller had dealt fairly with the consumer.

The Consumer Protection (Distance selling) Regulations 2000 (as amended)

The Unsolicited Goods and Services Act 1971 (now updated by the Consumer Protection (Distance Selling) Regulations 2000) made it a criminal offence for suppliers to demand payment for unsolicited goods and services to unsuspecting consumers. Furthermore, the receiver of these goods or services is under no obligation to return the items and may treat them as an unconditional gift and will be under no duty to pay for them. The supplier will be committing a criminal offence by demanding payment for them.

The Electronic Commerce (EC Directive) Regulations 2002

According to Verdict Research (www.verdict.co.uk) in the UK, web-based online retail sales in 2008 produced sales amounting to around £18.4 billion. This is an ever-growing market. As more and more businesses trade online, inevitably, problems will arise and laws are being introduced to control these problems and protect consumers.

Presently, there are various regulations which control the use of online selling with the main law being the Electronic Commerce (EC Directive) Regulations 2002. These regulations place restrictions on businesses that use electronic commerce as a way of selling items on the Internet. However, it is difficult to ensure that all of the law has been followed. The regulations stipulate information that must be included on a business website, including:

- the company's full identity details – its name, a geographic address and an email address
- terms and conditions, which are easily accessible and fair to consumers
- a description of the goods or services being offered for sale
- pricing information – this needs to include any delivery charges or tax
- information on how long the offers or prices apply
- details of the stages involved in the ordering process, including any additional costs for delivery

- the steps to follow to enter into a contract – consumers must be made aware of what the process will involve and the point at which they will commit themselves and a contract formed
- information about the availability, delivery and dispatch of goods
- information about substitutes in the event that goods or services are not available – this includes telling the consumer that the cost of returning unsatisfactory substitute goods will be refunded
- a clear complaints procedure and policy on returning goods
- information about withdrawal and cancellation rights
- a statement that UK law is the applicable law
- a statement indicating that, when buying goods and services on the Internet, the consumer is entering a legally binding contract
- the technical means for identifying and correcting input errors prior to the placing of the order

- a data protection statement
- a privacy policy and information about security issues
- a cookie (unique identifier) policy
- details of any registration scheme to which the seller belongs and its registration number
- details of relevant professional bodies where the business is registered
- details of any Code of Practice to which the business subscribes to
- VAT number (if appropriate).

Consumer organisations are increasingly concerned about the growth of this area of business and the Office of Fair Trading announced that it will be investigating whether or not stricter controls might be required to protect the consumer. To find out more information on what OFT is doing, go to its website: www.oft.gov.uk for more details.

Assessment activity 21.2

P4 P5 D1 BTEC

Look closely at either the contract you chose for Assessment activity 21.1 or one supplied to you by your tutor. Prepare a presentation which includes the following:

- a description of the meaning of the significant terms in a standard contract **P4**
- an explanation of the effect of these terms
- how statutes affect these standard contractual terms **P5**
- evaluation of the effectiveness of these terms for the needs of all the parties involved. **D1**

Grading tips

1. You should clearly describe the express terms and implied terms in the contract and explain how they are each affected by statutory protection. You should make direct links between the terms and the statutes.

Remember that the statutes are Acts of Parliament, such as the Sale of Goods Act 1979 or the Unfair Contract Terms Act 1997, and you should make direct links between the terms and the statutes you have learned about. **P4 P5**

2. You must evaluate the terms from the point of view of all parties to the contract. You should consider how well the business protects itself from things like loss from non-payment or failure of delivery as well as consider how the buyer is adequately protected from issues such as late delivery or poor quality. Remember evaluation means judgement so you should look at what is positive about the terms and what needs to be improved before discussing how well the terms meet the needs of both parties. **D1**

PLTS

Explaining the meaning of terms in a contract will help you to develop your skills both as a **reflective learner** and as a **self-manager**.

Buying flight tickets online

As the online holiday industry continues to grow, so too do the risks associated with the failure of those businesses. A good example of this is the failure of low cost airline firms going into liquidation leaving customers without flights. According to the Transport Select Committee, around 40 per cent of all holiday flights in the UK are booked via the Internet. Many of these bookings are on low cost airlines that may not be members of government-funded schemes for compensation, such as the Air Travel Organiser's Licence (Atol).

In January 2005, Air Polonia, a privately owned Polish airline that flew from destinations in Poland to Stansted Airport, collapsed and disappeared from the Internet. More than 50,000 passengers lost their bookings or were left stranded at various airports. There is little chance of any of them receiving any money back from the airline – most passengers were left to claim the money from their holiday insurance.

Think about it!

1. Are there any laws that would have protected the consumers from Air Polonia's collapse?

2. Explain how customers might try to get their money back.

3. Evaluate whether controls on Internet selling are adequate. If not, how would you strengthen them?

3   Understand the impact of statutory consumer protection on the parties to a contract

3.1 Sale of goods

Activity: Different types of consumer contracts

In small groups, try to come up with as many different types of consumer contracts. List all the examples you can think of for each type. You can use the Internet to help your research.

As an extra challenge, try to find the largest type of contract, the smallest and the most bizarre!

PLTS

Working together as a group to put together the lists in this activity will help you to develop your skills as a team worker.

The key piece of legislation which controls contracts regarding the sale of goods and protects consumers is the Sale of Goods Act 1979, which covers all types of consumer contracts. The Sale of Goods Act 1979, **S2 (1)** defines a contract of a sale of goods as:

'a contract by which the seller transfers or agrees to transfer the property in goods to the buyer for a money consideration called price'.

This definition is very important because only those contracts which fall within it are covered by the Act.

Definition of goods

Goods include all tangible items of property such as: food, clothes and furniture.

Land and money, however, are excluded from the definition.

Implied terms

Generally, the parties to a contract are free to agree between themselves the details of their contract, but the Sale of Goods Act 1979 has a series of conditions that are automatically included in every contract dealing with the sale of goods. These conditions are known as implied terms and include information dealing with title, description, fitness and quality. They are dealt with in sections 12 to 15 of the Sale of Goods Act 1979.

Title

In **S12**, there is an implied condition on the part of the seller having the right to sell the goods. For example, it is an implied condition that car dealers sell cars that actually belong to them; they can legally pass ownership (title) to another person. A seller will be liable for breach of contract if they cannot pass a good title to the buyer.

Description

In **S13**, for any contract for the sale of goods, by description, there is an implied term that the goods will correspond with that description. The description of the goods may cover such matters as size, quantity, weight, ingredients and origin as well as how the goods are packed. The slightest departure from this description gives the buyer the right to reject the goods for breach of condition of the contract.

Case study: FW Moore & Co. v Landauer & Co. [1921]

FW Moore & Co. agreed to supply to Landauer & Co. 3,000 tins of Australian canned fruit, packed in cases containing 30 tins each.

When the goods were delivered, it was discovered that, although all 3,000 tins were there, about half the consignment was packed in cases of 24 tins.

The Court agreed that FW Moore & Co. could reject the whole contract.

1. **Why did the Court side with FW Moore & Co?**

2. **Why are terms about quantity, quality and description important in a contract such as this?**

3. **Do you agree with the Court's decision? Why or why not?**

Fitness and satisfactory quality

There is no general duty placed on private sellers to make sure that the goods sold are of correct quality and suitability. This preserves the principle of **caveat emptor**, which is a Latin term meaning 'Let the buyer beware'.

Key term

Caveat emptor – from the Latin term meaning 'Let the buyer beware'. Today it is used to mean that a buyer is purchasing a product 'as is' and should be aware of defects in it.

For example, should you buy a camera from a friend, and the camera does not work, there would not be much you could do. However, if your friend was selling the camera in the course of their business **S14** includes two implied conditions:

- the goods are of satisfactory quality
- the goods are fit for a particular purpose.

When a seller sells goods in the course of their business, the goods supplied should of **satisfactory quality**, except to the extent of defects which are brought to the buyer's attention before the contract is made, or ought to have been noticed by the buyer if they have examined the goods. The quality of goods includes their state and condition. **S14** does not impose absolute standards of quality with which all goods must comply. However, goods must be satisfactory to a reasonable person. This means that goods do not have to be absolutely perfect, but satisfactory in the usual run of events.

The goods supplied should also be **fit for the particular purpose**. This ensures that they are safe, durable and long lasting. In the course of a business, when the seller sells goods, it is implied that the buyer has expressly made known to the seller or at least suggested the particular purpose they need the goods for. It is vital that a seller is told if a particular product is to be used for a particular purpose as this will offer them a degree of protection under the legislation.

Activity: Fit for purpose

Read the following cases and then work with a partner to answer the questions that follow.

Grant v Australian Knitting Mills [1936]

Dr Grant bought a pair of woollen underpants from the Australian Knitting Mills. The pants contained a chemical that should have been removed before sale, and the buyer contracted dermatitis.

It was held that the items were not fit for the purpose and the Court ruled for the claimant.

Griffiths v Peter Conway Ltd [1939]

Mrs Griffiths bought a tweed coat from Peter Conway Ltd. Unknown to the defendants, Mrs Conway suffered from exceptionally sensitive skin. After wearing the coat she contracted dermatitis.

In this case, it was held that the defendants were not liable and ruled against the claimant.

1. What general principle of law do these cases raise?

2. How are these cases similar? How do they differ?

3. Explain why the outcomes of the case differ. Comment on whether or not the purchaser should have to declare any special requirements as to fitness for purpose. Analyse whether this places the seller at a disadvantage or not.

Case Study: Rogers v Parish (Scarborough) Ltd [1987]

Rogers bought a new Range Rover for £16,000. Within six months of delivery, the engine became defective and the bodywork began to deteriorate. The purchaser wished to reject the vehicle even though it was driveable and repairable. The Court held that the buyer was entitled to do so.

1. How did the Sale of Goods Act 1979 S14 help decide this case?

2. What sort of quality standards are implied into a consumer contract for purchasing a new car?

3. How long would you expect a new car to be free from defects? Would this time period change depending on what product was purchased?

Sample under the Sale of Goods Act 1979 (as amended)

The Sale of Goods Act 1979 **S15** provides that in a contract of sale by sample there is an implied condition that:

- the bulk will correspond with the sample in quality
- the buyer will have a reasonable opportunity of comparing the bulk with the sample
- the goods will be free from any defect making their quality unsatisfactory which would not be apparent on reasonable examination of the sample.

Activity: Research consumer cases

In small groups, look at consumer websites or journals to research some real cases where consumer contracts have led to real disputes and real court cases. Use the Sale of Goods Act 1979 as a guide and find at least one of each of the following case:

- based on S12, incorrect title
- based on S13, description
- based on S14, fitness and satisfactory quality
- based on S15, sample.

Report your findings back to your class. Remember to include the courts' decisions.

PLTS

Participating actively while also collaborating with others to come up with the various court cases for this activity will help you to develop your skills as a **team worker**.

3.2 Supply of goods and services

The Sale of Goods Act 1979 only applies to contracts where goods are sold for money. It does not cover other methods of obtaining goods nor does it cover the provision of services. The Supply of Goods and Services Act 1982 was passed to give terms that had previously been implied by common law in contracts for services a statutory footing.

Definitions

Legislation has been passed to protect commercial transactions that are not covered under the sale of goods. This covers contracts for **supply of goods and services** for work and material including building work, car repairs, installation work such as central heating and double glazing, hairdressing and gardening, contracts where no money changes hands such as exchange or barter, contracts for free gifts (where a buyer is given a free product if they buy another) and contracts for hire of goods (including the hire of cars, machinery and clothing).

Implied terms for hire of goods under Supply of Goods and Services Act 1982

The Supply of Goods and Services Act 1982 deals with implied terms that apply to contracts where one person agrees to bail goods to another person by way of hire, such as the hire of cars or machinery. Different sections of the Act deal with the various implied terms and conditions. Remedies for breach of contract will be broadly the same as for breach of contracts for the sale of goods.

S7 defines that there is an implied condition that the **bailor** has the right to transfer the goods. For example, if a person hires a car via the Internet from a car hire firm, it is implied that the car picked up at their holiday destination will be owned by that firm and that they will allow the hire to take place.

S8 provides that when there is a contract for the hire of goods by description, there is an implied condition that the goods will match that description.

S9 states that where goods are hired in the course a business, there is an implied condition that the goods are of a satisfactory quality and reasonably fit for the purpose hired.

S10 covers implied conditions in relation to contracts for the hire of goods by sample whereby the bulk must match the sample.

Key terms

Supply of goods and services – services that do not have consumer contracts, where one party actually provides a service to the other, such as a plumber or hairdresser.

Bailor – the person providing the hire.

Implied terms for supply of goods and services, work and materials

S2 of the Supply of Goods and Services Act 1982 contains an implied condition that the **transferor** has the legal right to transfer the property.

S3 states when the transfer is for goods or services by description, then there is an implied condition that the goods will correspond to that description. For example, if your computer were to break down and you sent it to a computer repair shop to be repaired, the invoice should describe the work and the parts fitted. This invoice would be implied into the contract that the actual work and parts had been provided.

S4 provides that when goods are transferred in the ordinary course of business there is an implied condition that the goods are of suitable quality and fit for the purpose.

S5 refers to the transfer of goods for a sample; there is an implied condition that the bulk will correspond with that sample.

Activity: Contracts for sale of goods and contracts for supply of goods and services

Compare and contrast the terms of a contract for sale of goods versus the terms of a contract for supply of goods and services. Make a list of the similarities and differences.

3.3 False trade descriptions

When the parties to a contract begin negotiations and start to form a contract there will be several representations made by the seller about the items being sold. Those representations may involve a description of the product. Any descriptions of goods and services, given by a person acting in the course of a trade or business, should be accurate and not misleading. Misleading descriptions of this type are called false **trade descriptions** and are against the law.

Trade Descriptions Act 1968

The Trade Descriptions Act 1968 makes it a criminal offence to mislead a consumer by a false description. A description of goods that are sold or hired must be accurate. That description could be:

- in writing
- in an advertisement
- in an illustration
- given orally, e.g. in a sales pitch.

The description itself can cover a range of factors, including:

- quantity and size
- composition
- method, place and date of manufacture
- fitness for stated purpose
- endorsements by people or organisations.

For more information on consumer protection law, see pages 252–3.

Link to misrepresentation

Consumer contracts for goods and services are strongly protected and terms are implied into contracts by law. Businesses that break these terms will be in breach of contract and in certain cases might face criminal prosecution.

If offering to supply services, accommodation or facilities, it is a criminal offence for the bailor or transferor to make a statement that is known to be false or misleading. This includes recklessly making a false or misleading statement about the provision, nature, manner, location or approval of the services, accommodation or facilities. If a person is found guilty of an offence under the Act, they could receive an unlimited fine or up to two years imprisonment. Breaking the Trade Descriptions Act is a criminal offence and also makes the person liable for misrepresentation for which damages may also be awarded.

Key terms

Transferor – the person who is providing the goods or services.

Trade description – a description made by a seller about the goods they are selling.

Case study: Marks & Spencer

In September 2005, Marks & Spencer was fined £10,000 for breaking the Trade Descriptions Act. It was found guilty of making misleading claims about a collection of new men's clothing.

Trading Standards investigated complaints from customers and found clothes in the company's Birmingham store clearly labelled *made in Italy*. Investigations found that the clothing was in fact from Egypt, India and Romania. The high street chain admitted five breaches of the Trade Descriptions Act by suggesting items in its new

Italian range were made in Italy. The store was fined £2,000 for per offence.

The clothing range now states *inspired by Italy*.

1. In your own words, explain why Marks & Spencer was found guilty?

2. Do you think firms like Marks & Spencer should be criminally prosecuted for such acts? Justify your answers.

3. Discuss the *inspired by Italy* branding and whether you think this could be misleading.

Did you know?

You can keep up to date with news stories about local businesses and how they commit trading standards offences by contacting the local Trading Standards Office for details of local companies or, for a more national feel, look at www.tradingstandards.gov.uk.

Assessment activity 21.3 (P6) (M2) BTEC

You are the owner of a kitchen installation service. A client has come in with questions about the sale and supply of goods and services. Prepare a report describing, in your own words:

- the essential points of a contract to protect consumers for the sale of goods such as the purchase of the new kitchen
- how a consumer might be protected in a contract for the supply of goods and services such as faulty plumbing of the new kitchen **P6**
- how consumers are protected in the event of breach of contract for the supply/sale of goods or services. **M2**

Grading tips

1. You should refer to both the Sale of Goods Act 1979 and the Supply of Goods and Services Act 1982. Include information about quality and fitness for purpose, making sure that you relate them to the goods and services as stated in the activity. Also remember to include information about quality and delivery of the services as required. **P6**

2. You should analyse specific issues relating to the creation of the contract, such as exclusion clauses, and how consumers might be protected in the event of a breach of one of these contracts and discuss how it is affected by the legislation. Remember to include both the benefits and weaknesses. **M2**

PLTS

Analysing the Acts and explaining how a consumer would be protected will help you to develop your skills as a **creative thinker**.

Functional skills

Writing the report for this activity will help you to develop your **ICT** skills.

4 Know the remedies available to the parties to a contract

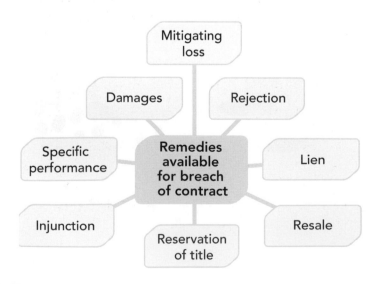

Figure 21.3: Different remedies available for breach of contract

4.1 Remedies

When one of the parties breaks the terms of the contract, the other, injured party will be able to gain some form of compensation for the loss of the contract. This is known as a **remedy** and is aimed at ensuring that the injured party has not lost out. These remedies can be written into the contract or exist as equitable remedies, and come from the historical idea of equity or fairness. The main remedy available is usually damages, which can be split into two types:

- liquidated damages
- unliquidated damages.

Key term

Remedy – solution for the victim of a breach of contract.

Liquidated damages

In the business world, it is quite common for parties to agree in advance the amount of damages that will be paid in the event of a breach of contract. These are known as **liquidated damages**.

An example of a common form of agreed damages can be found in most holiday booking confirmation forms as illustrated in Table 21.1.

Table 21.1: Charges from a standard holiday booking form relating to money that will be paid in the event of the firm cancelling a customer's holiday

Notification period	Amount paid back to customer
More than 56 days	Deposit only
More than 28 days	100% of holiday cost + £5
More than 14 days	100% of holiday cost + £10
More than 1 day	100% of holiday cost + £15
Less than 1 day	100% of holiday cost + £30

Unliquidated damages

Unliquidated damages are those damages awarded for breach of contract where there is no prior agreement between the parties as to the amount of damages to be awarded. The aim of unliquidated damages is to put the person in the position they would have been in had the contract been carried out correctly.

The damages are designed to compensate only for loss suffered. Therefore, if no loss has been suffered, the damages awarded will only be nominal to recognise that there has been a breach of contract. Courts use the following guidelines when awarding damages.

- The damage can include sums for financial loss, damage to property, personal injury and distress, disappointment and upset caused to the claimant.
- An injured party cannot necessarily recover damages for every kind of loss.

Breaches of contract can cause an unforeseen chain of events; thus, there has to, legally, come a point after which the damage becomes too distant from the original breach to be recoverable. Courts have to decide how much in way of damages is payable, provided that the loss is not too distant.

Mitigation of loss

Once a breach of contract has occurred, the innocent party is under a duty to mitigate or lessen their loss as soon as possible. A victim cannot simply stand back and allow their losses to get worse. **Mitigation** is the idea that a person will try to regain as much of their loss as possible if the contract is in breach. So, for example, a seller whose goods or services have been rejected must attempt to get the best price for them elsewhere.

Rejection

A party who is the victim of a breach of contract may reject the entire contract. We have already discussed examples where this is possible such as circumstances where the contract fails because of inability to deliver on time, delivering the wrong quantity or delivering goods of poor quality. Even if they reject the goods, the injured party will still be allowed to claim damages.

Lien

The owner of goods may be able to exercise what is known as a **lien**, which is a right to retain possession of the goods until the contract fee has been paid. An example of this would be where a person leaves a television set to be repaired. A contract is formed that the set will be repaired and the owner will pay for the services. The television repair technician now has a lien over the television and can retain possession of it until the bill is paid.

Key terms

Liquidated damages – damages agreed at the negotiation stage.

Unliquidated damages – damages awarded which were not agreed on the contract.

Mitigation – something done in order to reduce losses.

Lien – the right to retain possession of goods until they are paid for.

Case study: R v Turner (No2) [1971]

Mr Turner left his car to be repaired at a local garage. When the garage telephoned to say it was ready for collection, Mr Turner told them to leave it outside on the road and he would come in the next day to pay the bill and collect the car. Using his spare keys, he collected the car later that evening and refused to pay the bill.

The garage called the police. Mr Turner was arrested and convicted of stealing his own car!

1. Explain what a lien is and how it relates to this case.
2. What other remedies were available to the garage?
3. Do you think this type of remedy was fair?

Resale

Resale can be a remedy that occurs when a seller has goods that remain unpaid. Reselling of the goods will be allowed:

- when the goods are perishable and likely to spoil
- when the seller has told the buyer of the resale and the buyer fails to respond
- where the term of the contract allows the seller to do this.

This resale will not affect the seller's right to claim damages.

Reservation of title

A remedy that is often expressly written into the contract is the right of the seller **to reserve title** until the contract price has been paid. This will enable the seller to recover the goods in the event of liquidation or bankruptcy of the buyer. The seller's goods therefore are not lost to the buyer's creditors.

Injunctions

An injunction is an order by the court requiring the party at fault to keep to the contract. Injunctions are mainly used to enforce promises in certain contracts, for example, an employment contract which restricts employees from working in a similar capacity for rival employers.

Specific performance

Specific performance is an equitable remedy granted as an alternative to damages in cases in which damages are not considered an adequate solution. Specific performance requires the party in breach of contract to carry out their contractual promises. This remedy might occur when a person is compelled to perform a contractual obligation, such as a DJ who breaches his contract for a personal performance at a nightclub.

Activity: Specific performance

SCSC Enterprises music promoters has booked a famous singer to perform as the headline act at a large concert. Everything has been confirmed, the venue, the supporting acts and all of the tickets have been sold. Unfortunately, the singer has had a row with one of the producers of the show and is now refusing to perform. SCSC's lawyers have gone to court to gain a remedy.

In groups, discuss the following questions.

1. What is the contractual position between the parties?
2. What remedy do you think SCSC Enterprises will be trying to get?
3. Are damages suitable in this case?

Functional skills

Discussing specific performances to answer the questions for this activity will help you to develop your **English** skills in speaking and listening.

Key term

To reserve title – to retain ownership of the goods.

The Scales of Justice at The Old Bailey, the Central Criminal Court in England

4.2 Application of remedies

In the previous examples, when a breach of contract has occurred, the parties have been able to claim one or more of the remedies described. This is not an automatic right and the injured party, known as the claimant, will have to go to court to get their remedy.

Courts

In the event of a contractual dispute, it may be necessary to resort to apply to the civil courts to have a claim heard and hopefully be resolved to a satisfactory conclusion. The civil court system was transformed under the **Woolf Reforms**. This resulted in the Civil Procedure Act 1997 and Civil Procedure Rules. The three main civil courts that can hear cases initially are the Small Claims Court, the County Court and the High Court.

If an individual or company is in a dispute, they must apply to the court. Their case will then be given to a judge who will be assigned as case manager. The case manager will allocate the case to the correct court depending on its seriousness. This is known as the track system. The small claims track deals with Small Claims Court cases, the fast-track deals with County Court cases and the multi-track system deals with complex High Court cases.

Key term

Woolf Reforms – a series of changes to the civil courts led by Lord Woolf.

Small Claims Court

The Small Claims Court is a special court, which is part of the County Court, and deals with minor claims including contractual and business disputes where the claim does not exceed £5,000. This will include claims such as failure to supply goods, failure to pay for goods and other business disputes. These cases are not expected to raise any difficult questions of law.

If the case is simple and both parties agree, the district judge may make a decision on the documents alone, without a hearing. Alternatively, the judge may give directions, such as about certain documents which need to be produced in advance or the number of witnesses allowed, and sets a date for a hearing. If the case goes to full hearing, the proceedings are very informal and are often **uncontested**.

Parties in small claim cases are encouraged not to have legal representation from a solicitor or barrister; payment for legal help is not allowed. The courts are trying to reduce the parties' cost burden.

Did you know?

There is help available with small claims at www.hmcourts-service.gov.uk.

County Court

The County Court deals with fast track cases worth between £5,000 and £15,000. They also have **jurisdiction** to hear cases concerning the recovery of land, bankruptcies, company winding-ups, consumer credit and copyright matters.

Cases at the County Court are more formal than at the Small Claims Court and will be heard by a circuit judge. It is also normal for the parties to have legal representation. As with the Small Claims Court, there is help and advice available from the court itself and a person can now even make a claim against another person online using www.moneyclaim.gov.uk.

High Court

The High Court is the most senior of the first instance civil courts. Based in London and larger cities, it is split into three divisions dealing with different branches of civil law: the Queen's Bench Division, the Chancery Division and the Family Division.

The Queen's Bench Division hears multi-track contract cases involving large sums of money or involving complex points of law. It also acts as a Commercial Court dealing with business matters such as insurance, banking and the meaning of commercial documents. Its Divisional Court will also hear civil appeals from the County Court.

The Chancery Division deals with matters of equity (or fairness), including trusts, mortgages, partnerships, companies, bankruptcies and taxation.

The Family Division deals primarily with family law matters such as divorce and adoption so has little role to play in the law relating to businesses.

Activity: Alternatives to court

1. Describe the problems for parties using the civil court system.
2. Using the Internet, do some research and suggest alternative methods of resolving disputes.

Time limits

All breaches of contract will allow parties to claim remedies. These remedies may have to be claimed via a court case. However, the right to claim for breach of contract does not last forever. The Limitation Act 1980 imposes time limits to bringing an action. Simple contract dispute must be brought within six years of the breach and for disputes for contracts made under deed, such as the sale of land, the time limit is within 12 years of the breach. This time limit can be extended where fraud is involved, or where the person making the claim is suffering from a disability or lacks capacity.

Key terms

Uncontested – when the other party does not disagree.

Jurisdiction – to have the power to hear cases.

Assessment activity 21.4

(P7) (M3) (D2) BTEC

The same client from Assessment activity 21.3 is about to sign the contract with your kitchen installation company. However, the client now has some questions regarding breaching of the contract. Prepare a report which, in your own words:

1. describes the remedies available for a breach of contract **P7**

2. analyses the remedies available to a business provider in the event of a breach of contract for the supply of goods or services **M3**

3. evaluates the statutory protection given to a consumer in their dealings with a business and the remedies available. **D2**

Grading tips

1. You should include a description of damages, how these damages are assessed and the different types of remedies available. You should be able to describe issues such as reservation of title and issues of retention of ownership until the contract has been paid. **P7**

2. Using the damages and remedies you have described in P7, you should now consider the strengths and weaknesses of each when applied to a breach of contract situation. Remember to describe how well they seek to resolve the situation. **M3**

3. You should give a judgement, based on evidence you have collected for M3, about how well the law protects the consumer and business; include damages and equitable remedies. You should include evaluation of the court process, features of the process and suggest ways to resolve the dispute. **D2**

PTLS

Looking at how remedies are applied to breach of contracts will help you to develop your skills as an **independent enquirer**.

Just checking

1. What is the definition of a contract? Give some examples.
2. What is the difference between an offer and an invitation to treat?
3. What is consideration? Give an example.
4. What is the Small Claims track? What other tracks are there?
5. How are purchasers on the Internet protected?
6. If a sample and the bulk order do not match, what can the buyer do?
7. What is an express term? Give an example.
8. Explain the difference between liquidated and unliquidated damages.
9. What implied terms are in a contract for sale of goods?
10. What is the purpose of an exclusion clause? Give an example.
11. What punishment might a seller of a defective product receive?
12. Explain what a false trade description is.

edexcel

Assignment tips

1. Do not be put off by what looks like a very difficult topic. You will not be able to remember everything you have studied. To help you, read back through the pages and make summaries of the relevant law.

2. Try to find more modern case examples to put into your work.

3. Try to relate the issues of contract law to everyday situations you might be able to apply the law to.

4. Remember the main thing to think about is whether or not the elements of a valid contract have been formed.

5. Do not forget that contracts can be broken. You should be able to explain when a contract is broken and what can be done to put things right.

27 Understanding health and safety in the business workplace

Every year in Britain over 200 people die in the workplace, tens of thousands are injured and millions of working hours are lost due to employees needing time off because of injury or illness. It is clear from these figures that there are many potential risks to health and safety in the business workplace. These vary greatly depending upon the workplace environment and employers need to be aware of all the risks associated with their business. Employers must also meet a range of legal requirements to ensure that their workplace and the employees in it are safe and secure.

This unit will provide a background to the key health and safety legislation and regulations that affect businesses, as well as what businesses can do to protect their staff and who might be responsible for this. An important focus of this unit is the role of risk assessments in identifying, monitoring and preventing safety and security hazards in the workplace. Managing potential danger at work involves recognising a problem, deciding what to do about it and putting solutions in place that make employees as safe as possible.

Learning outcomes

After completing this unit you should:

1. understand how health and safety legislation and regulations affect a business working environment
2. know the requirements for healthy, safe and productive working conditions
3. understand the role and responsibilities of key personnel
4. be able to assess and manage risk.

Assessment and grading criteria

This table shows you what you must do in order to achieve a **pass**, **merit** or **distinction** grade, and where you can find activities in this book to help you.

To achieve a **pass** grade the evidence must show that the learner is able to:	To achieve a **merit** grade the evidence must show that, in addition to the pass criteria, the learner is able to:	To achieve a **distinction** grade the evidence must show that, in addition to the pass and merit criteria, the learner is able to:
P1 explain the legal requirements and regulations for ensuring the health, safety and security of those employed in business **See Assessment activity 27.1, page 126**	**M1** assess the implications of health, safety and security legislation and regulations for a business role in a workplace environment **See Assessment activity 27.1, page 126**	**D1** make recommendations for improving health and safety standards and practices in a selected work environment **See Assessment activity 27.4, page 157**
P2 describe the requirements for a healthy and safe workplace, as applied to the physical environment and equipment used, in a selected business **See Assessment activity 27.2, page 143**		
P3 explain the roles and responsibilities for health and safety of key personnel in a selected workplace **See Assessment activity 27.3, page 152**	**M2** analyse the roles and responsibilities for health and safety of key personnel in a selected workplace **See Assessment activity 27.3, page 152**	
P4 plan a risk assessment for a selected administrative work environment **See Assessment activity 27.4, page 157**	**M3** conduct a detailed risk assessment of a selected workplace **See Assessment activity 27.4, page 157**	

How you will be assessed

In this unit you will be assessed by producing work that explains the legal requirements and regulations for ensuring the health, safety and security of those employed in a business and make recommendations for improvement. You will also need to be able to describe the requirements for a healthy and safe workplace. You will then need to explain and assess the roles and responsibilities for health and safety of key personnel in the workplace and, finally, plan and conduct a detailed risk assessment of a workplace of your choosing.

David, 18, BTEC student

I chose to study this BTEC course because my father owns a large timber yard employing over 50 workers and I wanted to find out more about how businesses work. I was especially keen to study this unit as an employee at my father's yard was badly injured three years ago when he put his arm into an old unguarded sawing machine. Until then my father had run the business for 20 years with little changing in terms of technology and safety in that time. The yard was closed whilst an investigation took place by the Health and Safety Executive and my father was prosecuted for health and safety breaches.

When the yard reopened, my father had to make quite a few changes to make it a healthy and safe place for his employees. He had to complete risk assessments that assessed the many potential hazards in the yard. He then had to act on the findings, which often involved replacing old machinery and putting in place effective control measures to prevent harm to his employees. My father has now been running the yard successfully without a single accident or injury ever since. I am looking forward to applying the knowledge I have gained from this unit when I join the family business next year. Together, we can make sure the timber yard continues to be a safe place to work.

1. What is the purpose of health and safety law for the workplace?

2. How will studying this unit help you with your understanding of health and safety principles?

3. How do you think health and safety law is enforced?

1 Understand how health and safety legislation and regulations affect a business working environment

In pairs or small groups, discuss the following questions.

*   Why do you think we need health and safety protection in the workplace?
*   What might happen if there was no legislation to protect workers from harm?

Now choose a business you are familiar with and identify as many potential hazards in this workplace as you can. For each hazard you have identified, suggest a measure that would protect employees from harm.

In this section you will be looking at the range of health and safety legislation and regulations that affect the working environment. You will look at the requirements of the legislation and see how the law impacts on the running and organisation of a business.

Of course, we take health and safety seriously!

Why is employee safety so important in business?

1.1 Legislation

It is estimated that there are around 1.6 million accidents each year in the workplace with a cost to British industry of around £700m. This sounds like a lot of accidents, but compared to many other countries the safety record of workers in Britain is good. The reason for this is that we have a very strong set of laws passed by Parliament and the European Union that aim to protect employees.

Statutory duties of employers and employees relating to health, safety and welfare

In the past, health and safety in the workplace was very much the employer's responsibility. Now, employees have more rights and responsibilities and the emphasis has shifted so that current health and safety legislation is focused on employers and employees working together in partnership to ensure that everyone is safe in the workplace.

There are several explicit duties that an employer has towards their employees. Employers must provide:

*   the maintenance of safe plant and safe systems of work

- arrangements for ensuring safe means of handling, use, storage and transport of articles and substances
- information, instruction, training and supervision relating to health and safety
- a safe place of work and provision and maintenance of safe access to the workplace.

An employer also has a statutory duty to ensure that employees have adequate welfare facilities. Employees also have specific duties laid down by law. Employees must:

- take reasonable care for the health and safety of themselves and others who may be affected by their acts at work
- co-operate with the employer or any other person to enable the employer or other person to perform or comply with any legal requirement.

The Management of Health and Safety at Work Regulations 1999

The duties laid out in this piece of health and safety legislation are constantly being modified and updated. The main aim of the regulations is to reduce harm by requiring the assessment of all potential risks and the creation of action plans for emergencies. The regulations impose a duty on employers to assess all risks for all of their workers. Employers must complete and review risk assessments at set times and make modifications to safety standards if there are any significant changes in working practices or equipment. These risk assessments must form part of a systematic safety record. A risk assessment should:

- identify hazards in the workplace
- identify those workers who might be harmed and how
- evaluate the seriousness of the risk of harm from the identified hazards
- record the significant findings in a record that can be stored and used again.

Special risk assessments should be completed in cases where a business employs workers who are below the legal school-leaving age as they do not have the same experiences of older workers to recognise the risk of harm. These types of risk assessment should:

- provide training so that hazardous situations can be avoided

- identify any significant hazards.

You will look at risk assessments in greater detail on pages 152–4.

The usual way for a business to comply with the regulations is to appoint an employee to perform health and safety tasks such as planning, organisation, control, monitoring and review of health and safety arrangements. This person would then be the organisation's **health and safety representative**, whose role it would be to focus on preventative and protective measures to minimise employees' exposure to potential harm.

Activity: Health and safety representative

Identify who the health and safety representative is in your school, college or workplace. Ask them if you can interview them to find out more about what they do. Alternatively, you could ask if they could come to talk to your class or work colleagues to explain what they do. You may also be able to workshadow them to assess exactly what their role involves.

Health and Safety at Work Act 1974

The **Health and Safety at Work Act 1974** is one of the major pieces of legislation in this country to affect businesses and the workplace. It is an enabling act, which means that other legislation can be added to it without having to change the Act itself. The Health and Safety at Work Act has five main aims:

- to protect people at work
- to protect people not at work from those who are
- to ensure that explosive or highly flammable substances are stored, used and transported safely
- to replace existing safety legislation
- to remain up to date.

Key terms

Health and safety representative – a person appointed by a business or trade union who focuses on protection of workers from harm in the workplace.

Health and Safety at Work Act 1974 – the key piece of legislation concerning health and safety in the workplace.

The Act states that if a business employs more than five people, the employer must have a written health and safety policy consisting of three parts, outlined below.

- The aims and objectives for what will be achieved in terms of health and safety for the company.
- An organisation chart stating who is responsible for health and safety within the company.
- A system that contains all the necessary procedures for compliance with the relevant laws affecting the company, e.g. risk assessment procedure, along with all risk assessments, a fire evacuation procedure and relevant training records.

The Health and Safety at Work Act has created duties and responsibilities that must be followed by employers and employees alike. The Health and Safety (Offences) Act 2008 has increased the power of the legislation by imposing tough sentences on those who fail to follow the 1974 Act, which now includes sending someone to prison.

The Workplace (Health, Safety and Welfare) Regulations 1992

These regulations have been law since 1995 and apply to all workplaces except transport, construction sites and what are known as 'extractive industries' (mines, agriculture and forestry industries) away from any

Activity: Health and Safety Law poster

If a business has employees, it is required by law to display a copy of the Health and Safety Law: What you need to know poster. Locate a copy of this poster in your school, college or workplace and complete the following activities.

1. Make a summary of what the poster says.
2. Is the poster easy to understand? Why is this?
3. Create your own version of the Health and Safety Law poster for your school, college or workplace. Use your own words and design and ensure that it is easy to understand.

main buildings. The regulations apply to employers, landlords or persons in control of business premises and the self-employed.

The aim of the regulations is to ensure that the basic welfare needs of employees are dealt with. These welfare needs are broken down into two broad areas:

- the working environment
- facilities.

Table 27.1 lists what is covered under these headings and how each requirement affects employees and employers.

Table 27.1: Requirements under the Workplace (Health, Safety and Welfare) Regulations 1992

Requirement	Notes
The working environment	
Temperature	Should be reasonable for indoor workplaces. There should be a sufficient number of thermometers provided to allow checking of temperature.
Ventilation	Must be effective and suitable to ensure a sufficient quantity of fresh air.
Lighting	Every workplace shall have suitable and sufficient lighting. Where it is practicable, the lighting shall be by natural light. Suitable and sufficient emergency lighting shall be provided.
Room dimensions and space	Every room where persons work shall have adequate floor area, height and unoccupied spaces for purposes of health, safety and welfare. The minimum space requirement is $11m^3$ per person (minimum floor space $3.7m^2$).
Workstations and seating	All workstations should be set up so that it is suitable for any person at work in the workplace who is likely to work at that workstation. Adequate seating is provided for every person at work where work can or must be done sitting.

continued

Requirement	Notes
The working environment	
Cleanliness and waste materials	All workplaces and the furniture, furnishings and fittings shall be kept clean. Surfaces of the floor, wall and ceiling of all workplaces inside buildings shall be capable of being kept clean. Waste materials should be collected in appropriate holders and disposed of.
Floors and traffic routes	Every floor and traffic route in a workplace shall be of a construction which is suitable for the purpose for which it is used. Safe passage of pedestrians and vehicles must be wide enough and marked where necessary.
Falls or falling objects	Areas where there is a risk from falling objects must be clearly indicated and access restricted.
Windows and transparent or translucent doors/gates	Risk assessments should be completed to ensure that windows and doors are protected from being broken. Transparent surfaces of a wall or door where they could be walked into must be clearly marked so that the risk can be identified.
Windows, skylights and ventilators	There must be a safe method for using any adjustments or opening mechanisms on windows, skylights and ventilators. People must not be able to fall out of open windows or skylights. Restricting devices should be fitted.
Ability to clean windows safely	All windows and skylights in a workplace must be able to be cleaned safely.
Facilities	
Sanitary conveniences	There must be suitable and sufficient sanitary conveniences. The rooms containing them must have adequate lighting and ventilation. They must be kept clean and orderly.
Washing facilities	There must be suitable washing facilities. They should be in or near the sanitary conveniences and soap and hot and cold water must be available.
Drinking water	An adequate supply of drinking water shall be provided for all persons at work in the workplace.
Other facilities	Facilities must be provided for changing clothing in places where special clothing is used for work. Rest facilities must be provided for pregnant women and nursing mothers.

Did you know?

The Health and Safety Executive is a public body responsible for workplace health, safety and welfare. You can find out more about the HSE by visiting the website at www.hse.gov.uk. If you click on the 'Guidance' tab you can find out more about the legislation covered in this section.

Activity: Welfare at work

Produce a checklist based on the information in Table 27.1. Use it to find out if your school, college or workplace meets the requirements of the Workplace (Health, Safety and Welfare) Regulations 1992.

The Reporting of Injuries, Diseases and Dangerous Occurrences Regulations 1995

You have already learned that there are over 1.6 million accidents at work each year. Unfortunately, over 200 of these result in the death of an employee. How do we know this information? We know because employers must report all injuries, diseases and dangerous occurrences that happen in the workplace under the Reporting of Injuries, Diseases and Dangerous Occurrences Regulations (RIDDOR) 1995.

Employers, the self-employed and anyone else in control of work premises has legal duties under **RIDDOR** that require them to record and report certain work-related accidents, as shown in Figure 27.1. Employers can report an incident by phone, post, email or online. You can find out more about RIDDOR by visiting the website at www.hse.gov.uk/riddor.

The Control of Substances Hazardous to Health Regulations 1994

There are many business situations where an employee might be exposed to dangerous substances, such as harmful chemicals. There are however strict guidelines in place to protect employees and they apply to virtually all UK workplaces. These are the Control of Substances Hazardous to Health Regulations 1994 (amended in 1999), also known as **COSHH**.

COSHH concerns information on the products and work practices associated with substances hazardous to health. Substances hazardous to health are those known to be capable of causing bad health effects or disease. COSHH defines them as:

- those which are very toxic, toxic, harmful, corrosive or irritant
- those where exposure is limited
- those which are biological agents capable of causing infection, allergy, poisoning or other health risk
- any significant amount of dust in the air
- any other substance that creates a health hazard.

They include most types of chemicals, fumes, dusts, vapours, gases and biological agents (germs).

Employers have a duty to ensure that:

- any risk to the health of employees is identified through a risk assessment completed by a competent person
- provision is made to either eradicate the risk or at least control it
- staff are adequately trained to deal with hazardous substances.

You can find out more about COSHH by visiting www.hse.gov.uk/coshh.

Key terms

RIDDOR (Reporting of Injuries, Diseases and Dangerous Occurences Regulations) – the regulations dealing with accidents/injuries or dangerous occurrences in the workplace.

COSHH (Control of Substances Hazardous to Health) – the regulations dealing with chemical use in the workplace.

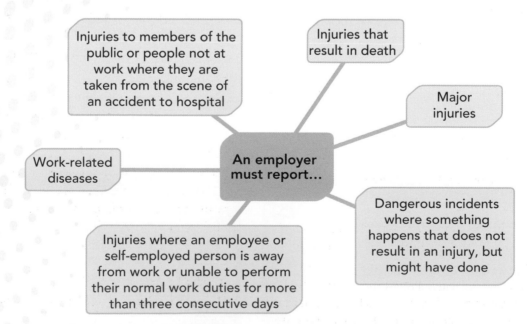

Injuries to members of the public or people not at work where they are taken from the scene of an accident to hospital

Injuries that result in death

Major injuries

Work-related diseases

An employer must report...

Dangerous incidents where something happens that does not result in an injury, but might have done

Injuries where an employee or self-employed person is away from work or unable to perform their normal work duties for more than three consecutive days

Figure 27.1: Incidents that must be reported under RIDDOR

Activity: Hazardous substances

For each of the following business types, use the Internet or other resources to identify possible hazardous substances employees might be exposed to. You could extend this activity by choosing one of the business types and for each hazardous substance finding out the measures that should be put in place by the employee to ensure the health and safety of employees.

- agriculture
- bakery
- beauty
- catering
- cleaning
- engineering.
- hairdressing
- printing
- vehicle repair
- welding
- woodworking

The Electricity at Work Regulations 1989

Each year about 1,000 accidents at work involving electric shock or burns are reported to the Health and Safety Executive. About 15 of these are fatal. To protect employees from the dangers of electricity, the Electricity at Work Regulations 1989 apply to all aspects of the use of electricity within the workplace, from electrical supplies to the use of electrical equipment. They place a duty on employers, employees and the self-employed to:

- have their electrical systems constructed in a way that prevents danger. This includes testing all new equipment to ensure that it is safe
- maintain their electrical systems correctly to prevent danger
- have repaired or closed any electrical system that causes danger.

The Display Screen Equipment Regulations 1992

The workplace is becoming increasingly dominated by the use of computers and other IT equipment. Unfortunately, continued work with display screen equipment can potentially cause health problems for employees. Reported problems include muscular strain and other physical problems, eye fatigue and mental stress. All of these problems can be prevented by the use of well designed office equipment and furniture.

These health problems have been recognised as a serious issue by the Display Screen Equipment (DSE) Regulations 1992 which place a strict duty on employers to:

- assess workstations and their users to see if there is any risk
- reduce or eliminate recognised risks
- ensure that workstations meet minimum requirements
- ensure that employees' work includes breaks and changes from screen use
- provide users with an eye and eyesight test and treatment where necessary
- explain to staff about the health and safety aspects of their job.

Users are defined in the Regulations as 'an employee who habitually uses display screen equipment as a significant part of their normal work'.

The Manual Handling Operations Regulations 1992 (as amended)

Over 25 per cent of injuries reported to the Health and Safety Executive each year are due to the lifting and carrying of loads, known as **manual handling**. This issue represents a serious and expensive problem for employers. In an attempt to minimise the risk, the Manual Handling Operations Regulations were created, which place a duty on all employers, so far as is possible, to avoid the need for employees to undertake any manual handling operations at work which involve a risk of their being injured.

Under the Regulations, a suitable and sufficient risk assessment of all manual handling operations should be carried out to quantify the risks and put suitable guidance and support in place to make sure risks are kept to a minimum. Employers are also expected to train staff where necessary in the correct way to manually lift and handle objects. To find out more about manual handling visit www.hse.gov.uk/contact/faqs/manualhandling.htm.

Key term

Manual handling – lifting and carrying things at work.

Activity: Display screen checklist

Complete the following checklist for the display screens in your school or college classroom, library or IT suite, or in your office/workplace.

DSE Regulation question	Yes	No
Is the room adequately lit?		
Has the screen got adequate contrast with no glare or distractions?		
Has distracting noise been minimised?		
Is there leg room to allow shifts in body movement?		
Is there window covering to prevent glare?		
Is the screen image stable, adjustable and readable?		
Is the keyboard usable, adjustable, detachable and legible?		
Is the work chair adjustable with foot support if needed?		
Is there excess pressure on underside of thighs and backs of knees?		
Is the position of the equipment such that it allows for forearms to be approximately horizontal?		
Is the screen height and angle correct to allow a comfortable head position?		
Is there space in front of the keyboard to support hands/wrists during pauses in keying?		
Does the work surface allow flexible arrangements, i.e. is it spacious and glare free?		
Are there obstacles under the desk?		

PLTS

Organising your time to complete this survey and prioritising action points from your own findings will help you to develop your skills as a **self-manager**.

Did you know?

According to the British Safety Council, in 2008 British businesses lost £250 a second in costs and payouts for needless accidents in the workplace.

I think I can manage it...

Why do you think employers have a duty to avoid manual handling in the workplace?

1.2 Implementation in workplace

The law relating to health and safety at work has developed well since the original act in 1974. As society has developed, so too has the complicated nature of the workplace. In the UK, we now have a very thorough and sophisticated legal framework to protect workers from harm, but the legal framework is only as effective as the way that employers implement the law in their own businesses. With accidents still being reported in the workplace each year, there are clearly still problems with the implementation of health and safety legislation.

Legal requirements

Whilst the legal requirements of health and safety legislation place duties on the employer and employee alike, the overriding health and safety obligation is towards the employer who must ensure that their employees are safe at work at all times.

Workplace policies for job role

Health and safety law states that employers must have policies in place that detail the training employees need to enable them to work safely. All employees also need to know how to work safely in their particular jobs. Workplace policies relating to job roles must show employees what hazards they might face in their particular job, ways to deal with them and how to react in emergency situations.

Health and safety training for jobs should take place during working hours and must not be paid for by employees. Employers should take particular care regarding the job roles of young or vulnerable workers, new employees, employees changing jobs, employees taking on more complex jobs and workers who are appointed as safety representatives.

Reporting procedures

As you have already learned, RIDDOR exist to ensure employers report all serious incidents to the Health and Safety Executive. This means that employers must put in place procedures by which accidents and incidents (including near misses) are reported by employees. Staff must be trained and encouraged to report such events as part of normal working procedures. Figure 27.2 on page 124 shows a typical accident reporting form used by many organisations. It provides details of the incident, how serious it was, whether the HSE needs to be informed and what actions are required by the employer to prevent reoccurrence of the incident.

Activity: Health and safety policies

Choose two different job roles. One should be an obviously hazardous job, such as a firefighter, and the other one should be a less dangerous job, such as an office worker.

Write a job role for each. Then think about the hazards each of them might face in their job and write an appropriate health and safety policy for that job role. For more help on this task visit the Business Link website at www.businesslink.gov.uk and enter 'create health and safety policy' in the search box.

Activity: Reasons for not reporting accidents at work

In 2007 the Health and Safety Executive produced a report called *An investigation of reporting of workplace accidents under RIDDOR using the Merseyside Accident Information Model* in which academics from Liverpool University looked at the very serious issue of employees not reporting accidents at a Liverpool Hospital. They found that only 33 per cent of workers reported an accident that had happened to them.

In small groups, discuss what factors might cause a person to not report an accident they had suffered. Be prepared to feedback your responses to the rest of the class.

Key personnel responsible for health and safety

Within any business it is important that all staff know who is responsible for health and safety in the workplace, although there is no hard and fast rule as to who is responsible for what safety role. Table 27.2 on page 125 shows some typical health and safety-related responsibilities and who is likely to be responsible for them.

Accident/Incident Report Form

Details of person completing this form

Name .... Position ....

Address ....

Contact tel. nos. ....

Signature .... Date ....

Details of accident/incident

What happened? Give as much detail as possible, continuing overleaf if necessary.

....

....

....

When did the accident/incident happen? Date .... Time ....

Where did the accident/incident happen? ....

Cause of accident/incident if known ....

Details of witnesses ....

....

Category of accident/incident being reported

☐ Near miss ☐ Property damage ☐ Minor ☐ Intermediate ☐ Violence ☐ Threat of violence
☐ Verbal abuse ☐ Major ☐ 3-day ☐ Dangerous occurrence ☐ Disease ☐ Death

---

Details of those injured

Name .... Position ....

Address ....

Contact tel. nos. .... Age ....

Details of injury ....

Treatment given and by whom ....

Taken to hospital? Yes/No Details ....

Time taken off work? Yes/No   No. of days ....

To be completed by Health and Safety Officer

Does the accident need to be investigated? Yes/No Give details ....

....

RIDDOR reportable? Yes/No Give details ....

....

Details of immediate remedial measures taken ....

....

Details of further measures required to prevent recurrence

Action   Date completed

1. ....

2. ....

Figure 27.2: An example of an accident/incident report form

Table 27.2: Typical health and safety responsibilities and key personnel responsible

Health and safety responsibilities	Key personnel
Overall implementation of policy Promotion of safety culture Auditing and inspection	Director
Organisation Training Promoting safety culture Monitoring and auditing Communication Risk assessment (on and off premises)	Head of operational performance
Implementation of health and safety regulations Testing of fire safety devices Emergency procedures co-ordination Accident reporting and investigation	Premises officer
Staff liaison/consultation with management Policy review Auditing/inspection Performance Premises safety Standards Control	Health and safety officer
Accident reporting and investigation First aid treatment Accident reporting/recording Replenishing first aid supplies	First aiders
Fire/emergency coordination Spot check of firefighting equipment Fire hazard reporting	Fire marshals
Support and guidance Preparation of accident statistics Collating risk assessment Record keeping	Health and safety administration/co-ordinator
General safety and the welfare of themselves and others	All staff

Activity: Health and safety structure

Choose an organisation you are familiar with. It could be your school or college, your workplace or another chosen business. Find out which members of staff are responsible for health and safety. Then create an organisational chart showing how their roles link together and how they fit into the business structure as a whole.

Harmful work practices

The legislation, procedures and systems that you have learned about so far all share the same aim of reducing harmful work practices. These can be the result of dangerous, untested or faulty equipment, untrained or inexperienced staff, carelessness and stupidity or negligence. Whatever the cause, the result is often a workplace accident resulting in injury or sometimes death. The effective management of health and safety within the workplace should reduce harmful work practices, thereby reducing accidents.

Organising own work area

A major focus of health and safety legislation is the requirement that all employers ensure that their workers are safe. But employees also have a duty to take care of their own health and safety and that of people who may be affected by what they do (or do not do). Employees must also co-operate with others on health and safety and not interfere with or misuse anything provided for their health, safety or welfare.

As part of their duty employees are also expected to organise their own work area to ensure that it is safe for themselves and any other person coming into it. They must report any accidents and any dangerous or defective equipment as soon as they see it. In these ways, employees play a very important part in the overall health and safety procedures within an organisation.

Activity: Work area health and safety checklist

Create a work area health and safety checklist for your classroom and assess whether your own work area complies with health and safety requirements. Highlight any issues where action may be needed.

Assessment activity 27.1

P1 **M1** **BTEC**

For this activity you will need to choose a business. This can be one that you have personal experience of, such as your school or college, your workplace, or another business, such as a large retailer or warehouse.

For your chosen business, prepare a written report outlining and explaining the legal requirements and regulations for ensuring the health, safety and security of those employed in that business. **P1**

Your report should also assess the implications of that legislation and regulations for a business role in the organisation. **M1**

Grading tip

You should choose a business or workplace that you are familiar with. Your report must show you have researched the legal requirements that the business must comply with regarding health and safety, and that the business is affected by the legislation. **P1** **M1**

2 Know the requirements for healthy, safe and productive working conditions

You have already seen how important it is to know about health and safety legislation in the workplace. It is equally important that employers and employees consider the effect of health and safety requirements in the actual physical workplace. This will involve assessing common hazards found in the working environment.

2.1 Physical environment

Employers must ensure that the physical environment of the workplace promotes healthy and safe working conditions so that workers feel secure in their workplace.

Impact of working environment

Workers may spend more than half their waking hours in the workplace. Employers should create a work environment that is not only compliant with health and safety legislation but is also as comfortable as possible.

The working environment can pose many dangers and employers and employees must both work to reduce the potential risk of harm. Accidents that occur in the working environment are commonly caused by things such as:

- falling objects
- hand tools
- moving objects.

When employers carry out risk assessments, they must consider the risk to employees of being struck by falling objects. They must ensure that:

- items stored above ground level, such as on storage shelving in warehouses, are secure and will not fall easily if disturbed
- heavier items are stored on or near the ground with lighter items stored higher up
- careful consideration is given to methods of stacking, handling and movement of goods to prevent objects falling
- all self-standing objects, such as gas cylinders, or objects leaning against walls are either stable if knocked or secured.

Hand tools, such as knives, pose a significant risk of injury for many types of business and employers should make sure that such tools are safely stored when not in use. In industries where knives are often used, employees should be given protective clothing to prevent injury.

The workplace can be a dangerous environment

Activity: Assessing the working environment

You have been asked to look at the working environment of employees in a local supermarket. The manager is concerned that the working environment may be hazardous and has given you three areas to focus on: falling objects, hand tools and moving objects. Identify the potential risks from these three environmental areas and suggest ways of minimising the risk. Copy and complete the table below to record your findings.

Environmental area of concern	Potential risks identified	Control measures to minimise risk
Falling objects		
Hand tools		
Moving objects		

Moving objects, such as pallet trucks, baking-racks and trolleys, pose a potential risk to workers. When completing their risk assessments, employers should take into account all areas of the workplace where there is the potential for employees to be hit by moving objects.

A common risk found in the workplace that has a significant impact on safe conditions is the existence of sharp edges and trailing leads, both of which can injure staff. Almost all businesses have desks, cupboards, drawers, doors, shelves and chairs in them. Over a period of time, these items may begin to show wear and tear and it is especially common for things like doors and tables to become damaged with sharp edges becoming exposed. Damaged items should be identified on risk assessments or reported by employees and either repaired or replaced.

Trailing electrical leads should be kept to a minimum as they present a very real danger to employees due to the risk of tripping and falling. If leads have to be exposed so that they present a hazard, then employers must secure them and cover them with safety tape to highlight the potential for danger.

Activity: Classroom check

Complete a safety check of your classroom.

- Is there any risk posed by falling or moving objects?
- Are there any sharp edges?
- Are there any trailing leads?
- What could be done to reduce the risk of harm caused by any of the above?

Evacuation assembly areas

Whilst the number of employees killed or injured by fire or serious incident such as an explosion is very rare, it is essential that all staff in any organisation know what to do in the event of a fire or other emergency.

Procedures for an emergency evacuation must be detailed in a fire safety policy document. Abbreviated versions of this policy should be found on the fire action notices that are posted on the walls of the building, usually above a break glass point. Employees should be trained on induction about fire and evacuation procedures so that they know what to do in the event of hearing the fire alarm, discovering a fire, or there being an explosion. Regular practice evacuation drills must be carried out so that employees know what to do and where to go.

On hearing the fire alarm, employees must leave the building by the nearest available exit and make their way to the designated **evacuation assembly area**. The location of this assembly area will be written on the fire action notices. Employers must appoint appropriate staff to the role of fire marshals to guide employees out of the building ensuring that they are the last to leave and that all doors are closed behind them. Fire marshals should also ensure, so far as is reasonably practicable, that they and those whom they are responsible for make their way to the assembly area by the safest route. They are responsible for ensuring that all staff under their control are accounted for. Special evacuation procedures should be in place for disabled employees.

Key term

Evacuation assembly area – a designated place to meet if the building has to be evacuated.

Evacuation assembly areas vary from business to business, but are usually located away from the building in order to protect staff. There may well be more than one evacuation assembly area and employees should go to the area as directed on the fire action notice in the room they are in or as directed by the fire marshal. Staff should only return to the building when the all-clear is given and it is safe to return.

Activity: Evacuation procedures

Familiarise yourself with the emergency evacuation procedures in your school, college or workplace.

- Locate and read the fire action notice.
- Where is your evacuation assembly area?
- How do you get to it?
- Why do you think this assembly area was chosen?
- What factors might change your emergency evacuation route and assembly area?

Did you know?

You can find out more information on the law relating to fire safety at work by searching for the Regulatory Reform (Fire Safety) Order 2005 on the Internet.

Site building works

From time to time, employees will be exposed to building works within their place of work. This can be very intrusive and can expose workers to new and additional risks beyond the normal risks of their job. They may find they have to enter hazardous areas, come into contact with hazardous substances or be exposed to noise pollution. Employers must complete additional risk assessments to take into account any building work with potential additional risks identified and controls put in place to protect workers.

Ideally, employers should make sure building work is kept separate from employees, but where this is impossible, all care must be taken to ensure employees are safe at work.

Off-site work

The workforce is becoming increasingly mobile as more jobs require employees to work away from the main site of the business. Such staff are known as 'off-site workers'. For the purposes of health and safety, these workers are treated exactly the same as on-site workers, although sometimes special considerations may apply. This means that all off-site work must be organised so as to minimise the risks to the health and safety of off-site workers.

Any risks associated with the off-site work must be assessed before it takes place with risks highlighted and controlled in the same way that they would be in the workplace. Significant risks must be highlighted and dealt with appropriately. Individuals involved in off-site working must be provided with appropriate information and training about the off-site activity to ensure healthy and safe working.

Activity: Off-site working

Make a list of some different types of off-site workers and identify the additional off-site risks for each. Copy and complete the table below to record your findings.

Type of off-site worker	Additional off-site risks

Organic infestation

The presence of organic pests in the workplace can be offensive, present infection hazards, contaminate foodstuffs, damage materials and structures and be a nuisance to employees. There are various types of organic pest that can infest a workplace, including:

- houseflies
- cockroaches
- ants
- wasps
- birds
- foxes.

They are a sign of poor health and safety procedures. Employers have a duty, so far as is reasonably possible, to ensure that there is effective management of organic pests. Employees have a responsibility to report all sightings of pests or evidence of their

existence to the appropriate person. As with most health and safety issues, there are many things that employers and employees can do together to eliminate the risk of organic infestation in the workplace, such as:

- covering or storing food items in pest-proof containers
- promptly clearing up spillages
- storing waste in a manner so as to prevent access by pests
- avoiding a build-up of static/stagnant water
- ensuring buildings are of sound structure and well maintained
- covering drains and repairing leaking pipe-work
- repairing cracks in plaster and woodwork, unsealed areas around pipe-work, damaged tiles, badly fitted equipment and kitchen units.

Vermin infestation

Vermin is a term commonly used to mean rats, mice and fleas. Workplace infestation by these types of pests is a serious issue. According to a 2006 survey conducted by the National Pest Technician's Association there has been a serious increase in the number of rats in the UK. The survey also states that

Why is vermin infestation prevention better than cure?

there had been 1.6 million reported infestations during that year in both domestic and business premises. Problems caused by vermin infestation in the workplace include damage to equipment, damage to electrical supply, contamination of the water supply and the threat of disease from droppings and urine.

Employers carrying out risk assessments should be aware of the signs of infestation and employees should report sightings of rat or mice activity. As with other types of infestation, prevention is better than dealing with the problem once it has taken hold and so employers should ensure that these types of vermin do not have the chance to enter the workplace. If a workplace does have an infestation of rats or mice the appropriate specialist pest controller should be contacted to eradicate the problem.

Although not presenting a serious health risk to workers in the UK, fleas present a difficult and annoying challenge in the working environment. Obviously, fleas are much harder to spot than rats or mice, so by the time evidence of infestation is present the amount of fleas in the workplace may be very high indeed. The usual way fleas are brought into the workplace is by human carriers, i.e. on employees' clothing and bodies. For an employer, this type of infestation is much harder to manage and control, but employers can make rules about bringing pets to work and insist that members of staff who might have been exposed to fleas are given protective clothing to wear.

Infestations can be prevented with good workplace hygiene, such as regular vacuuming and cleaning of carpets and fabric furnishings where fleas might live. If flea infestations become very bad professional help will be needed, usually involving the workplace being sprayed with a chemical. If this happens employers must ensure there is an appropriate risk assessment carried out and that workers are not exposed to harmful chemicals.

Did you know?

Restaurants, offices and other business premises are regularly closed down because of vermin infestations. In 2008 a fast food restaurant in Reading was closed due to the presence of rats, and in 2009 a local Council office had to be evacuated and temporarily closed down whilst it was sprayed to get rid of a flea infestation.

Activity: Effects of vermin infestation on a business

Choose three different businesses and carry out the following tasks.

- Assess their potential risks of vermin infestation.
- Analyse the potential negative effects on the business of vermin infestation.
- Discuss what control measures the business could use to prevent infestation.

Dampness and mould

Mould arising from damp conditions within walls and structures of the workplace can cause a range of health problems for employees. Workers may suffer from allergies and cold-like symptoms, such as itchy eyes and sneezing. Employees with pre-existing conditions like asthma should certainly not be exposed to damp and mouldy working conditions. Damp problems can also cause serious future respiratory problems for employees. Staff working in damp and mouldy conditions are likely to be working in generally very unpleasant conditions that could cause them serious harm.

The responsibility for preventing mould arising from damp problems in the workplace rests with the employer. There are several things an employer can do to prevent the build up of mould caused by dampness, including ensuring that:

- any build up of condensation around the workplace is dried up within 48 hours to prevent the growth of mould
- the workplace is properly ventilated to give moisture the chance to escape
- cold surfaces are insulated where possible as they are the places where condensation often develops.

Materials

Employees may come into contact with materials that are hazardous to their health and, if not dealt with properly, these can result in serious injury or even death. You have already learned about the health and safety legislation COSHH (see page 120) and what is clear from this is that employers must ensure that they minimise the risks to workers exposed to them. They can do this by:

- minimising the amount of harmful materials kept in the workplace
- storing chemicals and hazardous materials according to the correct instructions
- making sure that staff know how to take delivery of harmful substances
- keeping substances apart that can become volatile when kept together
- making sure that steps are taken to prevent leakage of harmful substances
- training and equipping staff with ways to deal with harmful substances in the event of a leak or spillage
- cleaning up any spills that occur
- ensuring that staff take safety precautions when handling hazardous materials. These could include wearing overalls, gloves, facemasks and boots and ensuring that the workplace has sufficient ventilation to allow fumes to escape
- checking that all flammable materials are stored in protective containers away from heat
- making sure that employees know how to dispose of the substances safely.

Managers also have a duty to ensure that hazardous waste is correctly identified at each stage of production and appropriate measures are taken to protect the health of employees and contractors who transport or dispose of waste. These provisions are built into the Health and Safety at Work Act 1974 and the Control of Substances Hazardous to Health Regulations (COSHH).

Hygiene facilities

As part of the general welfare requirements for staff, employers must ensure that certain minimum levels of hygiene facilities are provided in the workplace. Under the Workplace (Health, Safety and Welfare) Regulations 1992 (see page 118), employers must provide adequate washing facilities for their staff in the workplace. The type of washing facilities will depend on the nature of the work the business does. Each area for washing must be in places that staff can get to easily. Ideally, the washing facilities should be near to or incorporated into the same room as toilets and any changing rooms. The washing facilities must be hygienic and well lit so that staff can see what they are doing and make sure they are clean. There must be hot and cold water, soap, and

either towels or electric hand dryers. Men and women should have separate facilities.

The Regulations set out the minimum number of washing facilities that employers must provide. These are, for each sex:

- one for 1–5 employees
- two for 6–25 employees
- three for 26–50 employees
- four for 51–75 employees
- five for 76–100 employees.

After the number of employees exceeds 100, an additional wash station is required for every 25 people. Where work is physical, dirty or could result in contamination of the skin by harmful materials, showers should be provided.

The Regulations also provide guidelines for the numbers of toilet facilities required in the workplace. The minimum numbers of water closets (WCs) in the workplace for mixed use are as follows:

- one for 1–5 employees
- two for 6–25 employees
- three for 26–50 employees
- four for 51–75 employees
- five for 76–100 employees.

After the number of employees exceeds 100, an additional WC is required for every 25 people. For male employees, the minimum number of urinals per male employee is as follows:

- one for 1–15 employees
- two for 16–30 employees
- three for 46–60 employees
- three for 61–75 employees
- four for 76–90 employees
- four for 91–100 employees.

There is no requirement for extra urinals for businesses with over 100 employees if extra WCs have been provided.

Activity: Showers in the workplace

In pairs or small groups, make a list of jobs where you think it would be necessary for employers to provide showers for their employees.

Safety in the workplace

In 2008 a munitions company was prosecuted in the courts and ordered to pay £50,000 in fines and costs of £15,000 after a worker was severely burned at its site in a workplace accident. The worker was disposing of flammable materials which caught fire burning his face, neck and both arms.

An investigation by the Health and Safety Executive found that the unsupervised disposal of these materials did not follow the company's policies and procedures, and senior managers did not check this.

Think about it!

1. Why was the company found guilty of an offence when it had created a safety policy on disposal of flammable materials?

2. What else could the company have done to ensure workers' safety?

3. Was a fine the correct punishment for the company? What other punishments could have been imposed?

The aim of the Regulations is to ensure that sufficient facilities are provided to enable them to be used without any delay. Whilst the facilities do not have to be within the workplace they should, if possible, be within the building. They should also be reasonably accessible at all times. Rooms containing the toilet should be ventilated, lit and clean. If the toilet is in an enclosed room, then provision for mechanical ventilation should be made. Each WC should be separate in a room or cubicle with a door that is lockable from the inside. To respect workers' privacy, urinals must not be seen from the entrance doorway when the door is open. The toilet windows should be made of frosted glass also to ensure privacy. A programme of cleaning should be developed for toilets so that it is clear who is responsible for cleaning them and when.

Under the Disability Discrimination Act (DDA) 1995 (amended 2005), employers have the duty to ensure that if they employ disabled staff they have access to adequate disabled washing and toilet facilities. The disabled facilities should meet the needs of all people with disabilities to allow safe access, including workers using wheelchairs. The facilities should have:

- drop-down grab rails and support rails
- emergency pull cords that meet specific requirements – they must be reachable from both the toilet (seated position) and the immediate floor area in case of a fall
- accessible wash basins, soap dispensers, toilet paper and paper towels.

Food preparation areas

Food preparation in the workplace usually falls into one of two categories:

- food that is prepared and sold to the public as part of a food business
- food that is prepared for staff in the workplace.

Activity: WC audit

In mixed sex groups, complete an audit of the toilet facilities in your school, college or workplace. Be sure to ask permission before you do this and ensure that you respect other people's privacy at all times. When you have completed your audit, discuss your findings with the rest of the class.

Audit point	Findings
Number of students/employees	
Number of male students/employees	
Number of female students/employees	
Is there an adequate number of WC facilities?	Yes/No
Are there enough urinals?	Yes/No
Are there any disabled students/employees?	Yes/No
Do disabled toilets have: • easy access • hand rails • emergency cords • accessible washing, soap and paper/dryer facilities?	Yes/No Yes/No Yes/No Yes/No
Are WCs in the same room as washing facilities?	Yes/No
Can urinals be seen from the entrance doorway to male toilet facilities?	Yes/No
Are the toilets clean?	Yes/No
Are the toilets well lit and ventilated?	Yes/No

In either case, health and safety considerations are very important as poor procedures can be the cause of serious health issues and result in the business losing its reputation due to poor hygiene or safety standards.

In any food preparation area, there must be strict rules laid down by the employer to prevent food from being contaminated. It is also the employer's responsibility to make sure that employees are not a risk to food safety. Employers need to focus on four key areas to ensure health and safety:

- personal cleanliness
- clothing
- reporting illness
- keeping the premises clean and safe.

Did you know?

In February 2009, The Fat Duck restaurant owned by television chef Heston Blumenthal was forced to close for several weeks when over 500 customers and staff came down with food poisoning from contaminated shellfish. The incident was investigated by the Health Protection Agency, which concluded that whilst raw shellfish poses well-known food poisoning risks, weaknesses in the restaurant's food preparation procedures made the situation worse. For more details about this case visit the Health Protection Agency website at www.hpa.org.uk and enter 'The Fat Duck' in the search box.

What are the possible consequences of not following health and safety procedures in a food preparation area?

Figure 27.3 opposite shows the minimum requirements employers must meet to ensure personal cleanliness in food preparation areas.

In terms of clothing, employers should ensure that:

- all staff working in food preparation areas are wearing suitable clothing
- clothing is be kept clean and should be changed and cleaned regularly.

A very important duty that rests with the employer is to train staff to report any illnesses that might affect food safety so that the employer can decide whether or not to exclude the employer from the business whilst they are ill. Employers must also ensure the food preparation area is clean and safe.

- All surfaces, including surfaces of equipment, in areas where food is handled, particularly those that are touched by food, must be maintained in a sound condition.
- Surfaces must be easy to clean and, where necessary, to disinfect. This means that surfaces need to be made of materials that are smooth, washable, corrosion-resistant and non-toxic.
- Staff must not store cleaning chemicals and disinfectants in areas where food is handled.

All items, fittings and equipment that food touch must be:

- kept in good order, repair and condition in a way that enables them to be kept clean and, where necessary, to be disinfected so as to avoid any risk of contamination

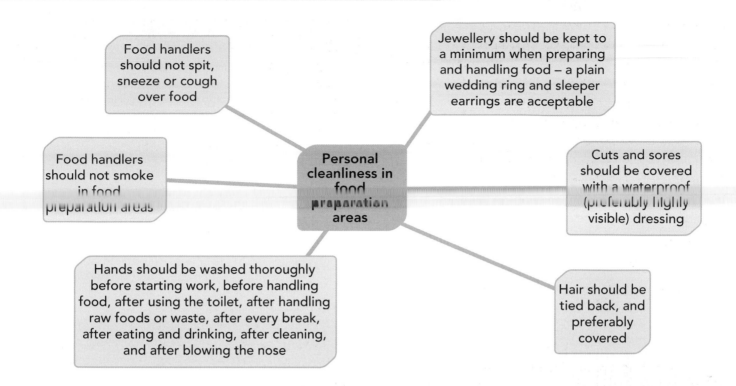

Figure 27.3: Minimum requirements for personal cleanliness in food preparation areas

- fitted, where necessary, with an appropriate control device, such as a temperature sensor to make sure that food is kept at the correct temperature.

The following requirements must also be met with regards facilities.

- There must be adequate facilities, where necessary, for washing food.
- Every sink or other facilities for washing food must have an adequate supply of hot and cold water.
- The water must be drinking quality. These facilities must be kept clean and, where necessary, disinfected.
- At regular intervals all machinery and food preparation areas must be deep-cleaned by professional cleaners.

To ensure that staff are doing their jobs properly, checklists should be created that detail cleaning, temperature and food storage. It is the duty of employees to ensure that these documents are correctly completed, but it is the employer's legal responsibility to ensure that all risks from contamination in food preparation areas are kept to a minimum.

Pest control

As you have already seen on page 129, employers have a duty to make sure that the workplace is free from pests. This ensures that staff are not harmed by them in any way and that all products produced are safe and free from contamination by pests. This means that the employer must do various things to control pests. These include:

- installing ultraviolet insect killers
- spraying insecticides to kill pests
- setting and maintain poisons and traps to kill vermin
- securing buildings to prevent pests from entering.

This is a difficult task, and often organisations will get outside professional help to make sure that they can show they have done everything they can to control pests in their workplace.

Noise and atmospheric pollution

Noise pollution in the workplace can be a serious issue employers have a duty to reduce any noise pollution that might lead to hearing damage, conditions like tinnitus (ringing in the ears) and associated stress problems from working in a noisy workplace. Since

2005, the Control of Noise at Work Regulations have placed certain legal duties on employers, as shown in Figure 27.4.

The Regulations do not apply to workers exposed to low level noise and only apply to workers exposed to noise of 85 decibels or more whilst in the workplace. Prolonged exposure to this level of noise will damage an employee's hearing.

Table 27.3 lists some sources of noise found in the workplace that produce very high levels of noise pollution.

Table 27.3: Common sources of noise pollution in the workplace

Belt sander 82–92 dB	Impact gun 91–107 dB
Bandsaw 94–95 dB	Impact wrench 104–107 dB
Wood planer 94–95 dB	
Blower/pump 95–96 dB	Metal saw 105–108 dB
Brake riveter 97–99 dB	Grinder 87–110 dB
Welding machine 99–100 dB	Diesel generator 107–111 dB
Cross cut saw 98–101 dB	Gas turbine 92–112 dB
Guillotine 94–103 dB	Mining drill 108–113 dB
	Compressor 101–123 dB

The types of machinery shown in Table 27.3 can cause hearing damage and employers must provide adequate protection for workers using this type of equipment.

Did you know?

According to Goines and Hagler, writing in the *Southern Medical Journal* in 2007, noise pollution has been likened to a 'modern plague' producing serious issues for persons suffering it. Common problems caused by noise pollution include:

- hearing impairment
- interference with spoken communication
- cardiovascular disturbances
- disturbances in mental health
- impaired task performance
- negative social behaviour and annoyance reactions.

Activity: How loud is too loud?

Perform an Internet search to find out more about decibels (dB). See if you can find out the decibel levels of some common sounds. Look for examples of sounds that exceed the safe exposure limit. Does exposure have to be continuous to cause hearing damage? Have you ever been exposed to noise pollution and, if so, what was the source and how loud was it?

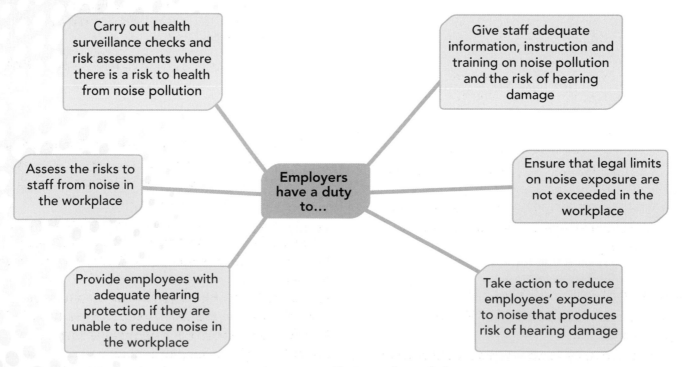

Figure 27.4: Legal duties of employers with regards to noise pollution in the workplace

- Carry out health surveillance checks and risk assessments where there is a risk to health from noise pollution
- Give staff adequate information, instruction and training on noise pollution and the risk of hearing damage
- Assess the risks to staff from noise in the workplace
- Ensure that legal limits on noise exposure are not exceeded in the workplace
- Provide employees with adequate hearing protection if they are unable to reduce noise in the workplace
- Take action to reduce employees' exposure to noise that produces risk of hearing damage

Employers have a duty to...

As well as controlling noise pollution in the workplace, employers also have a duty to ensure that their workers are not exposed to atmospheric pollution, also known as air pollution. Atmospheric pollution is any particulate matter present in the air that has the potential to cause negative health effects, such as dust, fumes and gases. The effects of atmospheric pollution in the workplace vary, although commonly workers' skin, eyes, nose, throat and lungs are usually affected, depending on the pollutant. Flu like symptoms may also be experienced together with blocked or runny noses; occasionally nausea may accompany these symptoms. These effects are potentially very serious and can cause long-lasting or life-threatening health problems for some, including asthma, damage to the central nervous system, brain damage, lung damage, liver damage, cancer and permanent damage to the eyes.

Workers can potentially be exposed to more subtle forms of air pollution due to naturally occurring substances such as ozone. Ozone is a gas that is naturally present in high concentrations in the upper atmosphere, although concentrations in the lower atmosphere can increase due to pollution. It can then become an atmospheric pollutant, reducing air quality and causing health problems. Ozone can accumulate in some workplaces where there is equipment that creates electrostatic discharge, such as arc welding equipment in workshops and photocopiers and laser printers in offices.

Any health condition caused by atmospheric pollution has the potential to be very serious for those in the workplace. Not only can employees become very ill, but productivity is also affected and employers can be sued for compensation. Employers therefore have a legal duty to ensure that adequate risk assessments for atmospheric pollution are completed in the workplace. Effective and suitable provision must be made to ensure that every enclosed workspace is ventilated by a sufficient quantity of fresh or purified air to prevent harm to workers. Pollutants such as dust must be controlled and minimised by adequate cleaning and vacuuming.

Temperature and ventilation

The Workplace (Health, Safety and Welfare) Regulations 1992 state that:

'The temperature in workrooms should provide reasonable comfort without the need for special clothing. Where such a temperature is impractical because of hot or cold processes, all reasonable steps should be taken to achieve a temperature which is as close as possible to comfortable.'

The minimum temperature allowable in the workplace is 16°C, although if the work involves physical labour the minimum temperature is 13°C. Whilst no maximum temperature is set in the guidelines, it has been suggested by the HSE that the maximum temperature in which a person is able to work comfortably is 30°C. If workers are exposed to temperatures that are too low or too high, the employer must make provision to ensure workers are as comfortable as possible.

Did you know?

Coal miners are one type of worker at serious risk from atmospheric pollution. Continued exposure to coal dust in enclosed spaces has resulted in serious lung diseases for some. A large number of those affected have been awarded compensation from the government, although they still have to suffer with their disease and may face severe disability or even death.

Activity: Noise and atmospheric pollution

In small groups, choose two different types of business or organisation. One should be a heavy or manufacturing industry, such as a steel or engineering works, and one should be a light industry, such as computing. Then carry out the following activities.

1. Identify the types of machinery or equipment that might be found in each business or organisation.

2. level in decibels produced by each piece of machinery or equipment.

3. Identify the ways in which workers might be exposed to atmospheric pollution in your chosen organisations.

4. How could both employers reduce the risk of exposure to noise and atmospheric pollution to their staff?

Activity: Too hot, too cold

In pairs or small groups, visit different areas of your school, college or workplace with a thermometer and record the temperature that students or staff are working in. You could carry out this activity twice at different times of the year, e.g. winter and summer.

Write a report based on your findings about what your school, college or workplace could do to improve current temperature conditions.

Workplaces also need to be ventilated properly so that employees have the opportunity to breathe fresh, clean air when they are working. Ventilation can be as simple as sufficient windows for the workplace or properly installed and maintained mechanical systems. The air should be taken from a source outside the workplace so that it has not been polluted by contaminates in the workplace and should then be circulated throughout the workplace.

Ventilation systems in the workplace should also remove and dilute warm, humid air, which can be uncomfortable to work in, and give adequate air movement, which produces the effect of breathing fresh air. Ventilation systems are especially important in organisations where workers are exposed to heat, dust, gas, fumes or other materials liable to cause breathing difficulties.

Activity: Breathing easy?

In small groups, draw up a plan of your school, college or workplace showing all of the ventilation points in the building. Assess how well the school, college or workplace is ventilated and whether any improvements could be made.

2.2 Equipment

To help maintain a safe working environment, a range of safety equipment and warning signs is commonly used to protect workers from harm. We will now look at some of the more common forms of safety equipment used in the workplace.

Safety guards

Many serious accidents at work involve machinery. The guarding of dangerous parts of machines used at work has been a legal requirement for many years under the

What could be the effects of working in an environment that is too cold or too hot?

Health and Safety at Work Act 1974 and the Supply of Machinery (Safety) Regulations 2008. Employers must also ensure that dangerous machinery is only used by appropriate staff who have received the required training.

Ideally no worker should be exposed to dangerous machinery, but in some businesses this is unavoidable and part of the job role. Figure 27.5 shows some types of dangerous machinery commonly found in the workplace.

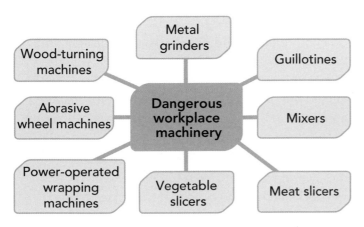

Figure 27.5: Examples of dangerous machinery that can be found in the workplace

Dangerous machinery, such as that shown in Figure 27.5, must not be used by untrained staff and young workers. As part of their risk assessments, employers need to check that these types of machines are fitted with a safety guard that is strong enough to protect workers and, if fixed, that it cannot be too easily removed. Workers using these types of machines must also be made aware of where the emergency stop button is so that in the event of a problem the machine can be turned off quickly.

Warning signs and sound signals

A common safety feature in the workplace is the warning sign which can be used to alert employees to potential risks or danger. Warning signs may also instruct workers on what to do in the event of an emergency. Since 1996 the law on warning signs has been governed by the Health and Safety (Safety Signs and Signals) Regulations which were introduced to create specific warning signs to be used in all organisations. Common warning signs in the workplace include:

- corrosive material
- flammable material
- explosive material
- no unauthorised entry
- toxic material
- first aid boxes
- general hazards
- safety helmets must be worn
- no smoking
- fire exits and fire exit routes
- location of firefighting equipment.

The Regulations state that certain signs, such as fire exits signs, must be able to light up in an emergency and must also be fitted with audible alarms. Training must be provided to all employees so that they understand the information or instructions being conveyed by any warning signs in their workplace.

Activity: Warning signs

In small groups, assess your school, college or workplace for evidence of sufficient warning signs. Create or find a plan of the building and note where every warning sign is located and what type it is. Are there any other warning signs that might be needed in certain places?

Case study: Safety equipment saves lives

In October 2009, an engineering firm was fined £10,000 and ordered to pay nearly £15,000 legal costs for failing to provide adequate safety precautions for a worker using an asphalt mixer. The worker lost four fingers and part of his thumb when his hand got caught in this piece of machinery.

1. Why was the business prosecuted?
2. What could have been done to prevent the accident?
3. Is a fine the best punishment for businesses that break health and safety laws?

As part of the general safety requirements for staff in the workplace, all workers should also be aware of any sound signals that the business uses in an emergency situation. Sound signals, often referred to as acoustic signals, are classed as safety signs and staff should know what to do if they hear them. Common types of sound signals used in the workplace are for:

- fire evacuation
- gas/fume evacuation
- explosion
- bomb alert
- water sprinkler use
- unauthorised opening of fire exits
- general evacuation.

Where used, sound signals must:

- have a sound level considerably higher that that of the normal working noise without being excessive or painful
- be easily recognisable and clearly distinct from any other signal or background noise.

Whatever type of sound signal is used, staff must be trained to know what the signal means and what they have to do in the event of hearing it. Where a sound signal is used to order evacuation, the signal should continue throughout the evacuation and staff must be given practice in what to do by way of practice drills.

Maintenance frequency

Many accidents at work are caused by faulty or poorly maintained work equipment. Employers have a duty to ensure equipment is maintained and in good working condition. They must make sure that maintenance logs are kept up to date showing when machinery and equipment was last serviced and inspected. This is not required for all equipment, but must be in place for all high risk equipment, such as dangerous machinery, electrical equipment, fire alarm systems, water sprinklers and fire extinguishers. The maintenance frequency of workplace equipment depends on various factors, such as the working limits and maximum use of equipment, how it is used and the risk to safety of malfunction. It is normal that some maintenance is carried out in-house, for example, in your school or college you may have a premises or maintenance team that deals with minor maintenance issues. But for

more serious maintenance of high risk equipment, your school or college will use professional experts to carry out the maintenance.

Did you know?

According to the Health and Safety Executive, around 25 workers die each year at work from using poorly maintained electrical equipment.

Protective clothing

Some job roles require workers to wear protective clothing. Protective clothing can make a job easier, prevent injury and even save lives. Examples of such clothing are gloves, helmets, footwear, face masks, chemical suits, high-visibility vests and eye protection.

Under the Personal Protective Equipment at Work Regulations 1992, it is the responsibility of the employer to make sure that the protective clothing provided matches the potential workplace hazards. Employers must also make sure that workers understand why protective clothing must be worn and when to use it correctly. This will often involve some sort of staff training on its use.

Employers must provide personal protective equipment and employees have a responsibility to use it

Activity: Protective clothing

Look at each of the following jobs and identify what types of protective clothing might be needed in order to safely carry it out. You should also state why each item is required.

Job	Protective clothing required	Reason for protection
Mechanic		
Refuse collector		
Welder		
Miner		
Nurse		
Police officer		
Soldier		

Accessible emergency exits

As part of their emergency risk assessment, employers must consider whether, in the event of an emergency like a fire occurring, all persons in the workplace could leave safely and reach a place of safety. To this end, they must provide accessible fire exits. Each employee should be no further than 18 metres from the nearest accessible emergency exit. Emergency exits should be clearly signposted with signs that can be illuminated and alarmed.

Emergency exits must be kept clear of all obstructions that could stop someone escaping. They must never be locked. The emergency exits should lead to a place of safety away from the workplace. Staff should be trained to know where all the emergency exits are in their place of work and should know what to do in the event of an emergency.

Fire extinguishers or sprinkler systems

Within the workplace, employers must provide the means for staff to deal with small fires. The most common way to do this is with the correct use of fire extinguishers. As part of the organisation's fire management plan, as required by the Regulatory Reform (Fire Safety) Order 2005, the workplace must have the correct fire extinguishers with staff that know how to use them.

The number of extinguishers required in a business will vary and depend on the size of premises and whether it is a low or high risk business. The general requirement is that in a low risk workplace staff should be no more than 30 metres from their nearest extinguisher. Usually, extinguishers are sited next to a potential fire risk, such as a heater or computer, and close to exit doors and stairways. As part of the warning and safety signage requirements you have already looked at on page 139, extinguishers must be clearly sited and labelled.

There are five main types of fire extinguisher, each designed to deal with a specific type of fire hazard, although some can be used on more than one type of fire.

- Water – used for Class A fires, which are those that involve common hazards, such as wood, straw, paper and coal.
- Foam – used for Class A fires, but also suitable for use with Class B fires, which are those that involve flammable liquids, such as petrol and paints.
- CO_2 (carbon dioxide) – used for electrical fires and flammable liquid fires.
- Powder – suitable for many different types of fire, so good to have on business premises where fires could involve flammable liquids, gas or electricity, as well as Class A fires.
- Wet chemical extinguisher – designed specifically for fires involving cooking oil and fat, for example, a chip pan fire, but can also be used on Class A fires.

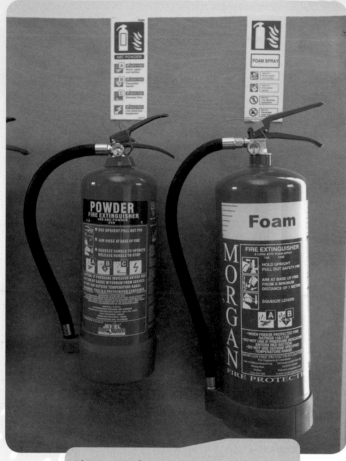

Always use the correct extinguisher

Employers need to train staff so that they are able to recognise the best type of extinguisher to use on a fire and so that they know how the extinguishers work. It is also the employer's responsibility to ensure that fire extinguishers are maintained and ready to be used if needed. Fire extinguishers need to be tested or serviced every year by a qualified engineer, and many extinguishers need to be discharged and refilled at specific intervals to ensure that they work correctly. The engineer will sign and date each extinguisher to indicate when the test or service took place. Extinguishers should also be visually inspected regularly to check that they have not been tampered with.

A far more effective way of dealing with fires in the workplace, and recommended by the Fire and Rescue Service, is the installation of a water sprinkler system. These are activated when a fire is detected and water, fed from the water supply, puts the fire out. These systems are seen as far more safe and effective than conventional fire extinguishers as:

- workers are not put at risk by attempting to put out fires themselves
- they protect people in the room where the fire starts as the sprinkler system only activates in the area where the fire is
- they deal with fires when they are small and more easily controllable
- they control/extinguish 99 per cent of fires
- they limit the production of smoke and fumes
- they reduce the damage caused by a fire and therefore minimise disruption to the business
- they work even when the business premises is empty, for example, at night
- generally, a sprinkler system for a new property would only amount to one to two per cent of the total build cost if the building was destroyed by fire

- they cost very little to maintain

- the protection they offer can reduce the need for other fire safety measures

- they bring about financial benefits resulting from insurance premium reductions

- they are environmentally friendly as they use around 5 per cent of the water the Fire Service uses to put out a fire and they do not give off chemicals like conventional extinguishers

- businesses using sprinkler systems show that they have done all they can to minimise loss of life or injury by fire.

However, sprinkler systems can be seen as more complicated than fire extinguishers as the system needs to be tested regularly. Both the alarm system and the water system has to be tested, usually once a month, by an appropriate person to ensure that it is working correctly. The system will also require regular maintenance servicing by a qualified engineer.

Assessment activity 27.2

(P2) BTEC

Using the same business you selected for Assessment activity 27.1, describe the requirements for a healthy and safe workplace, as applied to the physical environment and equipment used in the business. (P2)

Grading tip

To complete Assessment activity 27.2 you should use the information you have learned so far as a basis for your work and then describe which of these are required for your chosen business. You could present your findings as a PowerPoint® presentation. (P2)

2.3 Legislation

The main legislation concerned with healthy and safe working conditions is the Health and Safety at Work Act 1974 (see page 117) and the various laws and regulations that have developed both from this and other European laws.

As we now live in an increasingly technological age, a range of associated laws that impact on health and safety management in the workplace have been developed. The four main pieces of legislation that we will be looking at in this section are:

- Data Protection Act 1998

- Computer Misuse Act 1990

- Copyright, Designs and Patent Act 1988

- Freedom of Information Act 2000.

Data Protection Act 1998

The Data Protection Act (DPA) was passed to protect individuals' rights with regards to the increasing amount of personal data organisations and businesses hold about them. In the workplace, strict controls are now in place to ensure that data about employees, such as date of birth, address, bank details, pay, pension, discipline, training and health and safety, has to be kept safely and securely by the business. The business must appoint a person known as the data controller to manage the accuracy and validity of information about employees that is held by the business. The data controller must be registered with a government appointed person called the Information Commissioner. Businesses should be aware that it is now a criminal offence to hold employee information without permission of the Information Commissioner.

The DPA also gives rights to employees regarding the information held about them. Employees have the right to see the information (subject to the Freedom of Information Act 2000, page 144), the right to stop information being held, the right to stop the information being passed to third parties for marketing purposes, the right of compensation for mistakes made and the right for errors to be corrected.

Employers are duty bound to retain accurate information records about various aspects of their employees' work records, as well as the organisation's own health and safety records for certain periods of time known as the retention period. Table 27.4 overleaf shows some of the main records that need to be held, along with the retention period for each.

Table 27.4: Information record types and retention periods

Record	Retention period
Accident books, accident records/reports	3 years
Medical records and details of biological tests under the Control of Lead at Work Regulations	40 years
Medical records as specified by the Control of Substances Hazardous to Health Regulations (COSHH)	40 years
Medical records under the Control of Asbestos at Work Regulations	40 years
Records of tests and examinations of control systems and protective equipment under the Control of Substances Hazardous to Health Regulations (COSHH)	5 years
Assessments under Health and Safety Regulations and records of consultations with safety representatives and committees	Permanently
Personnel files and training records	6 years after leaving job

Computer Misuse Act 1990

As you have just read, an employer must keep different records for certain periods of time under the DPA. The main reason for this is to prove that health and safety procedures are taking place in the workplace. Under the Computer Misuse Act 1990, it is a criminal offence for anyone to gain access to a computer system to interfere with computerised health and safety records.

Copyright, Designs and Patents Act 1998

Electronic records, including health and safety records, may be the subject of copyright. This means that ownership of the records stays with the business and they are the legal owner of them. This means that no other person other than the owner of the contents of the record may gain access to them or use them without the owner's permission.

Freedom of Information Act 2000

The Freedom of Information Act was passed in 2000 to allow anyone to request copies of information held about them by public bodies. This is potentially very intrusive for many organisations and certain exceptions have been created within the Act to protect sensitive information. One of those is Section 38, which allows refusal of disclosure of information if it is likely to endanger the health and safety of any individual.

Activity: Data protection

1. Find out who the data controller is in your school, college or workplace. Prepare a questionnaire or some interview questions to find out what they do.
2. Looking at Table 27.4, assess the reasons why information must be kept for the specified periods of time.

Activity: Legislative information

In small groups, produce a short presentation and accompanying information leaflet that explains the legal effect on health and safety in the workplace of the Data Protection Act 1998, the Computer Misuse Act 1990, the Copyright, Designs and Patents Act 1998 and the Freedom of Information Act 2000.

Functional skills

Producing the presentation and information leaflet about legislation will help you to develop your **ICT** skills in IT systems and functional IT skills, and will also help you to develop your **English** skills in speaking and listening, and reading and writing.

3   Understand the role and responsibilities of key personnel

In any business, there must be members of the organisation that deal with health and safety in the workplace. It is crucial for the successful management of health and safety within the workplace that key personnel with specific responsibility for health and safety can be identified by staff and outside agencies. It is equally important to understand the roles, responsibilities and accountabilities of those persons involved.

3.1 Identification of responsible person

As you saw on page 123, there is a range of personnel who can be responsible for health and safety in the workplace. The names given to each position can vary from business to business, but some of the more common are discussed in this section.

Facilities manager

According to the British Institute of Facilities Management, the facilities manager in any business has an important role.

> 'At a corporate level, it [the role] contributes to the delivery of strategic and operational objectives. On a day-to-day level, effective facilities management provides a safe and efficient working environment, which is essential to the performance of any business, whatever its size and scope.'

Visit the British Institute of Facilities Management website at www.bifm.org.uk for more information.

The facilities manager should be easily identifiable in any business as they will be responsible for so many cross-organisation functions. Typical responsibilities of the facilities manager might include:

- being the building manager, ensuring statutory compliance for health and safety matters
- being the first contact for all building maintenance and development matters
- undertaking risk assessments, organising emergency procedures and liaising with staff
- liaising with other managers, to undertake specific health and safety audits
- ensuring that all legislative requirements are met

- liaising with, reporting and maintaining standards on departments, such as maintenance, catering and cleaning
- liaising with internal and external providers to obtain the best level of health and safety provision
- co-ordinating all aspects of health and safety and fire safety in the area(s) of responsibility.

The role of facilities manager also has a very important part to play in linking the business strategy and objectives within the organisation to high levels of health and safety.

Human resources director

Like the facilities manager, the human resources director is a very senior position within the business. They too will have strategic responsibilities with specific training, as well as health and safety responsibilities. The role is varied and differs from organisation to organisation, but common responsibilities in this role include:

- planning, developing and implementing a strategy for human resource management and development, including health and safety training and development of a safety culture within the business
- ensuring business activities meet with and integrate with organisational requirements for quality management, health and safety, legal stipulations, environmental policies and general duty of care
- creating a suitable and relevant health and safety policy
- maintaining a safe workplace without risk to health
- ensuring safe equipment and machinery and safe movement, storage and use of articles and substances
- provision of adequate first aid and welfare facilities and support
- making sure there is provision of suitable and current information and supervision concerning health and safety policies and practices
- ensuring that there are proper assessments of risks to health and safety and implementation of measures and arrangements identified as necessary from the assessments

- providing training on emergency procedures, first aid facilities, safety signs, relevant protective clothing and equipment and incident reporting to the relevant authorities

- making sure that the workplace satisfies health, safety and welfare requirements for ventilation, temperature, lighting, sanitary, washing and rest facilities

- preventing and taking precautions against staff exposure to hazardous substances, and danger from flammable, explosive, electrical, noise, radiation and manual handling risks

- recruiting and selecting health and safety direct-reporting staff.

Much of the role of a human resource director is aimed at providing adequate health and safety measures within the business. As a director, they will have legal accountability and responsibility on behalf of the business to ensure health and safety policies, procedures and systems are followed correctly.

Did you know?

The Corporate Manslaughter and Corporate Homicide Act was passed in 2007. The introduction of this Act means that for the first time in the UK, senior managers, such as directors, can be found guilty of corporate manslaughter as a result of serious management failures resulting in a gross breach of a duty of care, such as failing to implement satisfactory health and safety procedures.

Department heads

Department heads are usually much lower down in the organisational structure of a business than facilities managers and human resources directors, but they still have very important responsibilities concerning health and safety. In many cases, department heads who manage department teams are given responsibility from their senior managers to ensure that health and safety procedures are correctly followed. They are often given checklists to work from to ensure health and safety measures in their departments and can take action where necessary to correct defects and report serious issues. Figure 27.6 opposite shows a typical department head checklist that might be used in the business environment.

Enlisting department heads to manage health and safety ensures that problems are spotted and dealt with at an early stage and demonstrates the importance of involving as many members of staff in the health and safety system as possible.

Individual employee obligations and responsibilities

The majority of responsibility and accountability for health and safety in the workplace is placed on directors, senior managers and heads of departments. But it is clear from what you have already learned so far in this unit that the Health and Safety at Work legislation also places obligations and responsibilities on individual employees as well.

Employees have an obligation by law to follow all of the health and safety training they receive regarding working practices, safety procedures and the use of equipment. Employees must work together safely and take reasonable care of their own and other people's health and safety in the workplace. They also play an important part in the health and safety management cycle as they are often the first to spot health and safety issues in the workplace. Employees have a responsibility to tell someone (usually their line manager or safety manager) about any health and safety matter that could endanger themselves or other work colleagues.

First aider

As you will know by now, many people at work suffer injuries due to health and safety failings. Other staff simply fall ill in the workplace and require medical attention. Under the Health and Safety (First Aid) Regulations 1981, employers have a legal duty to provide suitably qualified staff who can administer first aid to injured or sick employees. It is important that employees receive immediate attention, and that an ambulance is called in serious incidents. The minimum requirements for first aid for any workplace are that there is a suitably stocked first aid kit, a qualified **first aider** and sufficient information provided to staff so that they know who that person is. The first aider must have attended an approved first aid training course paid for by the employer.

Key term

First aider – person responsible for giving emergency treatment to employees injured in the workplace.

Department Health and Safety Checklist			
Check procedure	Yes	No	Action required
Do you have a full copy of the organisation's Health and Safety Policy?			
Have all relevant actions identified on previous health and safety checklists been completed?			
Have fire safety checklists been completed on two occasions during the last 12 months and identified actions carried out?			
Are all staff aware of the need to report all accidents, dangerous occurrences and cases of ill health?			
Are all accidents, dangerous occurrences and cases of ill health investigated, either within the department or by the Health and Safety Manager?			
Are all new employees given information on health and safety matters specific to your department?			
Has the risk assessment system been fully implemented within your department?			
Have all reasonably practicable control measures been taken where identified by risk assessment?			
Has training been provided where identified by risk assessment?			
Has hygiene monitoring been carried out where identified by a risk assessment?			
Are floors/carpets, stairs and corridors sound?			
Do you have adequate numbers of first aiders or have you made arrangements for first aid cover?			
Are there adequate numbers of first aid boxes?			
Are the first aid boxes appropriately stocked?			
Are there signs identifying the nearest first aider?			
Are there adequate and appropriate health and safety notices and signs?			
Is storage of material and equipment adequate?			
Has all electrical equipment been PAT tested and labelled?			
Is hazardous waste appropriately disposed of?			
Have all pressure systems been examined and tested?			
Have all ladders and steps been visually inspected?			
Has all personal protective equipment (e.g. ear defenders, respirators) been examined and tested where necessary?			
Have all local ventilation cupboards been examined and tested?			

Signed .... Dated ....

Figure 27.6: A typical department health and safety checklist

- The number of first aiders required in the workplace depends on the size of the workforce and the nature of the business.

- In low risk workplaces, such as offices, there must be one first aider for every 50–100 employees, plus one per every additional 100 employees.

- In medium risk businesses, such as warehousing, there must be at least one first aider for every 20–50 staff.

- In high risk workplaces, such as construction, there must be one first aider for every 5–50 workers. There may also be the need to have additional specialist first aiders appointed, for example, in chemical plants, where additional first aiders should have skills for dealing with chemical injuries.

A first aid kit can be invaluable in the workplace, but should only be used by trained staff – why do you think this is?

Employers must provide sufficient information to employees about the provision of first aid in their workplace. This must include the location of equipment, facilities and first aid personnel. This information should be included in the induction training for new employees.

Fire marshals

Fire presents a rare but serious danger in the workplace. Employers have a duty to ensure that adequate fire precautions are maintained. One of the key features of an effective fire safety policy in the workplace is the appointment and training of **fire marshals**. The role of a fire marshal is, in the event of an emergency or drill, to assist with the effective evacuation of their area of the workplace and ensure staff gathers at the external fire evacuation assembly point.

Under the Regulatory Reform (Fire Safety) Order 2005, fire marshals in the workplace must be trained following approved training courses. Employers must have a fire marshal for each 'significant area' in each building and a fire marshal must cover all shift patterns the business operates. A 'significant area' is defined by the time it takes a designated fire marshal to account for a specified area as being safely evacuated. This area could be a section of an office or factory or anywhere else that employees and members of the public have access to. As a guide, it should take no longer than one minute for a fire marshal to be able to account for a significant area and reach the fire exit safely themselves. The number of floors the workplace has and the number of evacuation exits should also be taken into account.

Fire marshals also have to ensure the safe evacuation of persons other than employees using the premises, including contractors, visitors and customers. Consideration must be given to those with special needs in terms of evacuation support, and equipment must comply with disability discrimination legislation to ensure their safe removal from the premises.

Key term

Fire marshal – person appointed by an employer to ensure an area of a building has been evacuated in the event of fire in the workplace.

In the event of a fire evacuation or drill, fire marshals should be identifiable by staff and so usually wear fluorescent vests or jackets to make themselves known.

Head counts

In the event of an emergency in the workplace, such as a fire, it is vital that all persons are accounted for. Employers will need to devise specific ways of performing head counts to ensure that everyone is safe. This will need to be something that is practised in drills and training. Particular importance will be placed on the role of fire marshals to ensure their area has been evacuated safely, although, overall, it may be the responsibility of department heads or managers to ensure their staff are safe and then report this to the person co-ordinating the emergency.

Activity: Responsibility for health and safety

In small groups, using the information about key members of staff with health and safety responsibilities on pages 145–9, identify the personnel in your school, college or workplace who have any responsibility for health and safety issues. Find out the following information:

- Who are they?
- What is their job role?
- What are they responsible for?
- Who are they accountable to?

PLTS

Collaborating with others when working in groups to conduct research and evaluate the roles and responsibilities of health and safety personnel in your chosen business will help you to develop your skills as a **team worker**.

3.2 Roles, responsibility and accountability

You already know that the main responsibility for health and safety in the workplace lies with the employer, but there are other parties who have an important role to play too.

Tenant/leaseholder

Many businesses are run from rented or leased premises. Here the situation regarding health and safety is a little more complex. The overall responsibility for health and safety belongs with the owner of the property and they have a duty of care to ensure that the building conforms to health and safety legislation. Increasingly the day-to-day responsibility for health and safety is shifting away from the owner of the property and onto the tenant or leaseholder, but the ultimate responsibility still remains with the owner of the building.

Tenants or **leaseholders** cannot abandon their responsibility for what goes on in the workplace and so must ensure that the workplace meets a number of basic requirements under health and safety rules as an employer.

Depending on the type of agreement, owners and landlords may share the costs of these requirements and may ask tenants and leaseholders to make a contribution via a service charge. The tenant should also co-operate with other tenants in the same building on health and safety issues.

The division of health and safety responsibilities will often be the subject of negotiation between landlords and tenants. It is important to check what is set out in the lease as commercial tenancy agreements often put the duty for safety on the tenant.

Key terms

Tenant – person renting the business property.

Leaseholder – person who has bought the right to occupy the business property for a certain period of time.

Maintenance agencies

Under health and safety legislation, employers have a duty to ensure that the workplace is safe and well maintained. The majority of maintenance work can be performed in-house, but there will inevitably be times when the business needs to use the services of outside agencies to carry out maintenance. A good example of this is the maintenance of fire extinguishers and sprinkler systems (see page 141).

It is the duty of the employer to ensure that maintenance takes place and that it is of the required standard. Whilst maintenance agency personnel are on-site, the employer must ensure that they work safely and that they are treated in the same way as other employees in terms of health and safety.

Contractors and sub-contractors

There may be occasions when businesses have to allow contractors and sub-contractors into the workplace to carry out work, such as building or electrical work. In such a situation, both the organisation and the contractor have duties under health and safety law. Similarly, if the contractor uses sub-contractors to carry out some or all of the work, all parties will have some health and safety responsibilities. In essence, the procedures to protect contractors' and sub-contractors' safety are not substantially different from those that ensure the safety of employees.

Emergency services

Unfortunately, sometimes things will go wrong in the workplace that make it necessary to call the emergency services. This might be calling an ambulance for a member of staff having a heart attack or calling the police because of a shoplifter or break in. In general terms, employers owe the emergency services the same duties of care under the Health and Safety Act as their own employees and must ensure, as far as possible, that they are safe when in the workplace. There will be times, though, when the emergency services have to deal with dangerous situations, such as a fire, and it will then be up to the commanding officers of the emergency services to assess the situation. In many cases, if the situation becomes so dangerous that an evacuation takes place, the employer will not have any say over matters involving health and safety until the all clear is given by the emergency services.

Freelance consultant advisers

There may be times when the business will employ the service of a freelance (self-employed) consultant or adviser. This might be done to look at things like productivity or streamlining the work force. Whatever capacity this person is employed in, an employer will need to treat the consultant or adviser in the same way in terms of health and safety as if they were employed as a member of staff.

Trade union representatives

In many workplaces in the UK, workers' rights are represented by trade unions. Staff have the option to join a union that represents their industry and gain protection by being a member. It is normal practice for a union to appoint a trade union health and safety representative in the workplace. Under the Safety Representatives and Safety Committees Regulations 1977 and Health and Safety (Consultation with Employees) Regulations 1996 employers are legally obliged to consult with trade union health and safety representatives on matters relating to the health and safety of union members in the workplace. Employers must consult with their employees or trade union representative on the following issues:

* the introduction of any measure that may substantially affect the health and safety at work of employees
* the information given to employees on the risks and dangers arising from their work or workplace
* measures put in place to reduce or remove these risks and what employees should do if they are exposed to a risk of harm
* the planning and organisation of health and safety training
* the health and safety consequences of introducing new technology.

Clearly, the more involvement employees or their representatives have in the consultation process regarding their own health and safety, the more likely it is that any health and safety policy or procedure created will be accepted and followed by staff.

Activity: External parties

Look at your own school, college or workplace and list the different types of external parties who might affect the business, such as builders. Then create a chart showing the health and safety responsibilities and accountabilities the employer might have for each.

Implementation

The implementation of health and safety procedures within the workplace will vary from business to business, but there are usually areas of common practice. At the most senior director level, the policy for health and safety will firstly be devised. This may be discussed with and agreed upon by trade union representatives and senior managers. The policy may well then be given to various departments such as human resources in order for appropriate training to be arranged. Procedures will then be cascaded down through the organisational hierarchy so that the policy is fully implemented throughout the business.

Monitoring working conditions

One of the key challenges relating to health and safety procedures in the workplace is ensuring that systems put in place actually work and that workers are in fact safe and secure. The most effective health and safety systems are those that have procedures in place for monitoring working conditions. There are many ways working conditions can be monitored, including:

- health and safety officers checking working conditions
- staff feedback
- numbers of accidents at work
- numbers of days off work due to work-related illness or injury
- risk assessments by managers
- safety representative feedback
- audits by external inspection teams such as Fire Safety Officers.

If working conditions are regularly monitored and improvements made, then workers will feel valued, safe and secure and, ultimately, will work better.

Identifying and documenting improvement

Where the monitoring of working conditions has identified issues that require improvement, it is important to ensure that these improvements are made to improve the overall health and safety system. In cases where serious health and safety issues are identified, such as problems with fire extinguishers or an electrical fault, it is a requirement that these faults are documented in writing showing what action is required and what has been done to rectify the fault. By doing this, an employer will be able to prove to any relevant authority that they have done all they can to improve health and safety in the workplace.

Upgrading and compliance

There will be times when employers have to upgrade certain parts of the workplace. This might be, for example, through new building work or the introduction of new IT equipment. Whatever the upgrade, health and safety will be an important consideration. New risk assessments will need to be drawn up to incorporate the upgrading work and staff will need to be consulted about what is happening.

There are some aspects, such as the legislative requirements of health and safety, that a business cannot ignore. So when new changes in health and safety law are made, if they apply to a business, it must comply and follow those laws exactly.

Budget allocations

According to a survey of UK businesses carried out by Cowling and Bevan in 2007, only 29 per cent have an explicit health and safety budget, and the average amount of money spent per year on health and safety is £200 per full-time employee. In many businesses, the decision to spend money from the budget on health and safety is not a major priority. This is the wrong approach. If budget allocations do not reflect a commitment to health and safety procedures, then serious injuries and even deaths may occur, staff may feel undervalued and inevitably productivity will suffer.

4   Be able to assess and manage risk

Managing health and safety in the workplace is a complicated and difficult task. Employers have to balance legal requirements with financial constraints, all the time being aware that failure to correctly implement health and safety procedures effectively puts workers in danger of harm. The best employers will be able to assess risk through the effective use of risk assessments and manage risk in the workplace by monitoring risk and preventing harm.

4.1 Risk assessments

One of the best ways to manage risk in the workplace is by the completion of risk assessments. A **risk assessment** is a method of looking at work activities, assessing what could go wrong and then identifying suitable prevention measures to minimise loss, damage or injury. They are now a legal requirement in the workplace. The Management of Health and Safety at Work Regulations 1999 ensure that all employers and the self-employed assess the risks from their work on anyone who may be affected by their activities.

Key term

Risk assessment – a document used to record hazards, risk of harm and the controls put in place to minimise the risk and harm.

Format

There is no compulsory format required for a risk assessment in the workplace as they will be specific to the business. Businesses might use a generic risk assessment that is applicable to all risks, they might use ones for specific risks, such as fire management, or they might use one-off risk assessments, such as for school/college trips. Whatever format is used, if the business employs more than five staff the document must be able to be recorded and kept as a legal record that a risk assessment has taken place. This could be paper or electronic format, but it is more usual to use a paper document in order to have a written record of the risk assessment.

Frequency

The frequency of a risk assessment will depend on the type of risk being assessed and the severity of the risks identified. Employers may be able to complete a risk assessment for all workers identifying the risks in the workplace that may last for some time, but if new working practices are introduced into the workplace, a new risk assessment will be needed.

Content

Although there is no set content for a risk assessment, it is a working document aimed at assessing and controlling risk. Its content will need to reflect this and so, whatever else it contains, it should identify hazards in the workplace and which staff might be harmed, identify how they might be harmed and include an evaluation of the risks with ways to avoid them. There should also be a grading of the risk of harm, either numerically or simply low, medium or high.

Once the risks have been identified, they should be recorded on the assessment and control measures put in place to minimise the risk. There should also be the ability for the assessor to review the risk assessment and update it if necessary.

Safety and security hazards in the workplace

The purpose of a risk assessment in the workplace is to identify hazards that pose a threat to workers' safety. Hazards can be broken down into two main types: safety hazards and security hazards. Common safety hazards around the workplace might include:

- loose or trailing cabling
- wet, slippery, unclean, badly surfaced or damaged floors
- poor lighting/broken lights
- inadequate ventilation
- poorly stored and disposed chemicals, including cleaning substances
- flammable substances stored incorrectly
- faulty or untested electrical equipment
- poorly managed waste
- bad drainage
- ladders that are not fit for the purpose they are intended
- poorly designed workstations
- exposure to vibration from tools, equipment or processes
- insufficient rest breaks
- inappropriate and poorly maintained protective equipment
- inadequate training
- exposure to excessive workload.

Security hazards are a little more difficult to assess, but might include:

- unauthorised persons in the workplace
- unlocked doors that should be locked
- suspect packages
- broken monitoring equipment
- inoperative alarm sensors
- evidence of computer misuse/hacking.

A good risk assessment of the workplace should identify these hazards, assess who is at risk from them and identify control measures that can be put in place to reduce risk.

Activity: Safety and security hazards

Choose a business other than your own school, college or workplace, for example, an airport or hospital. Identify as many safety and security hazards within your chosen workplace as you can.

Industry best practice guidelines

When creating risk assessment documents, employers should refer to any relevant legislation or standards covering the particular hazards in their workplace. For example, the Construction (Health, Safety and Welfare) Regulations 1996 for construction site hazards and the Safety, Health and Welfare at Work (Chemical Agents) Regulations 2001 and its Code of Practice for chemical hazards.

Many industries will draw up their own guidelines for best practice which aim to minimise particular risks. For example, any food producer that has identified that there is a potential risk of metal contamination within their products must install a metal detector. It is common practice for the producer's customer (e.g. supermarkets) to insist that the chosen metal detector conforms to a standard specification, such as the BRC (British Retail Consortium). This gives those appointed to carrying out risk assessments extra information and helps them in assessing and controlling the risk of harm.

Activity: Identifying best practice guidelines

In pairs or small groups, choose five different types of industries and identify industry-specific best practice guidelines relating to risk assessments.

Checks on suppliers' premises

A problem faced by businesses that trade with other suppliers is that whilst their own business may comply fully with all health and safety legislation, including risk assessments, there is no guarantee that their supplier is doing the same. There are several options available to businesses when choosing their suppliers.

- Accept a supplier and ignore any health and safety issues, risking bad publicity and other consequences if the goods or materials supplied are not fit for purpose or dangerous.
- Reject the supplier.
- Accept the supplier on the provision that they provide written evidence that risk assessments are taking place.
- Accept the supplier and insist on visiting the supplier's premises. The supplier does not have to allow this.

The only thing a business can insist on seeing from a supplier is a fire test certificate under the Regulatory Reform (Fire Safety) Order 2005 which proves they conform to current fire risk assessments.

What might be the consequences for a business if its suppliers are not managing risks?

Did you know?

Clothing store Primark had one of its suppliers checked for working conditions. In April and December 2008 it found that the supplier had adequate risk assessment systems in place. Yet, in January 2009, undercover reporters found extremely poor working conditions and workers working for very low wages.

Industry-related experience

Because health and safety legislation is so complicated and in many business people are not qualified in health and safety law or in things like risk assessments, businesses can get into trouble by conducting poor or meaningless risk assessments that leave workers exposed to danger.

A good example of this is in the area of fire risk assessments. In the workplace, the responsibility for fire hazard risk assessments rests solely with the employer. There is some limited written guidance available from the Fire and Rescue Services, but no physical help. Many employers struggle with very complex and technical risk assessments and so many ex-fire officers offer their services as a fire safety consultant. This type of industry-related experience would be of great help to the inexperienced risk assesser.

4.2 Monitoring and prevention

While risk assessments identify hazards, employers should, as a matter of course, monitor their workplace to prevent hazards occurring. We will now look at some of the many ways in which this can be done.

Training and staff development

The health and safety procedures in any business are only as good as the staff that use them. The key to a successful health and safety policy is the training and development of staff. Key training should cover many aspects of health and safety and will vary with job role and business, but common health and safety training should include:

- general safety induction for all new staff
- safety refreshers for existing staff
- display screen safety
- general COSHH safety
- fire safety procedures
- manual handling.

To further develop staff's knowledge and understanding of health and safety issues, employees should be encouraged to take part in other health and safety activities in the workplace. These might include:

- carrying out **generic risk assessments**
- carrying out specific risk assessments
- first aid training
- becoming a safety representative
- fire marshalling.

All health and safety training and development courses must be recorded as proof that it has occurred with details entered in staff records.

Industry-related awareness of hazard

When the appointed person is conducting workplace risk assessments, they should be suitably experienced and trained to identify hazards specific to the industry they are assessing. For example, in the construction industry a common hazard is vibration from machinery which may cause injury, and in the printing industry a hazard is working in a fume-filled environment, which may lead to breathing problems. Carrying out risk assessments with no industry-related awareness of hazards can result in meaningless risk assessments.

Activity: Identifying industry-related hazards

Look at each of the jobs in the table below and investigate which hazards are specific to that industry.

Industry	Industry-related hazards
Computer programmer	
Car paint sprayer	
Baker	
Supermarket cashier	
Lorry driver	

Departmental representatives

In an effort to improve the quality of their health and safety processes, many organisations encourage staff involvement in health and safety matters. Some businesses will appoint departmental health and safety representatives who may well be the first point of contact for staff with health and safety issues. These representatives will be encouraged to go on training courses and will be able to carry out risk assessments in the workplace. They will work closely with staff in their department, department heads, the appointed health and safety representative and senior managers to help maintain a focus on health and safety in the workplace.

Awareness raising across organisations

For a successful health and safety policy in the workplace, all staff need to be aware of health and safety issues. Without this awareness, policies and procedures may fail to be implemented. It is very important to raise health and safety awareness across a business and employers can do this in a number of ways, including:

- health and safety poster campaigns
- consultation meetings
- the setting up of cross-organisational health and safety committees
- bringing in outside trainers to train staff.

Benchmarking

One of the more effective ways of monitoring health and safety procedures is through a process known as 'benchmarking'. This is a planned process by which an organisation compares its health and safety processes and performance with others to learn how to:

- reduce accidents and ill health
- improve compliance with health and safety procedures.

By using benchmarking, businesses can continuously learn from others and, in turn, learn more about their own strengths and weaknesses and act on them to improve their own health and safety performance.

Use of equipment in accordance with manufacturers' instructions

One of the easiest ways of preventing harm at work is to have all staff using equipment and materials in the correct way. All equipment and machinery in the workplace will be delivered with manufacturers' instructions and staff should be trained to use all equipment in the correct way by referring to these.

Activity: Using equipment correctly

Use the Internet or your own knowledge to make a list of as many examples of incorrect use of equipment as you can think of, for example, using a waste paper bin to get rid of a cigarette.

Rest breaks

One of the simplest ways of preventing accidents at work is to ensure that staff are not too tired. Employers can be held responsible for contributing towards accidents if it can be shown that they are placing 'unreasonable' work demands on their workers. This may be by asking them to do extra shifts, not giving sufficient breaks, ignoring signs of tiredness and badly planning and implementing shift work. It is vital that staff are given the correct rest breaks at work as laid down by the Working Time Regulations 1998. These are as follows.

- Adult workers (over 18) have the right to a 20-minute rest break if they work more than six hours at a time. Young workers (under 18) who work for more than four and a half hours must get a rest break of 30 minutes.

- Adult workers have the right to a break of at least 11 hours between working days. Young workers must get 12 uninterrupted hours' rest in each 24-hour period in which they work.

- Adult workers have the right to either an uninterrupted 24-hours clear of work each week or an uninterrupted 48-hours clear each fortnight. Young workers must take two days off each week.

Safety devices

An effective way of preventing loss and injury at work is to have safety devices fitted. One of the most serious risks is the risk of fire and there are steps businesses can take to prevent fire damage being too severe.

Workplaces should have arrangements for detecting fire, and for many workplaces automatic smoke and fire detection equipment may be needed. These can be of different types and employers should take advice on the correct type of detection device needed for their business. Whichever smoke or fire detection device is used, employers should check that it conforms to British Safety Standards, is fitted correctly and is maintained and tested regularly.

Where a fire has started, employees may be trained in using fire extinguishers. You have already looked at these safety devices earlier in the unit (see page 141) and you will be aware that they can be very useful in preventing a small fire spreading and causing more damage.

Regular checking of equipment and procedures

As part of the ongoing health and safety monitoring process, there should be regular checking of equipment and procedures. This process should occur across all areas of the workplace with each department checking individual health and safety processes in their area. The results of these checks should be collated and passed to a senior manager who should then keep these records to show that they are taking place and continue to monitor them. Checks may be daily, weekly, monthly or annually, depending on the type of check taking place. In addition, regular safety drills should also take place with at least two fire evacuation drills each year. The drill should be logged in the safety record so that it can be proven that it has occurred.

Procedures for recording and reporting accidents and dangerous occurrences

As you have already learned, RIDDOR exist to enable employers to report all serious incidents to the Health and Safety Executive. Employers must have procedures in place for recording and reporting accidents and dangerous occurrences. Figure 27.2 on page 124 shows a typical form used by businesses to record such incidents.

Organisational and legislative requirements

One of the ways of preventing harm in the workplace is to have an organised approach to health and safety, which has numerous benefits, including:

- contributing to the well-being and productivity of all the people who work for the organisation

- decreasing the risk of injury and ill health to people who work for the organisation and others

- improving the reputation of the organisation in the eyes of customers, suppliers and other stakeholders

- ensuring the organisation meets legislative requirements, thus minimising the likelihood of prosecution and consequent penalties.

Review of records and action planning

As part of the monitoring process, safety records should be reviewed by appropriate senior personnel and action should be taken where the checks show that health and safety procedures are failing. Action will range from matters that can be immediately resolved to those that require longer-term solutions, maybe because they involve major decision making on expenditure, such as engineering or maintenance work or procedural or staff changes. Action plans should be developed, which will be linked to the requirements coming from the review. In this way, there can be a continuous improvement in the overall provision of health and safety in the workplace.

Public liability insurance

In any business things can go wrong as health and safety failures do happen. Businesses should, therefore, insure themselves against injury or damage to members of the public or customers that visit the business. They can do this by taking out public liability insurance. Premiums are based on the type of business and rated on an estimate for the level of activity of the business. For most businesses this will be the turnover, although other factors may be taken into account. For example, premiums for a hotel might be calculated on the number of beds available as this reflects the number of guests, or in a restaurant the number of tables which reflects the number of diners.

Assessment activity 27.4

P4 M3 D1 BTEC

1. One of the most important requirements of health and safety in the workplace is the carrying out of risk assessments. Select an administrative work environment, such as the IT department or finance department of your chosen business, or school or college. Either individually in the workplace or in groups in school or college, using the knowledge you have learned from this unit, make a plan of what should go into a risk assessment for that work environment and then physically create it. **P4**

2. Once you have created the risk assessment document, still in your groups, actually conduct the risk assessment for that work area and record your observations on the risk assessment form. **M3**

3. The risk assessment you have carried out may highlight health and safety issues in your selected workplace. It is now your job to act on what you have found and write a report recommending improvements in health and safety standards and practices in the chosen work environment. **D1**

Grading tip

Think about what you are trying to achieve with your risk assessment. Who is going to use it? How will it be communicated? What type of language should be used? **P4** **M3** **D1**

PLTS

Analysing and evaluating information from your risk assessment and judging its relevance and value in order to make recommendations will help you to develop your skills as an **independent enquirer**.

Just checking

1. What is the most important piece of health and safety legislation?
2. What does RIDDOR stand for?
3. What do COSHH guidelines deal with?
4. Describe three things to consider when checking display screen use.
5. What is an off-site worker?
6. Name three types of organic infestation.
7. How many toilets will a business employing 120 males and 380 females need?
8. What is the maximum decibel limit at work without ear protection?
9. What is the lowest normal minimum temperature allowed in the workplace?
10. List five types of warning sign found in the workplace.
11. Name five different types of fire extinguisher and their uses.
12. Which extinguisher would you use on a computer fire?
13. How long should an accident book be kept for?
14. What legislation governs information kept about workers?
15. Explain two functions of the human resources director.
16. How many first aiders are required in a workplace with 750 staff?
17. What is a risk assessment?
18. What should a risk assessment contain?
19. What is benchmarking?
20. What is public liability insurance?

edexcel :::

Assignment tips

1. As you study the unit, make a note of all of the legislation and regulations relating to health and safety in the workplace.

2. Do not be put off by the amount and complexity of the law. Refer back to your notes and this unit to help you understand what you are learning.

3. Apply what you learn from this unit to your own school, college and/or workplace.

4. You should be able to look back at all the points you have learned in this unit to produce an accurate, relevant and effective risk assessment that should identify, minimise and control risk.

29 Understanding retailing

Retailing plays an important role in our lives and is an important part of the UK economy. It is one of the most significant industries in the UK, currently employing over 2.5 million people, and is set to increase in size by 15 per cent over the next five years, taking its value to just over £312 billion (UK Retail Futures 2011: Sector Summary, Datamonitor). More than 10 per cent of people working in the UK work in retail operating from around 280,000 retail outlets.

This unit identifies the function of the different retail sectors. There are many different aspects and types of retailers, and once you have learned about the structure of the retail industry, you will look more in depth at the industry's role. You will see that while the retail world sells personal and household items, it also needs to provide customer service. Sales activities and customer services are essential and crucial elements of any successful retailer. We live in a changing world. Retailing, therefore, needs to be flexible and meet the needs of today's consumer. This unit will enable you to understand how the sector deals with modernisation.

Learning outcomes

After completing this unit you should:

1. know the structure of the retail industry
2. understand the role of retailing in the distribution of goods and services
3. understand the sales and service functions in retailing
4. know how the retail sector responds to internal and external change.

Assessment and grading criteria

This table shows you what you must do in order to achieve a **pass**, **merit** or **distinction** grade, and where you can find activities in this book to help you.

To achieve a **pass** grade the evidence must show that the learner is able to:	To achieve a **merit** grade the evidence must show that, in addition to the pass criteria, the learner is able to:	To achieve a **distinction** grade the evidence must show that, in addition to the pass and merit criteria, the learner is able to:
P1 describe the structure and organisation of the retail sector **See Assessment activity 29.1, page 173**	**M1** compare the function of formats and locations in retailing **See Assessment activity 29.1, page 173**	**D1** evaluate the distribution systems in delivering goods and services for a selected organisation **See Assessment activity 29.2, page 183**
P2 explain the process of distributing goods through different channels from the manufacturer to the customer **See Assessment activity 29.2, page 183**	**M2** compare the methods used to distribute products and services **See Assessment activity 29.2, page 183**	
P3 explain how focusing on the customer, by providing good customer service, is essential to retailing **See Assessment activity 29.3, page 191**	**M3** explain the ways in which sales techniques and customer service have developed in retail organisations **See Assessment activity 29.3, page 191**	**D2** assess the impact of different sales techniques and customer service in a selected organisation **See Assessment activity 29.3, page 191**
P4 identify the competitive factors in the retail environment a selected organisation faces **See Assessment activity 29.4, page 201**		

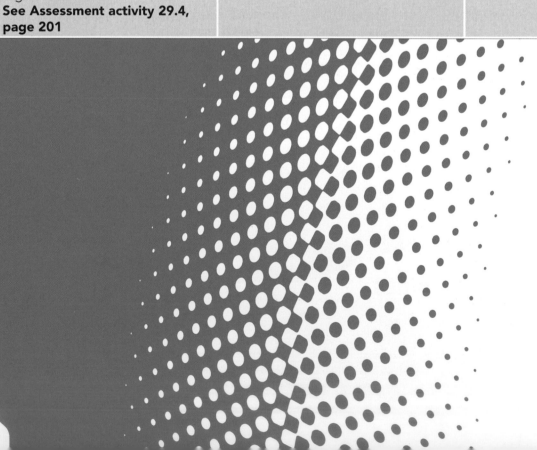

How you will be assessed

This unit will be assessed by an internal assignment that will be designed and marked by the staff at your centre. The assignment is designed to allow you to show your understanding of the unit outcomes. These relate to what you should be able to do after completing this unit.

Your assessment will be in the form of:

- presentations
- case studies
- practical tasks
- written assignments.

Ashton, 21, Administration assistant

After finishing my BTEC National Diploma in Business, I knew that I wanted a career in the retail sector. The Understanding Retailing Unit made me aware of all the different opportunities there were within this sector.

I had worked for a small independent DIY shop on the weekends and this gave me a taste of what the retail sector was all about. However, not until I did the BTEC National Diploma in Business, did I realise how much there was involved in buying, selling and dealing with suppliers. I also learnt about the online selling element.

After finishing the course, I was able to secure a job as a buyer's administration assistant at a large out-of-town DIY store. I support the buyers in their everyday activities which includes raising and following up orders. This unit, in particular the section covering the role of retailing in the distribution of goods and services, gave me a great insight into the retail sector, and these skills definitely help me in my job.

My ultimate ambition is to become a buyer; first I need to become an assistant buyer and have some additional training. When I eventually become an assistant buyer, my role will change dramatically. I will be expected to help plan and select products according to the demands of the customer.

My advice to anyone who wants to work in the retail sector is to get some experience and undertake a course like the BTEC National Diploma in Business, as this combination will give a good insight as to what is required. Potential employers will be aware that you know something about the sector you are aiming to make your career.

1. What areas of this unit might you find challenging?
2. Which section of this unit are you most looking forward to?
3. What preparation can you do in readiness for the unit assessment(s)?

1 Know the structure of the retail industry

1.1 Organisation

Definition of retailing

Retailers provide service to customers at a profit. They are able to do so since the aspects of retailing – operating from an appropriate location, offering attractive product assortments, ensuring enough stock is available to meet demand – add value to the products bought from suppliers and eventually sold to customers. Retailers cut their bulk deliveries from suppliers so individual customers can buy the quantity they require – very often a single item.

Did you know?

The term retail comes from the old French word *retaille* meaning 'to cut again'.

Types of store

There are several different types of retail store, as shown in Table 29.1.

Online and physical stores

All retail stores now offer an **eRetailing** option which allows customers to buy products using the Internet. The Internet has three main advantages compared with traditional retail outlets.

- Convenience – shopping via the Internet saves travel time, the cost of car park charges and the hassle of standing in a queue at the checkout.

Key term

eRetailing – selling of retail goods on the Internet.

Table 29.1: Table showing the different types of retailers

Type of retailer	Example
Department stores	John Lewis Partnership, Debenhams, House of Fraser
Multiple chains	WHSmith, Mothercare, Boots the Chemist
Independents	Spar, Londis
Supermarkets	Sainsbury's, Tescos, Morrisons
Specialist outlets	PC World, Waterstones
Catalogue stores	Argos
Membership clubs	Matalan
Discount stores	Superdrug, Currys
Internet stores	Amazon.co.uk
Internet auction	eBay

- Choice – access to a massive range of products and services from all over the world can be gained through using the Internet for shopping. This is by far the biggest advantage of buying over the Internet.

- Cost – many goods or products sold online are cheaper than those sold in shops. This is because costs of shop premises and sales staff are invariably less for Internet retailers than for the traditional bricks and mortar retailers.

Clicks and bricks

Many businesses merge traditional physical outlets with online services via the web. **Clicks and bricks** is a business model that involves a business combining its physical shop with an online web store. For example, Argos allows the customer to order a product online and then pick up the item at the store. Also, any product bought online can be taken to a store for a refund or exchange should the customer need to return it for any reason. Alternatively, a kitchen or bedroom retailer may have displays at a local store from which the customer can order via the web for delivery.

The clicks and bricks approach is used by retailers who have a successful distribution network. It is considered far easier for a traditional physical retailer to establish an online presence than for a new Internet business to launch a traditional presence. The success of this approach has destroyed the concept that the Internet would make traditional retailers obsolete, though many have seen their **market share** reduced.

The advantages of clicks and bricks retailers are that they:

- utilise existing suppliers, which ensures problem-free delivery of products and an assured supply

- use established and trusted brands already known to the customer

- bring with them economies of size, such as being able to buy in larger quantities and qualify for bigger discounts from producers

Key terms

Clicks and bricks – businesses that offer online services via the web as well as the traditional retail outlets (offline) staffed by people.

Market share – amount of a product or service (usually expressed as a percentage) that a business sells in a given market area.

eRetailing means that the consumer can purchase a wide range of items without having to leave their home

- have the benefit of **learning curve** gains, which apply to organisations that have been in an industry for some time.

A major disadvantage for click and brick retailers is the extra expenses associated with the website as well as the costs associated with a physical business. These can lead to prices that are not always competitive.

Emerging store types

There are a number of new store types which have emerged recently.

- Shopping villages offer a wide range of designer products and brands at discount prices. The goods on sale are invariably surplus stock from the high street or special buys and are usually sold through stores run by the brands themselves.

- Factory shops or factory outlets are usually attached to a factory. They normally sell 'seconds' or imperfect goods, produced by the adjacent factory.

- Teleshopping is an enormously popular way of shopping. There are a large number of television shopping channels in the UK where purchases can be made over the phone or via a website. Digital television will eventually allow the customer to order instantly with the use of their remote control.

Key term

Learning curve – the process of gaining experience and knowledge as a result of learning from mistakes.

The advantages of teleshopping include:

- being able to shop from home and have the goods delivered to your door
- avoiding traffic congestion and parking problems in towns and cities
- wider availability of choices, especially for rural areas where there is not a variety of shops to choose from
- allowing people who are confined to their homes, such as the elderly or disabled, the chance to shop.

The disadvantages of teleshopping include:

- other members of the household are unable to use the television for viewing purposes
- a risk of error when ordering and difficulty of establishing responsibility for any mistakes.

Case study: QVC Television shopping channel

QVC launched in October 1993 as the UK's first television home shopping channel selling a variety of products including home wares and jewellery. QVC has been a success and is regularly viewed by over 15 million people via cable, Freeview and Sky. It uses a variety of methods to sell its products: interactive television, its website and telesales.

The key to QVC's success is its ability to take sales information instantly and respond quickly to market trends. Its central-ordering system enables QVC to attain sales information in real time. Because of this, QVC is able to concentrate on its customers' needs and focus less on areas that do not capture the viewers' attention. It is also able to monitor sales so if an item is sold out it can be announced instantly on the television and removed from the website.

QVC's philosophy for a successful business is to keep all technology below the surface and

ensure that it does not intrude on the shopper's experience. An enjoyable shopping experience is key to getting return customers. QVC wants to ensure that shopping with the channel will always be easy, and while it wants to keep ahead with modern technologies, it thinks that customer service is the most important thing.

Switch on to the QVC television shopping channel. You will also need to visit QVC's website (www.qvcuk.com).

1. What are the different elements of customer service the company offers?

2. Are these elements different from what is offered on the website?

3. What other customer service functions could QVC offer in the future?

Hybrid stores

Hybrid stores offer a 'new' combination of products in the same store. A good example would be where a bookshop and a coffee shop have been combined to offer a dual experience for the customer.

Service versus product retailing

Most shopping centres or streets have a high proportion of service retailers, including banks, building societies, beauty salons and hairdressers, estate agents, travel agents, cafes and restaurants. These organisations want to provide an effective **extended marketing mix** as they now realise the importance of including three extra elements: people, physical evidence and processes in gaining customers – see Table 29.2.

Table 29.2: The implications of using the different types of marketing

Extended marketing mix	Ways used by service retailers
People (staff)	Should be naturally polite, sincere and courteous. Must know about products and policies of the business. Need to have excellent selling and negotiation skills.
Physical evidence	Brochures available in attractive folders. Give away gifts with some intrinsic value, such as a diary or a calendar. Staff dressed in appropriate uniforms, with name badges.
Processes	Various ways of processing payments or depositing money. Immediate appointment booking system and in some cases on-demand consultation.

Key term

Extended marketing mix – an addition to the traditional marketing mix of product, price, place and promotion (the four Ps) to include three further Ps, related more to marketing services, i.e. people, physical evidence, processes.

What are the benefits of combining products in the same store?

Activity: Retail positioning map

One method of analysing a retail market is to use a **retail positioning map**. One example for food stores is shown in Figure 29.1.

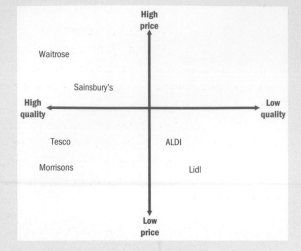

Figure 29.1: A retail positioning map

Using Figure 29.1, plot as many clothes retailers that you think of. Think in terms of the quality of the products and prices.

Some examples could be:

- Primark
- Marks & Spencer
- Burton
- River Island
- Topshop
- New Look
- Next
- Dorothy Perkins
- Moss Bros Group PLC.

Key term

Retail positioning map – a model used to identify where a retail store sits in the market compared to its competitors.

Classification of retailers

Type of activity

Retailers can be classified according to the type of products they sell. They are broken down into the following categories:

- food stores
- non-food stores including:
  ○ non-specialist stores
  ○ textiles, clothing and footwear stores
  ○ household goods stores and other stores
- non-store retailing.

Each of the categories has different strategies on products they sell and how they are sold, as shown in Table 29.3.

Table 29.3: Sales area and product strategy

Store type	Product strategy
Supermarkets, superstores, hypermarkets	Very large stores which sell a full range of food and non-food products. Supermarkets are stores with at least 200 m² of sales area, using self-service methods and having at least three checkouts. Superstores have 2,500 m² of sales area space and car parking facilities. Hypermarkets are large superstores that have 5,500 m² of sales area.
Discount stores	Retailers which concentrate on selling large quantities of consumer durables at discount prices.
Multiple stores	Organisations such as Marks & Spencer and House of Fraser, which offer a narrow range of products. Multiple retailers have more than ten branches.
Multiple variety stores	Stores such as Boots the Chemist and WHSmith, which offer fast moving product lines, usually selling nationally advertised brand leaders or own-brand merchandise.
Independent retailers	Includes convenience stores or c-stores such as Londis and Spar. They focus on selling essentials, fresh and convenience foods. Also features 'niche stores' which offer specialist products to a wide geographic area, e.g. walking and camping equipment. Independent retailers have fewer than ten branches.

Store size, number of employees, enterprises and turnover

Retailing in the UK is concentrated in the hands of a few major retailers with 34 per cent of sales turnover being generated in just 1.25 per cent of the enterprises. Although there are more small retailers in terms of the number of people that are employed, the retailers with more employees have the largest sales turnover, as shown in Table 29.4.

Table 29.4: Store size versus sales turnover

Size of enterprise by people employed	Number of enterprises	%	Sales turnover (£ billion)	%
0–4	167,480	60	30.5	12
5–9	62,990	23	40.6	16
10–19	28,480	10	38.1	15
20–49	12,325	4.5	33.0	13
50–99	3,575	1.25	24.5	10
100+	3,545	1.25	87.7	34

Table 29.5: Top ten retailers in recent years by turnover in the UK

Rank	Company	Turnover (£ million)
1	Tesco	38,200
2	Sainsbury's	18,910
3	Asda Group	18,250
4	William Morrison	14,530
5	Marks & Spencer	8,160
6	Alliance Boots	6,340
7	John Lewis Partnership	6,270
8	Home Retail Group (Argos, Homebase)	5,790
9	Co-operative Group	5,370
10	DSG International (Currys, PC World)	4,470

Activity: Sales figures

Visit the Office for National Statistics website (www.statistics.gov.uk) and locate the retail sales report for the latest month. Compare the retail sales figures with the same period last year, then put together a graph showing the differences in the sales figures.

1. What reasons can you think of that might have an effect on the sales figures?

2. Do you think the government considers the latest sales figures to be good or bad for the country as a whole? Why?

3. Discuss your findings with the class.

Functional skills

Comparing the sales figures and then interpreting and communicating the solutions will help you to develop your **Mathematics** skills.

Location

Different locations provide access to different consumer profiles. For instance, rural areas will have a different mix of consumers to urban areas. Some locations will have households with a large number of young families, whereas others will have a larger number of older people. The overall mix of these different consumers will help shape which retailers are in which areas. Free car parks and better in-centre facilities than other areas may influence shoppers when deciding where to shop.

Did you know?

The largest shopping district in the UK is London's West End, which does not contain any large shopping centres.

In-town shopping

In-town shopping is located within a town or city and can include both shopping centres and high streets. This is the largest overall category of retail location types and also accounts for the largest volume of retail employment and sales. A typical in-town high street has:

- multiples stores
- department stores
- service retailers.

The larger towns and cities have central shopping centres, also known as **malls**, which are important shopping locations incorporating a wide range of shops to choose from; this is the most significant advantage of shopping centres. More recently, supermarket retailers have also been opening up smaller stores aimed at people working in city and

Key term

Mall – a large, frequently enclosed, shopping complex which contains a variety of shops, businesses and restaurants that are accessible by common passageways.

town centres. These smaller supermarkets sell a limited range of goods and open for shorter hours. An example of this would be Tesco Express

In-town shops have to be more aware of shopper flow around the centres and try to eliminate congestion hot spots. In-town shops also need to avoid being too similar, and many local authorities and town centre managers now have the challenge to develop strategies to secure a sustainable mix of independent and multiple retailers within a particular area to maintain character and avoid empty premises.

Local

Local shops serve built-up, suburban areas or smaller towns. They usually consist of a number of stores located around one main street. It is increasingly evident that product shopping is becoming a secondary reason for using local shopping centres. The main reasons for visits are to:

- go to the bank
- visit civic establishments such as the town hall or library
- socialise, such as meet friends for lunch.

Local shopping centres have been losing their attraction to shoppers for some time. Customers perceive these locations to lack a variety of stores. Fashion stores, fresh food stores and specialist-find food stores are not generally represented in local centres. Niche businesses such as craft and hobby stores, designer goods stores, specialist bookshops and children's clothes stores are often suggested by consumers as the sort of stores that would enhance a local shopping centre.

There seems little prospect of local retailers in any location increasing their share of expenditure. The likelihood is that, because of a diverse range of options (including the Internet or teleshopping), locally based retailers will have to face the prospect of a declining share of retail sales from shoppers.

Out-of-town retail parks and regional centres

Massive regional shopping centres have been built in several out-of-town sites in the UK. Up until the early 1990s there was a huge growth in such shopping centres. They are usually located close to main roads, thus providing easy access for shoppers. These retail parks are also normally located near suburban housing estates; this ensures that there is a workforce for them. The development of out-of-town shopping centres

has been possible because of the increase in car ownership, and the customer's desire for shops with a wider range of products.

Many retailing outlets move to out-of-town centres because of business competition as well as the availability of large areas of unused land which are cheap in comparison to land in towns or city centres. Retail companies can build larger stores, provide free parking and offer a wide range of shops and complementary facilities, such as petrol stations, restaurants and leisure facilities – the emphasis being on shopping as a daylong activity. The shopping centres are usually under cover and pedestrianised.

Many retail parks feature stores such as B&Q, Comet, PC World and Currys. They are popular not only because of the parking facilities but also because their prices are competitive and the size of the outlet means a greater variety of goods on sale.

Table 29.6: The UK's largest out-of-town shopping centres

Rank	Shopping centre	Location	Size (m²)
1	MetroCentre	Gateshead	168,900
2	Central Milton Keynes	Milton Keynes	166,000
3	Bluewater	Dartford	155,700
4	Westfield London	London	151,453
5	Merry Hill	Dudley	151,267
6	Meadowhall	Sheffield	139,355
7	Trafford Centre	Manchester	137,347
8	Lakeside	Thurrock	133,180
9	Arndale	Manchester	130,060
10	Liverpool One	Liverpool	130,060

Did you know?

Escalators are placed in strategic positions in order to force shoppers to pass the maximum number of storefronts.

Activity: Implications of local shops

There are advantages and disadvantages for the different retail outlet locations, as well as a range of social and environmental implications. The in-town shop may be accessible and beneficial for the community, but land is expensive and there may be problems with traffic congestion and limited parking. While out-of-town retail parks may provide a wide variety of shops and plenty of parking, their construction may have an impact on the environment and they may not be accessible to some sectors of the population such as the elderly. The local convenience store may be accessible, but it does not stock a wide range of products.

In small groups, discuss the implication for the local shops of a small town if a large retail centre opened up close by. Present your findings to the class, remembering to include issues such as:

- fewer mobile members of the community
- the elderly
- environment
- parking
- employment.

Ownership

The ownership of retail outlets reflects the diverse nature of the industry.

Did you know?

Lord Sugar founded Amstrad (Alan Michael Sugar TRADing) at the age of 21.

Independent

Independent retailers are retail organisations with less than ten branches. They tend either to sell a specialist range of products such as medicines, or they are general convenience stores and sell a range of products including groceries, household goods, wines and spirits. Independent retailers try to offer a personal service and have a flexible approach to opening hours. Pricing, discounts and other trading policies are at the discretion of the owner.

The market share and number of independent retailers have been on the decline for a number of years. This is particularly common in the food sector, with the rise of supermarkets. The trend seems set to continue, especially as supermarket chains are now opening up neighbourhood convenience outlets to complement their larger stores.

Activity: Independent shops

Look at the website for a large town in your area and find out if there are any independent men or women's shoe shops locally. You can try looking under different headings such as: shoe shops, shoe shops – ladies, or shoe shops – men's. Once you find an independent shoe shop, take a look at their website, then answer these questions.

1. Who is the shop targeting?
2. What do you notice about its website?
3. Do you think the shop relies on online sales, offline sales or both?

Multiple

Multiple retailers are businesses with more than ten branches. Some multiples are classified as specialist stores, such as Accessorize, which concentrate on a narrow range of items. Their stores project a strong corporate identity, which makes them easily recognisable. Multiple variety chains like WH Smith and Boots the Chemist offer a wider range of products and services. They buy fast-moving branded products centrally and in bulk to obtain lower prices. Multiples tend to be located in busy shopping areas and clustered together with other well-known multiples. Prices are usually relatively low, generating volume sales.

Can you think of some examples of multiple retailers?

Table 29.7: Types of stores operated by Tesco

Format	Description and location
Tesco Extra	Tesco's largest store format. Tends to serve large and densely populated areas. Sells a full range of food and non-food items. Located in out-of-town areas.
Tesco Superstore	Large specialist food outlets; larger ones carry clothing and non-food items. Tends to serve smaller residential areas and are located in retail parks.
Tesco Metro	Found in busy high street city centres. This store type is significant in size and sells a range of everyday products catering for the increasing number of city dwellers and professional people looking to do important shopping near their place of work.
Tesco Express	A convenience store type of shop. It concentrates on a local residential neighbourhood selling fresh and convenience foods. Some are located in petrol forecourts and are the smallest of Tesco's store format.
One Stop	In January 2003, Tesco plc acquired T&S Stores, and the company continues to trade under the One Stop brand. One Stop is a retail convenience business. Open seven days a week, it aims to meet the needs of all its local customers.
Homeplus	Offers all of Tesco's non-food ranges in warehouse-style units in retail parks. Tesco is using this format because only 20 per cent of its customers have access to a Tesco Extra, and the company is restricted in how many of its superstores it can convert into Extras and how quickly it can do so. Large units for non-food retailing are much more readily available.

places include public libraries, coffee shops or even a borrowed office. An increasing number of people will soon be using third places and many individuals will spend approximately 25–35 per cent of their total time in these locations. Third place developments all have some common characteristics such as:

- access to tools such as computers
- access to knowledge through people like technicians
- support services such as catering services.

Additionally, the space in these developments can be used for several different things, including work, learning and civic activities.

Third places are likely to become anchors for economic development in our increasingly global, **knowledge-based economy**. They might offer a new retailing opportunity, with possibly a new retailing format.

Key term

Knowledge-based economy – economy based solely on the production, distribution and the use of knowledge.

What are 'third places' and why are they becoming increasingly popular?

Employment characteristics

The retail industry accounts for about 20 per cent of all part-time jobs and 6 per cent of all full-time jobs. It is heavily dependent on part-time employees – especially in London. The retail industry employs approximately 3 million people, which equates to one in nine or 11 per cent of the total UK workforce. The average gross weekly earnings in the retail sector are about £287, although in London it is nearly 30 per cent higher than in other areas of the UK.

Assessment activity 29.1   P1 M1   BTEC

You are a journalist for a local paper and have been asked by the editor to write an article on the retail sector.

1. Write an article which includes the following:
   - details of the structure
   - the organisation
   - different formats
   - rationale for location. **P1**
2. Compare the function of five different retail formats and shopping locations. **M1**

Grading tips

1. You must write your article using relevant criteria. Discuss the development of the article with your tutor to ensure you include all of the following:

   - size and trends in sales
   - location and size of stores
   - types of retailer including not-for-profit and public place retailers
   - trends in the number of retailer types
   - employment characteristics of the sector.

   Your presentation should contain visual materials to illustrate your work. **P1**

2. You need to compare means to emphasise the similarities and differences. Retail format and location are closely linked. In comparing the different formats, you should identify why retailers prefer different locations and explain the retail functions they perform. **M1**

PLTS

Investigating the structure and organisation of retail businesses will help you to develop your skills as an **independent enquirer**.

---

2 Understand the role of retailing in the distribution of goods and services

2.1 Distribution channels

Having produced a product or service, organisations need to consider how they are going to distribute and sell them to the customer. Distribution is concerned with getting a product or service to the right people, at the right time, taking into consideration the need for profit and efficiency. When a customer purchases a product or service, they may have bought it directly from the business or through a retailer or wholesaler. These ways of purchasing are known as distribution channels.

Availability of products (time, place, quantity)

Retailers are always faced with the challenge of being able to offer the right product at the right price, at the right time and at the right place. This occurs despite their gathering huge amounts of data about the buying patterns and tastes of their customers. In all probability you have gone to a shop only to find that it does not have the item you want – even though the shop has plenty of stock. Different customers react differently when items are not in stock:

- 31 per cent of customers purchase the item at another store
- 26 per cent of customers substitute for a different brand
- 24 per cent of customers either delay purchase or never purchase the product.

Did you know?

Every second, two Barbie dolls are sold somewhere in the world. Her full name is Barbara Millicent Roberts.

Movement of goods from manufacturer to retailer to consumer

There are several possible distribution channels with varying characteristics. For most products it is sensible to use more than one of them.

Organisations between the manufacturer and the customer are called intermediaries. The most common intermediaries are as follows.

- Retailers – these may be owned by the manufacturer (e.g. The Body Shop) or independent of the manufacturer (e.g. Iceland).
- Wholesalers – these range from cash and carry outlets, which offer minimal service, to full function

wholesalers, which provide credit, delivery and technical advice.

- Agents – these may represent the manufacturer, retailer or the wholesaler. Agents obtain orders for manufacturers, retailers and wholesalers, but they are not employed by the organisation. They are self-employed.

Distribution channels for different types of goods

The distribution channels used to deliver a product to the consumer can differ depending on the product as shown in Table 29.8 (opposite).

Wholesalers as intermediaries

Manufacturers may decide to sell their products to a wholesaler who will distribute the products in order to reach a larger number of consumers. The wholesalers then become the intermediary between the manufacturer and the retailer.

Wholesalers buy in bulk and then split the purchase into smaller quantities in order to sell the products on to the retailer. Some wholesalers offer further services such as packing, labeling and quick delivery as well as supplying promotional material.

Once the wholesaler purchases the product there are three main ways that it will reach the consumer.

- The wholesaler sells the product directly to the consumer.
- The wholesaler sells the product to retailers.
- The wholesaler sells the product to agents.

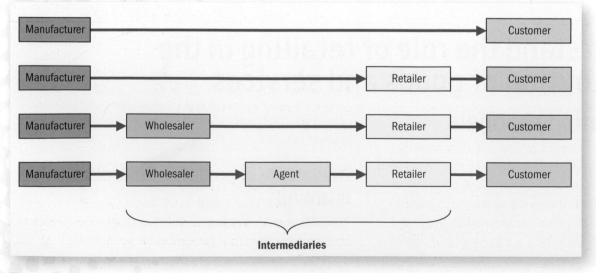

Figure 29.2: Products reach the customer in a variety of ways

Table 29.8: Differences between food and clothing distribution

Channel feature	Clothing	Food
Geographic areas from which products obtained	Abroad, largely the Far East.	Mostly from the UK but some from abroad.
Time between a retailer placing an order and receiving goods	Long time – can sometimes take up to a year.	Short time – especially fresh goods.
Responsiveness to consumer demand	Generally not so responsive – products available in store change on a seasonal basis rather than on what consumers are buying.	Responds quickly to changes in demand – but weather can dramatically alter demand for food products.
Special shipment requirements	Arrives flat packed in cartons or ready for hanging in store.	Special vehicles deliver fresh, chilled and frozen products. Other food products delivered in general purpose vehicles.
Intermediaries	Shipped in containers from abroad to the regional distribution centres (RDCs) of large retailers, to wholesalers or direct to stores.	Deliveries also to RDCs of large retailers who have special chilled and frozen goods storage facilities. Fresh products delivered direct to store or are crossed docked at RDCs, i.e. goods moved directly from supplier's truck into store delivery vehicle for immediate shipment to store.

One development in this area is the growth of cash and carry outlets such as Makro. Retailers who buy from this type of organisation are responsible for transporting the stock and paying in cash, but prices are lower than those obtainable generally at the traditional wholesaler.

Retail control of the supply chain

Own brands

Retailers are aware of the importance of their brand and have begun developing their names as brands rather than simply a name over the shop. The consumer knows the name of many major retailers rather than those of manufacturers' brands. Retailers use **own-brand** items to offer their customers different and better value. This has resulted in an increase of control by the retailer over the supply chain; they can decide the features, quality, packaging and price of such products.

Key term

Own brand – a name, a symbol or a design used to identify a specific retailer and make it appear different from its competitors.

Did you know?

In 1902 Albert Parkhouse invented the coat hanger after being frustrated at the lack of hooks available to hang up his coat at work. His company thought it was a good idea and patented the invention.

eRetailing

Retailers have come to understand the potential for the Internet which can act as a shop window where consumers can view and purchase products and services online. The Internet can also be used to promote products and services with an aim to secure more sales from other distribution channels. Many bricks and mortar retailers have established websites to sell their products or services.

The Internet has offered manufacturers the opportunity to deal directly with the customer, making the role of the retailer redundant. This process is called disintermediation. It is an attractive method for manufacturers as it allows them to offer products at a reduced price to the customers whilst making higher profits. This process has become a reality for some products such as music, books, films, software and

Jamile (Far Eastern) Limited

Jamile (Far Eastern) Limited is a Hong Kong-based manufacturer making teddy bears for the collectible market, mainly in the UK and Europe. One problem is the length of time it takes for the product to reach the customer. Jamile (Far Eastern) Limited has recently acquired other companies in the **supply chain** in order to reduce this time.

Before the decision was made, the company collected all relevant information concerning timings, starting with the purchase of the raw materials and ending with delivery to the final customer.

Jamile's supply chain is shown below.

Mohair stored in commodity warehouses before purchase	80 days
Felt stored in commodity warehouses before purchase	9 days
Wood wool stored in commodity warehouses before purchase	5 days
Components stored in commodity warehouses before purchase	8 days
Jamille (Far Eastern) Limited buying mohair	12 days
Jamille (Far Eastern) Limited buying felt	2 days
Jamille (Far Eastern) Limited buying wood wool	2 days
Jamille (Far Eastern) Limited buying other components	3 days
Transports all components to the factory	35 days
Store mohair, felt, wood wool and components	2 days
Transport mohair, felt, wood wool and components to the factory	40 days
Cut mohair to form teddy bear shape	8 days
Cut felt for paws	6 days
Sew mohair and felt together	3 days
Include components	2 days
Final finishes, i.e. nose and fill with wood wool	3 days

Think about it!

1. What were the major issues with the above supply chain?
2. What are the benefits of reducing the length of the supply chain?
3. Which type of company would you have recommended Jamille (Far Eastern) Limited to purchase? (For example, storage, transportation, raw material manufacturer.)

Key term

Supply chain – the network of retailers, distributors, transporters, storage facilities and suppliers that participate in the sale, delivery and manufacture of a particular product.

ChemistDirect and similar online retailers have become major competitors for Boots the Chemist

tickets. The retailer's control over the supply chain is severely weakened under such circumstances.

Provision of product enhancing functions

Transport

Retailers selling certain products such as furniture or large electrical goods will need to offer a delivery service. For other retailers, it will provide a competitive advantage. A delivery service is an important way of adding value to a product and for retailers to differentiate themselves from their competitors. Technological advances and services are making the delivery process much more effective. Most retailers, as part of their customer loyalty strategy, send delivery status emails to inform of the expected time of arrival of their products.

Storage

Effective storage techniques, whether in the warehouse or the store stockroom, can enhance and add value to the product by being available when the customer requires it.

- Vertical storage and minimising aisle width provides the space to stock the right quantities of a product.
- Layout should help to speed up the collection

and despatch of the products; frequently required products should be kept near the stockroom door adjacent to the shop.

- Handling of the product should be kept to a minimum to reduce the potential for damage; roll cages can be moved from the warehouse to the store shelf without any additional handling.

Did you know?

Amazon has huge warehouses to stock its products. These warehouses are called fulfilment centres and are generally located near major airports. Amazon also offers warehousing and order fulfilment services for other companies.

After-sales service

After-sales service is the support customers receive following the purchase of a product or service. It is as important as the actual sale of the product or service as it plays a role in ensuring customer loyalty. After-sales service elements can include the following:

- product delivery at a convenient time for the customer
- handling of complaints

- commonly required spare parts or consumables available
- repair and servicing facilities
- technical advice either in store or through an appropriately and adequately staffed telephone help lines
- commitment to the guarantee provided when the product was bought
- installation and removal of replaced items.

2.2 Distribution process

A retailer may have an attractive store, well-trained staff and a distinctive brand reputation in the market. However, these factors do not count for anything if products are not on the shelf when the customer is shopping. Therefore, ensuring products are available for the customer at all times is a vital process for retailers. The distribution process:

- heightens the need to improve quality service
- ensures a shorter order cycle time
- takes into consideration any environmental factors.

Activity: Distribution channels

Retailers use various distribution channels to source their products. Examine the different channels used by a catalogue store such as Argos and an online store such as Amazon.co.uk. Use retailer information, logistics information, textbooks and your own observations.

Supply chain

The main function of the supply chain is to provide products or services required by end consumers. The supply chain extends from raw materials through many processes to the final consumer; each link in the chain processes the material in some way or supports this processing. It can also include the disposal of any associated waste.

An efficient and responsive supply chain will:

- improve stock availability
- improve choice
- offer up-to-date products
- reduce stock levels and mark downs.

In overall terms, costs will fall whilst sales and profits increase.

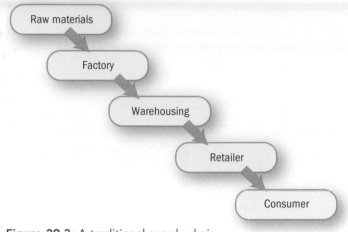

Figure 29.3: A traditional supply chain

Moving goods in the UK and mainland Europe

The UK and many countries within Europe have well developed road and rail infrastructures offering highly efficient and cost effective methods of transport, so road and rail are two of the most popular modes of transport used to move goods.

By rail

The freight rail network is highly developed in the UK. However, it is important that companies think about the entire journey that the goods take to ensure it is efficient enough for the goods to arrive on time. Transportation of goods, once in mainland Europe, could take some time and involve transshipment to a variety of different rail operators. It is better to ship large quantities of goods in one single shipment in order to be cost effective.

By road

The most popular method of transporting goods is by road; it is also the cheapest. There is a wide range of vehicle types available, so companies can design a transport system around their products. Consideration must be given to the type of goods being transported, however. For example, road transportation may not be appropriate for perishable goods. Assessment of the road network in both UK and mainland Europe should determine whether the infrastructure is of high enough quality to ensure that the products arrive on time and in good condition.

By air

Transport by air is a fast option and allows retailers to hold smaller stock levels. However, the cost for most products tends to be very expensive and this means of transport might be best for emergency stock or to meet a deadline such as Christmas. Problems can also occur with delays at airports, as goods have to be loaded and unloaded.

By water

This is a slow but economical method of transportation. However, delays may occur while waiting for suitable sailing conditions and consideration needs to be given to the time needed to load and unload goods.

By container

Most consumer products are transported by container. There are good levels of security and this results in lower insurance costs. However, containers are expensive to produce initially and returning empty containers increases costs. Special equipment is required to handle the containers and this limits the number of transfer points.

Did you know?

Transportation to and from mainland Europe has been transformed by the opening of the Channel Tunnel. It is now possible for goods to be transported by both rail and road using the Tunnel.

Sourcing (UK and internationally)

There are benefits for sourcing in the UK. These benefits include:

- shorter lead times
- shorter transit times
- ability to monitor the total production process more easily
- lower costs in terms of management time and communications.

A retailer may consider accepting higher prices in exchange for the lower risk and costs associated with sourcing from the UK or a geographically close country. Costs will be greater when sourcing from a distant or less developed country. However, some companies adopt a policy of sourcing from several different countries. Nike, for example, has shoes produced in Taiwan, Thailand, South Korea and Hong Kong.

Suppliers

Suppliers are crucial for any retail business. Retailers, depending on the products they sell, may need one,

Figure 29.4: International product sourcing process

two or even several suppliers. Suppliers are generally divided into four main categories:

- Manufacturers – the majority of retailers purchase through company salespeople or independent representatives who handle products from a variety of different companies. Prices from these sources can be quite low although this will depend on a retailer's location as an added cost of shipping freight might be incurred.

- Independent craftspeople – they tend to offer exclusive distribution of unique products and are usually offered by independent craftspeople, sales representatives or through trade shows.

- Import sources – domestic importers operate in a similar way to a domestic wholesaler. Some retailers, if they are familiar with different countries, will travel abroad to purchase products.

- Distributors – see below for further details.

Distributors

Distributors, also known as wholesalers, brokers or jobbers, normally represent an international producer in one of their important overseas markets. The distributor purchases in quantity from a variety of different manufacturers and warehouses the products for sale to retailers.

In general, distributors will:

- be situated in the market for which they have distribution rights
- have the financial strength to carry adequate stock levels

- be prepared to purchase in large quantities to minimise the expense of international transport
- be wholly or partly involved in promotion and any after-sales service requirements of the product
- be responsible for the business transactions in their market for the exporter's products
- accept the risks that are associated with trading in a particular market.

Logistics process

The logistics process refers to the management of resources within the supply chain to ensure the right product is available, in the right quantity at the right time.

There can be many costs involved in the transportation of goods and selecting the most reliable and accessible is important. Consideration must also be given to transit times, capability, security and, of course, one of the most important elements – cost. Table 29.9 gives details of the different types of transportation carriers.

Storage locations

Warehouses

Warehouses need to be efficient in being able to store, receive and stock goods. The items that are stored at a warehouse determine its precise layout. Modern warehouses can:

- break down larger quantities of stock received from manufacturers into smaller, more manageable amounts for the retailer
- put larger quantities of products together by consolidating small amounts of individual products into a bulk delivery to a single store or location

- organise deliveries to and from the warehouse in a manner acceptable to retailers
- put together special promotional packs where a free product (e.g. a cereal bowl) has to be attached to a packet and promotional labels applied to the combined item.

Did you know?

The first and longest lasting cartoon characters to promote a Kellogg's product are Snap! Crackle! Pop! from Rice Krispies cereal.

Distribution centres

Distribution centres serve as a warehouse for a variety of products. Their sizes can vary from a few thousand square feet to over 100,000 square feet. A distribution centre is part of a logistics chain which includes trucks delivering and picking up items from the warehouse, movement of goods via air, train or ship, dispatchers, brokers and transportation managers.

Most distribution centres are strategically located according to a company's needs and are usually sited in or around major transportation areas, which makes shipping products easier and more cost efficient. An international organisation would typically have distribution centres located around the country as well as in major countries in Asia and Europe. Distribution centres can also offer complementary services to their clients and become a full-service centre. For example, the centre may offer to take customer orders for the client's products and then collect outstanding monies for the client.

Table 29.9: Characteristics of different transport modes

Transport mode	Characteristics
Road	Offers access to all producers. Some legal restrictions to consider such as driver hours and weight limits.
Rail	Cost effective mode of transport (estimated to be one-tenth of the cost of road transport). Slower than road transport and rougher for the goods. Not as convenient as collection is required from rail head.
Air	Very fast mode of transport (one-tenth of the time of road transportation). Expensive compared to road transport – estimated at approximately five times more expensive. Less convenient as goods have to be taken to the airport.
Water	The most cost effective mode of transport. Much slower as boats average 20 mph on inland waterways. Much less convenient, with goods having to be taken to quayside.

Stock rooms

Depending on the type of retailer or the sort of stock being sold, the stockroom space will vary. However, all stockrooms should be conveniently located close to the retail selling areas. Other important factors which determine stockroom organisation are as follows.

- Accessibility – stock should be accessible with faster selling products located as close as possible to the sales area.

- Use of space – wall areas should be used to the maximum while full use of floor to ceiling height should be attempted.

- Grouping lines – lines should be stacked so that they follow the same pattern and layout as the store.

Use of ICT in the supply chain

The supply chain is increasingly influenced by the use of ICT. Many of the developments are designed to increase the responsiveness of the supply chain to customer needs. Companies need to use ICT and information sharing techniques in order to:

- focus on the reduction of response time

- streamline logistic functions across the supply chain in order to reduce costs and improve efficiency

- develop supply chain relationships

- enhance customer service for competitive advantage

- attain international standards and access to global markets.

There are many uses of ICT in the supply chain as shown in Figure 29.5.

Distribution of eRetail products and services

Fulfilment is the process of receiving, packaging and shipping orders for products. Any eRetailer selling products directly to customers through the Internet must deal with fulfilment.

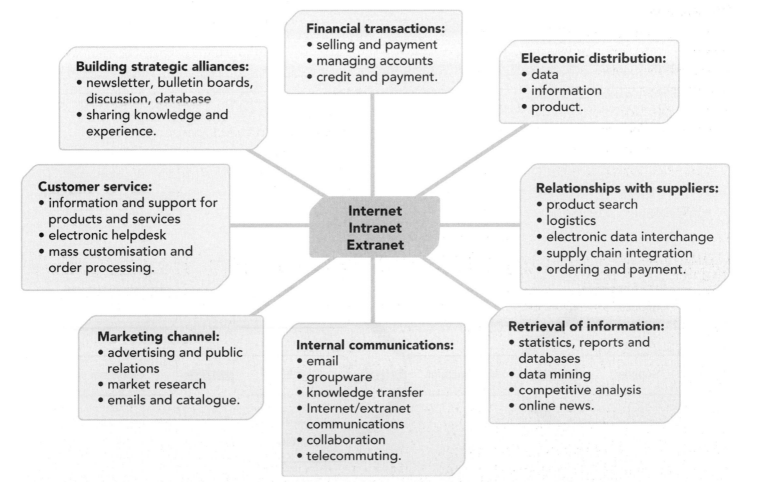

Figure 29.5: ICT use in the supply chain

For eRetailers, it is important to fulfill orders as efficiently and cost effectively as possible. There are two key methods used by eRetailers: store picking and dedicated warehouses.

Store picking involves using low levels of technology to assemble orders by picking products off the supermarket shelves. This method is currently used by Tesco Direct and Sainsbury's Order online. Advantages of using this method include:

- fast, low-risk expansion of the service in the early growth stages
- generally shorter delivery distances because stores cover a small, local catchment area.

Disadvantages of using this method include:

- out of stocks
- high picking costs
- capacity constraints
- store customer disruption.

Dedicated warehouses involve orders being assembled in a centrally dedicated facility using devices such as scanners and conveyor belts. Dedicated warehouses have many advantages, including:

- considerable reduction of out of stocks

- no capacity constraints; stores tend to have limited storage space locally
- no disruption to or from customers shopping in the facility
- consistent range of product.

Figure 29.6 illustrates the supply chain of an Internet company.

Home delivery is a service used by a customer who purchases over the Internet and has the products delivered later by the retailer, home delivery company, post or by courier.

Non-conventional channels

The grey market is concerned with the flow of new products through distribution channels other than those authorised or intended by the manufacturer. Only new products fall into the legal and accepted definition of a grey market.

Grey products are not illegal, unlike those on the black market. Instead companies that may have no relationship with the manufacturer of the products are selling them outside the normal distribution channels. This form of parallel import frequently occurs when the price of an item is significantly higher in one country than another. This situation commonly occurs with cigarettes and electronic equipment such as cameras. Entrepreneurs can:

- purchase the product where it is available cheaply (often at retail but sometimes at wholesale prices)
- import products illegally to the target market
- sell products at a price that provides a profit, but that is below the normal market price.

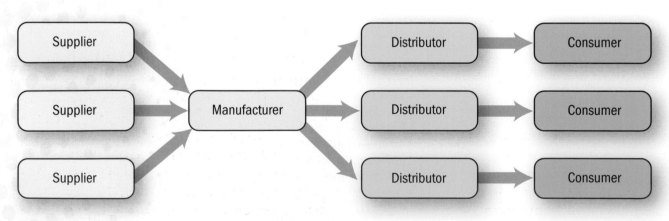

Figure 29.6: The supply chain of an Internet company

Assessment activity 29.2

You have been asked to do a report on Distribution in retailing.

1. Describe the distribution process through different channels from the manufacturer through to the customer for the following:
   - an independent retailer
   - a multiple retailer. **P2**

2. Select two products or services from different sectors and compare the methods used to distribute them. **M2**

3. Evaluate the system used in delivering goods and services for a retailer such as Tesco. **D1**

Grading tips

1. Use textbooks, company literature, websites and organisation logistics information to find the different distribution methods used by the two types of retailers. You could also interview retailers to gather information. **P2**

2. Remember that compare means to emphasise the similarities and differences. You can achieve M2 by distinguishing the distribution processes of two companies in different sectors. **M2**

3. Remember that evaluate means to make a judgement after looking at both the positive and negative aspects of an issue. The evaluation should consider the following issues: **D1**
   - responsiveness to consumers' needs
   - the costs incurred
   - the use of international or domestic suppliers
   - the use of intermediaries
   - the shipping arrangements involved.

PLTS

Investigating the distribution of goods will help you to develop your skills as an **independent enquirer**.

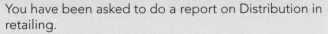

3 Understand the sales and service functions in retailing

3.1 Customer focus

Organisations must realise that the best way to reach their objectives is to concentrate on customer needs and ensure that they meet those needs better than the competition. For retailers this is probably best measured through customer satisfaction.

Customer satisfaction

Customer satisfaction refers to the extent that an organisation has lived up to the expectations of the customer. Happy customers are more likely to be loyal and use a wide range of services offered by the company. There are various factors that contribute to high levels of customer satisfaction including:

- products and services that are customer focused and offer a high level of value for money
- good customer service and personal attention to the needs of individual customers
- good and efficient after-sales service.

Customer satisfaction tends to occur when customers feel the products and services have been specially produced for them (or people like them). Depending on the needs of the customer this could include environmentally friendly products, products of certain colours or finishes or personalised services such as saving schemes that suit the individual. Conversely, many shoppers will walk out of shops without buying because of poor customer service.

In order to attract new customers, organisations need to know what consumers want and then tailor everything they do to pleasing them. Organisations that understand the importance of customer satisfaction tend to emphasise market research and marketing as the tools to find out what consumers want.

Did you know?

When Heinz launched its 'green' ketchup in 2000, it had its highest increase in sales in the brand's history.

Companies hoping to encourage repeat purchases from among its customers must offer good customer service. Poor customer service is damaging to an organisation's reputation. Of course, even more damaging is the fact that any unsatisfied customer will tell their friends and therefore further damage the reputation of the organisation.

Collection and uses of customer information

Retailers invest a lot of money and time in collecting and using customer information. Some of these are shown in Table 29.10.

Table 29.10: Collection methods and uses of customer information by retailers

Method of collection	Uses of customer information
Marketing research	Developing new retail services and the assessment of advertising messages.
Loyalty cards	Provides insights into characteristics of customers and their buying habits.
Complaints	Data helps to establish and assess appropriate store standards such as acceptable queue lengths at checkouts. Helps to improve retail services.
Website browser data	Indicates which products customers are buying and which ones they consider before buying. Customer reviews on the website can be very revealing.
Sales assistants	Identifies which sales promotions work and which advertising activities are genuinely effective. Usually a discussion point for staff meetings.

Activity: Customer satisfaction

If organisations need to find out how satisfied their customers are with their products and services, one way of obtaining this type of information is to do a customer satisfaction survey. Think about five products and services you have purchased in the last few weeks, then copy out and complete the survey below.

Customer satisfaction survey

Company name	Product/Service	Poor	Satisfactory	Excellent

Once you have filled out the survey, present your findings to the class. You will need to justify why you have decided to mark the company and product/service as poor, satisfactory or excellent. You should also state what improvements, if any, you think should be made by the company or regard the product or service.

Uses of ICT in communication with customers

Databases are used to assist retailers communicate effectively with their customers. Communication can be personalised, enabling individual messages to be sent to customers. This style of marketing is called micro-marketing.

Databases are being used for the following functions.

- To match new products and new offers to customers who are likely to be interested. For example, Amazon.co.uk notes the books or CDs customers have bought before and alerts them when a similar title or artist is published.

- To strengthen customer loyalty through, for example, reminders about key events. Websites ask surfers to register to access special information areas. This can involve giving some key details (including areas of interest), which are then used to communicate with that customer. This is called 'permission marketing' and is considered a more effective way to deal with customers. As a consequence the messages sent are individualised to that customer.

- To re-activate customer purchasing by providing something special to regain a customer. Databases can be used to send out materials just before a lapsed customer is about to purchase a product such as insurance once again.

Customer relationship management (CRM)

Customer relationship management (CRM) refers to how an organisation builds long-standing relationships with a customer. The main goals of CRM are to assist in the improvement of services that organisations provide to customers, and to use customer contact information for targeted marketing. CRM also takes into consideration the processes a company uses to track and organise its contacts with its current and potential customers. CRM software is used to support

these processes; information about customers and customer interactions can be entered, stored and accessed by employees in different organisational departments. Table 29.11 differentiates two different CRM approaches by retailers.

Table 29.11: Different approaches to CRM

Transactional approach (example: Argos)	Relationship marketing approach (example: a car dealership)
Focuses more on single transaction. Emphasis on product features. Some emphasis on customer service. Limited customer commitment. Little customer contact – but when it occurs there is the expectancy of a sale. Quality concentrated on product.	Focuses more on customer retention. Emphasis on product benefits. High emphasis on customer service. Higher customer commitment. Regular customer contact – without expecting an immediate sale. Quality is a priority concern, especially ones that impact on customer buying experience.

3.2 Customer service

Customer service covers all activities that affect the customer's experience when dealing with an organisation. Customer service encompasses the impressions created by the manner, appearance and training of staff, including the reality of how well the customer's needs and wants were satisfied. For example, when a customer visits a retailer to buy a kitchen, they may get the additional service of having the kitchen installed for them. At the same time, the retailer should be happy to help them with advice about the properties of different types of kitchen, repayment terms, delivery, etc.

Businesses offering high quality customer service will add value to their products and services, enabling them to charge a higher price, whilst still ensuring customer loyalty.

Customer service as an objective

In many retail sectors, price as a point of difference is losing its edge, although being price competitive remains essential for success. Retailers are turning to customer service as a means of providing additional points of difference. The long-term challenge is to maintain and sustain any competitive advantage a retailer can acquire for itself through customer service. Standards, it seems, need to continuously improve to maintain a competitive advantage.

Did you know?

Duracell, the maker of batteries, built parts of its international headquarters using materials from its own waste.

Advantages

Service standards are crucial to any organisation, although this is only one factor in a customer's decision to purchase. The advantage to an organisation of delivering excellent customer service is that retailers can create an emotional barrier to prevent customers switching to a competitor.

Problems

One problem facing retailers is the need for greater consistency in delivering the service levels demanded by customers. Various factors may prevent this consistent delivery.

- High staff turnover will have an adverse affect on customer service levels as staff are constantly learning on the job.
- Moves to reduce staff costs affect the training and development of staff.
- Ever increasing length of the trading week hinders the creation of a consistently effective customer service.

Activity: Customer service

In small groups, generate as many different phrases to complete the sentence 'Customer service is …'. Remember that customer service is not just one skill, attitude or behaviour, but many different things. Regroup and share ideas with the class. Count the total number of different phrases.

Target marketing

Retailers choose the level of customer service according to the demands of their target market; different organisations offer different levels of service. Department stores or large retail chains such as Marks & Spencer make it an important part of their overall appeal whilst other retail shops place less emphasis on customer service. The overall objectives of the organisation determine their approach to customer service. Carefully communicating to customers what they can expect once in a store is a key factor.

Identifying needs

Retail sales people should assist buyers in selecting products or services that meet their individual needs. Product selection tends to be influenced by the following factors.

- Source – some sources have a strong selling appeal, such as Japanese technological goods and Swiss watches.
- Durability – many buyers are prepared to pay more for items that are likely to last longer without the need for replacement. This is important in the case of consumer durables, but less so for clothing.
- Low running costs – what may be cheap to buy may be expensive to run or maintain. A consumer may be persuaded to choose a product that is economical to run, even if it costs a little more.
- Economy – price is invariably an important factor and not just with the lower income groups. Customers balance price with the subjective idea of value.

Pre-transaction, transaction and post-transaction

The standard of customer service offered before (pre-transactional), during (transactional) and after (post-transactional) a sale is important not only for the sale itself but also for whether that customer returns to purchase again.

Pre-transaction

Customer services relating to pre-transactional sales can include:

- store providing customer phones, cafés, banking machines, toilets, trolleys and children's rides and play areas
- treating customers effectively – first impressions are important

- providing information as requested
- agreeing to make an appointment if requested
- explaining the product features and benefits – matching them to the needs of the customer.

Transaction

Customer services relating to transactional sales can include:

- answering questions honestly and truthfully
- demonstrating products
- helping customers find the product they might be looking for
- assisting customers in making fast and efficient payment
- helping to complete any documentation such as guarantee registration
- thanking customers for purchasing the product and reassuring them they have made the right choice.

Post-transaction

Customer service relating to post-transactional sales can include:

- handling complaints effectively
- delivering and installing properly whilst removing and disposing of replaced product
- ensuring the customer is happy with product

What impact does customer service have on sales?

- contacting the customer to reassure them they made the right choice
- reminding customers that the product is due for a service
- suggesting buying a complementary product such as product care item
- identifying and undertaking any wrapping requirements.

Product offer

Customer service is an important part of any product as it gives an organisation competitive advantage. It can be used as part of a product offer. Good customer service is a unique selling point (USP) feature that could differentiate a product from its competitors. All organisations need to look at service USPs compared to those of their competitors. If a business does not have one, then it will struggle to attract customers, as it will only be able to compete on price (very difficult strategy in a competitive market). It is USPs that enable sales staff to convince consumers to buy from their shop.

All organisations need to be aware, regardless of their target customer market and the product or service on offer, of the significance of maintaining the highest level of customer service possible. Exceptional products or services attract customers but loyalty and competitive advantage can be maintained through excellent customer service.

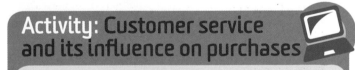

Activity: Customer service and its influence on purchases

In groups, discuss the following.

1. Think of an example of a time you have received good customer service.
   - List two reasons why you think you received this good customer service.
   - Did this service influence your decision to purchase the product/service on offer? Why?
2. Now think of an example of a time when you have received bad customer service.
   - List two reasons why you think you received this service.
   - Did this service influence your decision to purchase the product/service on offer? Why?

After-sales service

Good sales staff are crucial to any retail business as they get to know the needs of the customer and offer after-sales service. Customer service does not actually end when the customer leaves the shop. Customers have a variety of after purchase requirements, and by responding to these requirements, retailers encourage further purchases and further long-term customer relationships. Each retailer has to decide which aspects of after sales are important to the target customer and ensure that their sales staff are aware of what is available to secure sales. Some after-sales services include:

- fitting service for kitchens, bathrooms and bedrooms
- 24/7 helpline
- being able to talk to a person rather than a machine
- technical advice and help for products such as computers
- installation service for products such as washing machines and cookers

- removal of product being replaced, e.g. fridge freezer and tumble dryer
- extended warranty or guarantee for household appliances
- stock of spare parts.

Service quality

The majority of retail sales people naturally emphasise the quality of the products or services they are selling. However, from a retailer's viewpoint, it is the quality of its customer service that is important. Retail customer service should be:

- reliable
- responsive to the needs of the customer
- undertaken competently and effectively
- easily identifiable by the customer.

Service quality translates, on an operational level, to the shop floor. A store with good service quality should:

- be clean
- have correct signage

Activity: After-sales services

Retailers provide a wide range of after-sales service. Copy and complete the table by writing a short paragraph defining each of the types of after-sales services.

Type of after-sales service	Definition
Delivery	
Follow up advice/helpline	
Credit facilities	
Warranty/guarantee	
Information on new products/keeping customers informed	

- have tidy displays
- have good lighting
- have trolleys that work
- have clear aisles
- have short checkout queues
- have visible staff that are responsive to queries.

Furthermore, the time taken to resolve price queries at the checkout should not be long and the procedures for returning and exchanging goods should be considered excellent by the customers.

Sales process

Most retailers would like to focus all their energy on daily business operations and serving existing client demands. However, it is important to any retailer's success to focus also on gaining new sales from current and potential customers in order to grow and sustain then business.

There are various sales process models but they are all fundamentally the same. Nearly every sales process follows six main steps, whether they last several minutes or several months (see Figure 29.7 overleaf).

Activity: Customer service desk

What services and facilities do you think are provided by a customer service desk? Copy and complete the **mind map** by listing as many services as you can.

Discuss your findings with the class. Fill in any missing services.

Key term

Mind map – a diagram used to represent words, ideas, tasks or other items linked to and arranged around a central key word or idea.

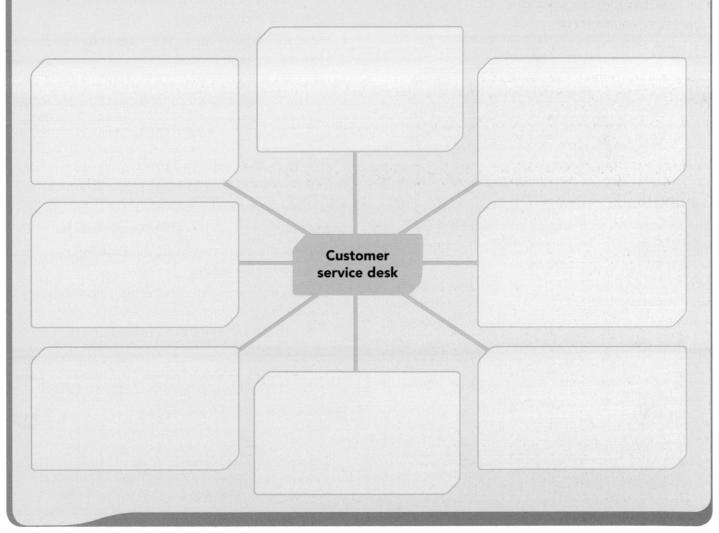

Customer service desk

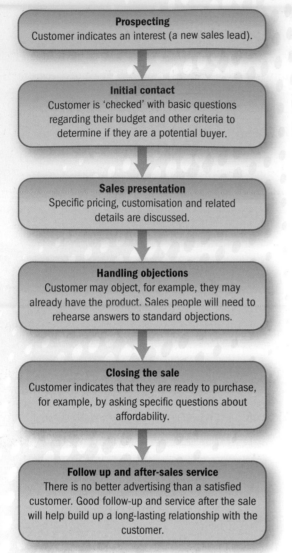

Figure 29.7: Six-stage sales process

Table 29.12: Buying motives

Buying motive	Implications for retail selling
Health	Customers purchase health foods, supplements to maintain their health and physical well-being.
Family affection	Customers purchase toys, branded clothing and other gifts; this is part of the pleasure of giving.
Imitation/ aspiration	Customers buy products to imitate those they admire. This is especially true of cosmetics and clothing.
Exclusiveness	A great deal of money is spent on clothing that underlines their self-proclaimed leadership through ownership of exclusive items.

Selling skills

The skill of sales staff is to be able to identify and select the product information that will appeal to the buying motive of the customer, which is generally referred to as the buying motive. Table 29.12 gives some examples.

Sales staff should also attempt to pay full attention to the customer and remember that listening requires self-discipline. Further selling skills include the ability to:

- learn from other, more skilful sales staff – remember to stay open to new sales techniques
- be sincere about wanting to help the customer – sales staff who have this attitude to selling will build long-term relationships with the customer
- provide more than just the product, e.g. provide product news updates and business advice as part of the service offered

- communicate directly by answering questions efficiently
- allow plenty of time to deal with the customer's questions and comments
- never be negative about the competition and definitely not the product.

Retail staff need to be aware of 'buying signals' and should be listening for these to ensure they are ready to close the sale when the buyer indicates a readiness to buy.

Examples of verbal buying signals include:

- 'Do you accept credit cards?'
- 'Do you have my size in stock?'

Examples of non-verbal buying signals include:

- the way the customer flexes the shoe to judge the flexibility of the leather
- the way the customer tries the item alongside something else (such as an accessory), which says, 'This will go with something I already have at home'.

Did you know?

William Wrigley was a baking soda salesman who, in 1892, started offering free chewing gum to his customers as an added bonus. When the chewing gum proved to be a more effective sales incentive, he ditched the baking soda and began selling Wrigley's Gum.

Sales support

Some sales transactions require important administration duties from the retailer. These can include:

- processing an order for the customer if the goods are out of stock
- ordering replacement stock from the warehouse if levels are becoming low
- organising delivery to a customer at the requested time on the right date
- recording the details of a customer complaint and the action needed to be taken
- processing a store charge card application.

Sales techniques

Some retailers lay down rules concerning the price, delivery policy and payment terms of products or services. However, certain retailers allow a certain amount of negotiation to take place. There are three main aspects to any negotiation.

- Sales staff must be aware of how much they are allowed to negotiate prices or changes to product or service features.
- Sales staff need to identify the exact needs of the buyer. This information can be used to determine the crucial factors in the buyer's mind and estimate the value to them of a concession.
- Sales staff should keep as many concessions in reserve as possible; concessions should only be given when absolutely necessary to achieve an order.

The sales techniques must ensure that the needs of the customer are satisfied by the product sold, otherwise retailers risk losing customers forever if they discover the product does not provide them with the benefits they were asking for.

Assessment activity 29.3

You are a freelance reporter and have been approached by a multinational retail company to write a report on different aspects of customer service.

1. Gather customer service information from three different types of retailer concerning what happens before, during and after a purchase.

   Write up your findings using a report format.

2. Explain how customer service is essential for effective retailing. **P3**

3. Choose two different types of retailers, i.e. department store and a multiple store, and compare the differences in the customer services they offer. Consider the key elements of effective customer service and selling skills. **M3**

4. Assess the impact of the different sales techniques and customer service offered by Amazon.co.uk by considering the future customer services it could offer to enhance those offered at present. Justify your conclusions. **D2**

Grading tips

1. You are required to undertake a customer service survey for three different types of retailer. You should identify the retailer's customer service policies and how they are applied at an operational (store) level. The elements should be categorised and discussed in terms of what happens before, during and after a sale. **P3**

2. You should consider the key elements of effective service and selling skills. You should also compare the customer services of two different types of retailers and establish why different types of retailers have different levels of customer service. **M3**

3. You are required to assess how the sales techniques and customer service used by Amazon.co.uk impact on the customer. Consideration should be given to future customer services that could be offered by Amazon.co.uk. Justify means giving reasons for and against your suggestions. You have to give a full account of the reasons why Amazon.co.uk could use each new customer service and why they are appropriate for the future. **D2**

4 Know how the retail sector responds to internal and external change

4.1 The retail environment

Macro-environment

Retailers are subjected to external influences over which they have no control. These external influences are also known as **macro-environmental** factors and can include:

- changes in consumer and business confidence
- changes in the housing market
- developments in employment levels.

Successful retailers are the ones that anticipate these influences and react accordingly. External factors should not be ignored as they may pose a threat to the long-term survival of an organisation.

A retailer's macro environment could be affected by the following external influences:

- changing consumer tastes
- retailers offering similar products at reduced prices
- rapidly changing market
- tough trading conditions
- war – could result in a slower economy
- increase in competition – locally, nationally and/or internationally.

It is usual for a business to undertake a **PESTLE analysis** to determine macro-environmental factors that may affect them.

Government policy

Government policy can have an influence on the macro-environment of retailers. For example, political decisions can impact on crucial factors such as education and health issues affecting the workforce,

trade barriers, legislation and economic infrastructure. Other government policies are considered below.

Trading hours

The Sunday Trading Act 1994 governs a retailer's right to trade on a Sunday. The Act allows shops to open, but restricts opening times of larger stores of more than 280 m² to a maximum of six hours. Most shops opening on a Sunday tend to open 10am to 4pm. The legislation was met with considerable opposition. Nevertheless, the shop worker's trade union USDAW (Union of Shops, Distributive and Allied Workers) finally agreed to support the six-hour Sunday trading in return for a promise that Sunday working would be strictly voluntary and premium pay would be offered.

Sunday trading has been deregulated in Scotland and as such shops are able to open any time. However, the right of workers in Scotland to refuse to work on a Sunday was later conferred by the Sunday Working (Scotland) Act 2003.

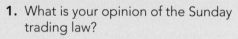

Activity: Sunday trading law

1. What is your opinion of the Sunday trading law?

2. Using the Internet, research information regarding the case for and against Sunday trading. Talk to your local Chamber of Commerce and ask its opinion on the Sunday trading laws. Talk to religious groups about their opinion on the Sunday trading laws. You should consider the implications for retailers, employees, customers as well as other relevant factors.

3. Discuss your findings as a group. At the end of the discussion, the class should vote for or against the Sunday trading law. Have you changed your original opinion as a result of this exercise?

Functional skills

By completing this task and researching the information on the Internet you will help to develop your **ICT** skills.

Key term

Macro-environment – the economy, technology, society, government and the competitive environmental factors that can influence an organisation but that are outside of its direct control.

PESTLE analysis – a model used by organisations to understand the external environment in which they operate. PESTLE stands for: Political, Economical, Sociological, Technological, Legal and Environmental.

Planning guidance

The Town and Country Planning Act directs local authorities to produce local structure plans. These plans show how shopping areas are likely to be developed over a ten-year period. Nowadays, retailers have to follow a particular sequence when seeking permission to build out-of-town centres. If a retailer puts forward a proposal, it must consider its store placement options in this order.

1. The town centre
2. An established edge of town centre
3. A local centre
4. Out-of-town location which can be made readily accessible by a variety of transport options

This Act makes it much more difficult for developers to gain planning permission for out-of-town developments. Local planners are particularly concerned that:

- any development would not harm the vitality and viability of any nearby town centre
- any proposals should not give rise to unacceptable vehicle or pedestrian traffic conditions.

Local authority development plans weigh the importance of industrial and commercial development with that of maintaining and improving environmental quality. Government planning guidelines found on the Communities and Local Government website (**www.communities.gov.uk**) make special reference to their definition of the importance of town centres.

'*Town centres that are attractive, well designed, and well managed, with a range of shops, arts and cultural uses, entertainment, good amenities, and good transport connections, are engines for economic growth, providing a focal point for business and social interactions. Vibrant town centres are good for business: they create jobs, attract investment and generate income. At their best, they create a local buzz and define the wider area, attracting people from near and far.*' (Communities and Local Government Good Practice Guide)

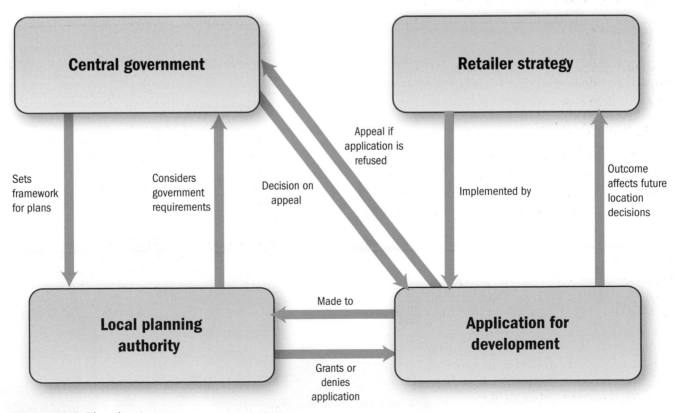

Figure 29.8: The planning process

Implementation of legislation

The Office of Fair Trading (OFT) was established by the Enterprise Act 2002, which enforces both consumer protection and competition law. The OFT's goal is to make markets work well for consumers by ensuring vigorous competition.

The OFT has three main operational areas which all affect retailing.

- Competition enforcement – enforces the Competition Act 1998. The OFT investigated the merger between Morrisons and Safeway. One of the recommendations was that Morrisons sold some former Safeway stores to other supermarket operators.

- Consumer regulations enforcement – enforces the Enterprise Act 2002. The online retailer of computers, software and IT services, Dell Corporation Ltd co-operated with the OFT and agreed to improve its consumer agreements.

- Markets and policies initiatives – the OFT has been asked by groups representing independent retailers to investigate the movement of supermarket chains such as Tesco into the convenience store retail market.

Activity: Office of Fair Trading

Visit the Office of Fair Trading website (www.oft.gov.uk) and link to the section *Newsroom*. Look through the press releases and then produce a summary of the research produced by OFT into scams and why people fall victim to them. Conclude with your views on the investigation.

Functional skills

Carrying out the OFT activity will help you to interact independently using **ICT** for a complex task. You may also have entered, developed and formatted information independently to suit its meaning and purpose using text and tables, images, numbers and records.

Social changes

As the community's social situation changes, the retail sector also needs to change. Shops need to stock products that meet the community's needs and demands. An example of this would be supermarkets now stocking more free-range poultry products to meet the demands of society.

Demographics

Retailers also need to be aware of their social responsibilities and take into account the changing demographics of society. They must look at the way they act towards the different parts of society that they come into contact with. The population of the UK continues to rise and people are living longer; more people are living beyond the age of 65 and there is an increase in people living to 85 and over. The UK has also had an inward migration of people in childbearing age ranges. All of these demographic trends have important effects on the retail economy. They impact both on the level of demand and also the pattern of demand for different products and services.

Household structures

The structure of households in the UK has changed significantly in recent years. With the decline of the

Why should retailers take into account the changing demographics of society?

traditional family, and the increase in single person households and co-habitation, retailers have had to target their products to suit different circumstances. Larger packages for families and smaller individual packs for single people have become the normal way for retailers to offer their products.

Mobility

Greater mobility of the customers has broadened the range of retailers and location that they can choose from. Out-of-town retail centres have captured a huge share of the expenditure. Shopping has become a leisure activity with more people travelling greater distances to shop rather than shopping locally.

New technologies

Technology is essential for ensuring a competitive advantage in a global marketplace. New technologies allow products and services to be produced cheaply and to a high quality and they offer the consumer a choice of innovative products and services, such as Internet banking. Flight, theatre and sports tickets can all be bought online eliminating the need to queue or telephone a reservation. These new technologies have also had an impact on traditional industries such publishing – books can now be downloaded from the Internet to a PC, an iPod or handheld digital book reader. Similarly, technology allows businesses to communicate with the customer through **customer relationship management**, banner ads and personalised messaging.

Did you know?

On a typical working day, the average person uses the Internet for approximately five hours. Two of these hours are for professional or work purposes, while the remaining three are for pleasure and leisure – including online shopping and socialising.

Information management

Information management in the macro-environment can generate both opportunities and threats for retailers. Customers can influence the information they receive and retailers must be careful to manage the collection, storage, analysis and use of information.

Opportunities can include:

* customers able to select promotional messages they want to receive (called permission marketing)

which is thought to be more effective than traditional promotional methods

* new ways of gathering important customer data, e.g. loyalty cards, and ways of analysing customer data, e.g. **data mining**.

Threats can include:

* consumers object to giving away so much personal information for organisations to use for promotional reasons
* greater potential for fraud, e.g. the use of cloned credit cards. Retailers must ensure they abide by the Data Protection Act guidelines for collection, storage, analysis and use of customer data.

Key terms

Customer relationship management – an integrated information system that can be used to plan, schedule and control pre-sales and post-sales.

Data mining – a technique that describes the process of exploring large amounts of data with the objective of revealing hidden relationships or patterns that provide an insight into customer behaviour.

Activity: Loyalty cards

Research two different companies that offer loyalty schemes and then answer these questions about each.

1. What is the name of the loyalty card?
2. How can a customer join the scheme and then subsequently earn points?
3. How does a customer spend points and on which products?
4. What other deals are offered with loyalty card?
5. How can the company get information about the consumer through the loyalty card? How does the company use this information?

Compare the two loyalty schemes and present your findings to the class using a short five-minute PowerPoint presentation. Your presentation should include any recommendations and conclusions that you have come across whilst doing your research for this activity.

Economic growth

Economic growth is measured by the yearly change in Gross Domestic Product (GDP) and is usually expressed as a percentage. It can be influenced by many factors, such as:

- higher business investment
- better productivity
- new skills
- new technology
- increased efficiency.

For retailers and consumers, economic growth offers benefits including:

- more disposable income
- creation of jobs
- reduction in lower paid jobs
- more goods produced resulting in a larger choice for consumers and businesses
- a higher standard of living
- society feeling better as a whole.

Economic growth does have its disadvantages, such as:

- extra pollution due to higher production levels
- reduction in non-renewable resources such as oil
- the affluent society may be the only ones that benefit.

Activity: Economic growth

1. If the economy was growing by 5 per cent per annum, what would be the likely impact on a retail company such as Marks & Spencer?

2. Look at the list of benefits of economic growth. Place them in order of importance for the retail sector and briefly explain the reasons for your order of priority.

Recession

A **recession** can have a massive impact on the retail trade and is usually accompanied by a decrease in the value of the **stock market**, an increase in unemployment and a decline in the property market. A recession is normally considered less severe than a depression though if a recession continues for a long period of time it is often then classified as a depression.

Typical characteristics of a recession include:

- rising unemployment as businesses make employees redundant and/or lay off contract staff to control their costs
- a sharp fall in business confidence and a subsequent decline in profits
- a decline in consumer spending as people become conscious of costs
- money in the form of bank loans and mortgages is much more difficult to attain from banks and building societies
- de-stocking and heavy price discounting – this leads to lower **inflation**
- reduced inflationary pressure in the labour market as unemployment rises
- falling demand for imports
- increase in government borrowing.

During a recession, people tend to cut back on many luxury products and services. However, some activities such as trips to the cinema experience growth during a recession.

Key terms

Recession – a period of general economic decline; usually defined as a fall in GDP for two or more consecutive quarters.

Stock market – a general term for the organised trading of stocks through exchanges and over-the-counter.

Inflation – the overall general upward price movement of goods and services in an economy.

Activity: Going to the cinema

In small groups, discuss the reasons behind the increase in popularity of going to the cinema during a recession.

Consider the following issues.

1. How important is pricing when it comes to stimulating demand for (a) cinema tickets (b) for food and drink products sold in cinema foyers?

2. What role has product innovation (for example, the different films on offer and/or the cinema environment) played in the growth?

3. Produce a PowerPoint presentation to present your findings to the class.

PLTS

Working in a group to discuss ideas about the popularity of going to the cinema during a recession will help you to develop your skills as a **team worker**.

4.2 The competitive environment

The retail environment is more competitive than many other industry sectors, although it is always worth looking at different categories of retail activity and making your own judgement. You may well find the answer surprising! For example, some sectors with greater competition are very often the ones experiencing the most change.

Michael Porter in his book *Competitive Advantage: Creating and Sustaining Superior Performance* developed a framework by which businesses can analyse the competitive environment within which they operate (see Figure 29.9).

Competitors

Retailing covers a wide range of sectors, from the price-led, value retailers through specialist teenage retailers to the more aspirational or older focused brands. On the surface, they may look as if they are competing with each other. However, each retailer within a particular sector has its own particular appeal, for example, Primark for competitive prices, Marks & Spencer for quality and Topshop for fashion.

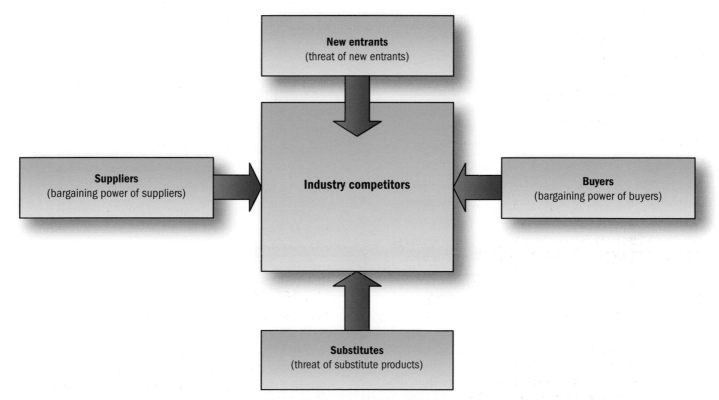

Figure 29.9: Porter's Five Forces Framework allows businesses to assess the competition and helps them to understand the factors producing it

Activity: Competition

Copy the table below and then place the following statements under the appropriate headings.

- A significant number of retailers selling similar products enter the market.

- Suppliers are charging premium prices for a particular resource.

- Consumers have become more price conscious and will look around for a bargain.

- Consumers are not particularly loyal to any one retailer.

- As a retailer, it is beneficial to purchase from a variety of suppliers.

Threat of new entrants	Threat of substitutes	Bargaining power of suppliers	Bargaining power of buyers

Market position

Market position can be described as a retailer's position in the market place and how the consumer perceives it. It is typically expressed relative to the position of the competition.

Barriers to entry

Barriers to entry are obstacles that are designed to block potential entrants or new organisations from profitably entering a market. The ability of existing businesses to maintain such obstacles will depend on their marketing and financial power. In other words, barriers to entry have the effect of making a market less desirable to other businesses. For example, a beauty salon, which is probably a relatively cheap market to enter because capital requirements are low and the training can be achieved fairly quickly, but compare this with supermarkets. The size of current competitors means they benefit from economies of scale, making it difficult for others to enter the market. Wal-Mart is the world's largest retailer and due to the expense of building new stores in the UK, decided to purchase the existing retailer ASDA.

Pricing

Retailers adopt a variety of approaches to pricing. The four main pricing strategies include the following.

- Premium pricing – used when retailers offer products and services at a high price. This strategy is used when the product or service is unique or when a significant competitive advantage exists. Examples include luxury accommodation such as the Savoy Hotel or executive class flights on aeroplanes.

- Economy pricing – used when retailers offer products and services at a low, no frills price. All elements of the business are kept to a minimum, including. marketing. Supermarkets such as Tesco have a value brand for products such as bread, washing powder and soups.

- Penetration pricing – used by retailers when they charge significantly lower prices than the competition in order to gain a market share. Once they have achieved their objective, they increase their prices again. Sky TV originally used this strategy.

- Price skimming – when retailers charge a high price because they have a significant competitive advantage. However, the competitive advantage is not sustainable and tends to attract new entrants into the market. Inevitably, the prices fall because of increased supply to the market. Most premium technology products are priced using this strategy.

There are many other types of pricing strategies depending on the type of retailer and their market. When selling online, the retailer may adapt some traditional methods.

- Premium pricing is used for selling products such as downloadable music.
- Economy pricing is used for basic products and services such as basic templates for websites.
- Penetration pricing is used by some online companies such as YouTube which offer free subscriptions.
- Price skimming is used to launch new products such as music albums or video games.

Online retailers may use other pricing strategies such as:

- optional product pricing whereby a customer can buy a holiday online with the option of purchasing travel insurance at the same time
- captive product pricing whereby a customer purchases an anti-virus software package and all updates are available through the manufacturer.

Product development

Retailers have a chance to alter their product mix when they have the opportunity to sell new products or services. Look at the examples in Table 29.13.

Table 29.13: New product opportunities for retailers

Retailer	New product opportunities
The Carphone Warehouse	New smartphones, 3G iPhones
Currys	64GB iPod Touch, iPod Nano
iTunes	Online store selling latest media
Dell	Online retailer selling customisable PCs

New products and services

Retailers are always on the look out for new products and services to offer their customers. Some examples are given in Table 29.14.

Table 29.14: Additional products and services for retailers

Retailer	Additional products and services
Tesco	Banking services, insurance, credit card facilities
Marks & Spencer	Autograph, Blue Harbour and other individual designer products
Virgin	Broadband and landline services
Currys	Free delivery and recycling on all orders

Activity: Pricing

1. Using the the pricing strategy grid in Figure 29.10, place the following statements in the correct segment.

   - EasyJet offers two new holiday routes to Europe.
   - Sainsbury's launches a new value product range aimed at students.
   - A new mobile phone company opens up in a town and wants to achieve a market share.
   - Sony launches a new video camera with innovative technological differences from its competitors.

2. Suggest four more examples of your own.

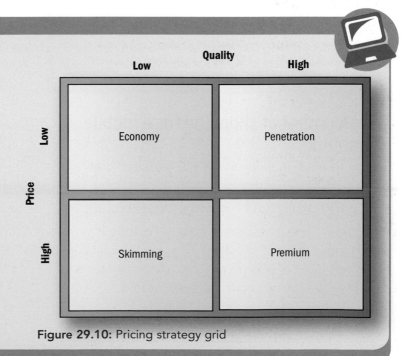

Figure 29.10: Pricing strategy grid

New retailing concepts

Consumers are continually looking for new leisure experiences and life changing activities which is having an impact on reshaping product and service retailing. This trend is already noticeable in the world of pubs and clubs whereby they are constantly changing their image and décor in order to reinvent themselves in the eyes of the customer. Shops will continuously have to keep reinventing themselves to maintain and retain their customers. Waterstone's, for example, has turned the traditional activity of purchasing a book into a wider leisure experience by offering coffee shop facilities in its bookshops. Its aim is to offer an experience that cannot be matched online by Amazon.co.uk.

Football clubs, who themselves are retailers by opening up extensive club shops and even superstores in order to sell their official club products, are taking on new retailing concepts. Some top football clubs also license a wide range of products. For example, Manchester United fans can now purchase a bottle of Manchester United mineral water, play a Manchester United Nintendo game and buy a toaster displaying the club's colours and logo. Fans can also buy different styles of clothing, all with the logo emblazoned on them.

Did you know?

The 1873 patent received by Levi Strauss and Jacob Davis for putting rivets in their denim apparel was titled 'Improvement in Fastening Pocket-Openings'. This simple improvement was the key component of what are known as Levi's jeans.

Development of shopping for a mobile population

The increase in mobility of the population is creating new retail opportunities for organisations. Some of these opportunities are discussed opposite.

Airports

Air travel continues to rise as the numbers of destinations being targeted by low cost airlines are on the increase. Airport management considers retail as an important factor in generating revenue. For example, Heathrow Airport's Terminal 5 offers a selection of retail outlets selling products such as traditional and modern souvenirs and gifts, luggage and travel-related products and jewellery, watches and accessories. They also attract high street retailers such as HMV, WHSmith, Accessorize and Boots the Chemist.

Railway stations

Passenger numbers are increasing on the national rail network. Convenience stores, confectionery and tobacconist shops are all enjoying an increase in demand. Products such as DVDs, music, electrical items, clothing and gift purchases are available at stations. They have also experimented with health and beauty operators such as Boots, The Body Shop and Superdrug. High value accessory retailers such as Vodaphone and the stationer Paperchase have also joined the market.

Motorway service areas

Motorway service areas (MSA) offer a range of food outlets including Marks & Spencer, Somerfield, Waitrose and Thornton's. They also have traditional high street retail outlets such as WHSmith and Fonebiz. Retail outlets within these MSAs are restricted on the size of their stores. They cannot sell alcohol; nor can they advertise their brands. A revision of these rules would allow these outlets to develop in line with consumer needs and wants.

Assessment activity 29.4

P4   BTEC

Identify the level of competition faced by SPAR. Write your findings using a report format. **P4**

Grading tips

Your report should include all aspects of how the retailing sector responds to internal and external change. You should include answers to the following questions.

- Is the market declining in terms of unit sales or value?

- Are there a significant number of independent retailers?

- Are the numbers of independent retailers in the market increasing or decreasing?

- Do customers tend to show loyalty to a particular retailer?

- Could the retailers easily serve more customers?

- Would it be difficult for retailers to convert their stores quickly and inexpensively to serve another market? **P4**

PLTS

Reflecting on the competitive factors faced in the retail environment will help you to develop your skills as a **reflective learner**.

Just checking

1. What percentage of the UK workforce is employed in the retail sector?
2. What type of retailers are the following?
   - Morrisons
   - Marks & Spencer
   - Argos
   - John Lewis Partnership
   - Londis
3. How has your local high street changed in recent years?
4. What are the advantages and disadvantages of becoming a franchisee?
5. Explain why independent retailers are declining in numbers.
6. Describe three advantages and disadvantages of online shopping.
7. Draw a flow chart showing the supply chain of products sourced from Europe.
8. Describe how retailers use ICT in the supply chain.
9. Explain the process for a retailer who wants to build an out-of-town shopping centre.
10. What are the advantages and disadvantages for retailers offering excellent customer service?
11. Name some retailers who regularly use the following strategies:
    - premium pricing
    - economy pricing
    - penetration pricing
    - price skimming.
12. Name four different ways that retailers collect and use customer information. Why do retailers want this information?

edexcel

Assignment tips

1. For all the assignments, select retail businesses that make it easy for you to highlight the similarities and differences between them. Many of the leading high street retailers offer information on their websites regarding these functions.

2. You can use textbooks, company website information and organisation logistics information to find the different distribution methods used by retailers. You could also interview retailers to gather information. You should emphasise the similarities and differences between the two retailers.

3. Choose retailers that offer information on their customer service policies. Ensure you identify how they are applied at an operational level. You will also need to include the key elements of effective service and selling skills and compare the customer services of two different types of retailers.

4. SPAR offers a lot of information on its company website. It is also recommended that you attempt to interview management of your local SPAR to assist you in answering the questions. This assignment should be presented in a report format.

Once you have completed all four assignments and they have been assessed, keep them carefully in your portfolio.

36 Starting a small business

Many people dream of starting up their own business. To be successful there are many aspects to consider when setting up a small business.

This unit looks at types of businesses, the attractiveness of the business idea, the target market and the need to balance personal and business needs. It will help you to understand the skills needed to support the business idea as well as personal development plans that may be needed to make the business a success. The legal and financial implications of starting up a business and how to devise an outline business proposal are also considered.

Learning outcomes

After completing this unit you should:

1. be able to present the initial business idea using relevant criteria
2. understand the skills and personal development needed to run the business successfully
3. know the legal and financial aspects that will affect the start up of the business
4. be able to produce an outline business start-up proposal.

Assessment and grading criteria

This table shows you what you must do in order to achieve a **pass**, **merit** or **distinction** grade, and where you can find activities in this book to help you.

To achieve a **pass** grade the evidence must show that the learner is able to:	To achieve a **merit** grade the evidence must show that, in addition to the pass criteria, the learner is able to:	To achieve a **distinction** grade the evidence must show that, in addition to the pass and merit criteria, the learner is able to:
P1 present the initial business idea using relevant criteria **See Assessment activity 36.1, page 217**	**M1** explain methods used to identify the target market for the proposed business **See Assessment activity 36.1, page 217**	**D1** present a comprehensive business proposal that addresses all relevant aspects of business start up **See Assessment activity 36.3, page 241**
P2 explain how to identify the target market **See Assessment activity 36.1, page 217**		
P3 describe the skills needed to run the business successfully and what areas require further personal development **See Assessment activity 36.2, page 239**	**M2** analyse the personal development needed to run the business successfully **See Assessment activity 36.2, page 239**	
P4 describe the legal and financial aspects that will affect the start up of the business **See Assessment activity 36.2, page 239**		
P5 produce a proposal containing the essential information for the start up of a business **See Assessment activity 36.3, page 241**	**M3** assess the implications of the legal and financial aspects that will affect the start up of the business **See Assessment activity 36.3, page 241**	

How you will be assessed

This unit will be assessed by an internal assignment that will be designed and marked by the staff at your centre. The assignment is designed to allow you to show your understanding of the unit outcomes. These relate to what you should be able to do after completing this unit.

Your assessment will be in the form of:

- presentations
- case studies
- practical tasks
- written assignments.

Lucy, 19, BTEC National Business Learner

My ambition is to one day open my own Internet café and this unit has helped me understand the requirements in starting up a business. I was particularly grateful for clarification on the legislation that needs to be considered and also the explanation on financial issues.

I enjoyed learning the whole concept of starting a business, which involves a lot more than I was aware of. It made me look at my own skills and helped me identify the personal development route I need to take in order to be successful. I also found the marketing aspect of businesses really interesting. This unit made me aware that I would need to understand who the customer would be at my Internet café.

In the lessons, we worked in groups and undertook many individual activities, which enhanced the learning experience. I had to use the Internet to research other start-up organisations and to look at the advantages and disadvantages of different types of businesses. Ultimately, the outline business start-up proposal was an enormous benefit as it is something I can use to go to my bank when I am looking for finance.

1. What type of business would you like to start up?
2. Would you prefer to purchase an existing business? If so, what type?
3. What type of research would you do before starting your business?

1 Be able to present the initial business idea using relevant criteria

New business start-up

In small groups, think of your local high street and the shops that are located there, then discuss the following questions.

1. How many shops are parts of a chain?
2. How many shops are individually owned?
3. Do these independent shops sell products and/or services that you cannot find anywhere else? What makes them different?
4. What ideas do you have for a business opportunity not currently found in your high street?

1.1 Criteria

Types of businesses

People choose to start their own business for a variety of reasons. For some it is an opportunity to escape working 9 to 5; for others, it may be through necessity after being made redundant; whilst some people have discovered a gap in the market or see an opportunity to open a business.

Whatever the reason or the motivation, there are three main areas to consider when it comes to looking at which route to follow: start a new business, purchase an existing business or become a franchisee.

New business

Setting up a new business using an original idea can be one of the most difficult strategies as well as one of the most satisfying. A venture is considered a new business if it is based on a unique idea that succeeds from the planning stage through to it generating **revenue**. There are many advantages to starting a new business including:

- less restrictive than purchasing an existing or franchise business as there are no predetermined rules and contracts
- control of all aspects of the business, including what products and/or services are being offered, marketing, location and staffing
- higher financial rewards than if employed by someone else
- creativity and personal satisfaction.

However, there are a number of potential disadvantages to consider when deciding whether to start a small business. These include:

- financial resources needed to start and grow a business can be extensive and, if unsuccessful, there may be substantial financial losses
- no guarantee of income
- stress caused by problems, responsibilities and decisions
- time commitment will be more than when working for someone else
- independence and working long hours might not be what were anticipated when started.

To stand the greatest chance of survival it is essential to research the market and this research must be made on an ongoing basis to stay ahead of the competition. Businesses must also start small; many business start-ups suffer from delusions of grandeur and spend money on totally unnecessary items. Finally, the new owner should have some knowledge or expertise in the chosen area of business. Without thorough market research, expertise and appropriate knowledge, the owner of any new business will start their venture at an extreme disadvantage.

Key term

Revenue – total amount of money received by the company for goods sold or services provided during a certain time period.

Activity: Suitable business ideas

1. Think about what people need and want in their everyday lives. Try to find something many people need done but where the people doing it right now aren't doing it satisfactorily – and do it better! Make a list of your ideas.

2. Take your list and circle the ones that you have a particular interest or expertise in. Then circle the ones that you would like to acquire an interest or expertise in.

3. Consider whether any of the circled ideas would make a good business venture. You should think about who your potential customers might be and who your competitors would be. Eliminate any business ideas that have become unviable due to lack of customers or too many competitors in the market. You should consider the following issues:
   - How difficult would it be to start your proposed business?
   - What are the advantages and disadvantages of your business idea?

4. Discuss your favourite idea choice with the rest of the class. Has anyone got suggestions which could help you look at your proposed business from a completely different angle?

Purchase an existing business

There are many advantages to buying a pre-existing business rather than starting one from scratch. There is risk either way. The decision depends heavily on the amount of risk a person is willing to incur. When taking on an existing business it is important to find an established firm with a solid customer base and a motivated workforce, rather than one with liabilities or a poor reputation. Existing businesses to buy can be found through the local press, estate agents, trade associations and websites dedicated to this sort of provision.

Advantages of buying an existing business are:
- some of the groundwork in getting the business up and running will already have been done and many of the problems will have already been discovered and solved
- easier to get finance as the business will have a proven track record
- a demonstrated market for the product or service
- established customers, a reliable income, a reputation to capitalise and build on and a useful network of contacts
- a business plan and marketing method should already be in place
- existing employees with experience that can be drawn on.

When purchasing an existing business, you would need to consider why the current owner is selling and how this might impact on the business. There are also some disadvantages, which should be considered, such as:
- often a need to invest a large amount up front, including professional fees for solicitors, surveyors, accountants etc., and if the business has been neglected it may need a larger investment to give it the best chance of success
- may need several months' worth of working capital to assist with **cash flow**
- possible need to honour or renegotiate any outstanding contracts the previous owner had
- the possibility that the current staff may not be happy with a new boss, or the business might have been run badly and staff morale may be low.

Key term

Cash flow – money coming into a business from selling its products and the money it spends on all aspects of production.

Research needs to be undertaken into any existing business in order to minimise risk before purchasing. Research should include looking into the past and current standing as well as the potential of the business to establish its future. Other things to consider are the location, the competition, the current reputation of the existing business, its internal operations and all financial aspects.

Franchise

Many high street chains are **franchises**. They are popular because they are usually a famous brand that is known and trusted by consumers. This means that it is easier to attract customers and therefore the business has a lower risk of failure. Another advantage is that this gives the franchisee a quick and cheap means of possible expansion.

The **franchisor** sells the licence of the original business to others who want to operate the business under the brand umbrella. As well as the licence, the franchisor sets out in the contract various details of how the business is to be run, gives advice on running the operation and takes a share of the proceeds. They also determine that nothing is ever done to damage the brand.

The **franchisee** buys the right to use the company name and logo, sell the company products and/or offer the company services. Many people find it easier to run a business this way because someone else has put all the effort into working out what will make it successful.

However, this type of business venture can be limiting, as there is no scope for using initiative or putting an individual stamp on the business. Furthermore, franchises can cost a lot of money to set up and the franchisor will expect a slice of the annual profits (a royalty). The cost of buying a franchise depends upon how famous the brand is. More information on franchising is available from www.british-franchise.org.

Aims

A business may have several **aims**, or goals it wants to achieve. In the private sector, one aim is to make a profit. Other aims may include surviving, expanding, maximising sales, being more competitive and being environmentally friendly.

Did you know?

Asda's aim is 'to provide goods/services that are cheap and affordable to consumers or the public'.

It is essential that any business owner determines the aim of the business to help **stakeholders** understand the direction of the company. When setting up a business, objectives should also be set that relate

to how the business will achieve its aims. Objectives should be SMART:

- Specific
- Measurable
- Achievable
- Realistic
- Time related.

An example of an objective could be 'to gain 10% of the market for computer sales by January 2011'.

Activity: Kitchen-fitting business

Sam and Katrina have decided to go into partnership together and set up their own kitchen-fitting business. Neither of them has any prior business experience, but Katrina has done an art degree and is good at design while Sam has studied accounts and has worked in the kitchen business.

In small groups, discuss what you think Sam's and Katrina's aims and objectives should be and give your reasons.

Business planning

Successful businesses invest time to create and manage budgets, prepare and review business plans and regularly monitor finance and performance. Structured planning can make all the difference to the growth of a new business. It enables the owner to concentrate resources on improving profits, reducing costs and increasing returns on investment.

Many businesses carry out the majority of the activities associated with business planning, such as thinking about growth areas, competitors, cash flow and profit. Converting this into a cohesive process to manage a business' development is not difficult or time-consuming. The key benefit of business planning is that it creates a focus for the direction of a business and provides targets that will help the business grow. It also provides an opportunity to review a business's

Key terms

Aim – broad statement of intent providing a direction for a business, from which more specific objectives could be set.

Stakeholder – a person, group or organisation that affects or can be affected by an organisation's actions.

performance and the factors affecting it. Business planning can give:

- greater ability to make continual improvements and anticipate problems
- sound financial information on which to base decisions
- improved clarity and focus
- greater confidence in decision making.

Attractiveness of idea

An attractive business idea could be an invention, a new product or service, or an original idea or solution to an everyday problem. It might also be:

- a gap in the market that can be filled
- a business related to work already being done
- an interest or hobby that can be turned into a business.

Did you know?

Motorola founder Paul Galvin came up with the name when his company started manufacturing radios for cars. It was originally called Victrola.

Unique selling point (USP)

A unique selling point (USP) is a feature that makes a product or service distinctive. A particular business, product or service may use unique branding, packaging, advertising campaigns, added quality or even simply a low price feature to make it different. Creating a USP is one of the most important things that a business can do. For an idea or product to be successful the USP should be obvious and attractive to the consumer.

Price can be an important USP but it is the hardest to sustain. That is why people change supermarkets. They will go to Asda for weeks, but then switch to Tesco if they can buy the same goods at a lower price. To try to combat this, many supermarkets have introduced USPs such as loyalty cards which offer benefits to loyal customers, or they have introduced services such as home delivery.

Demand for new business

One of the most important issues when starting up a business is to establish if there is a demand from consumers and if there are enough customers to support the business. It is important for any

Activity: USPs

In small groups, discuss the following questions.

1. What are the unique selling points of your favourite games console?

2. What attracts you to one particular games console instead of similar ones on the market?

3. Do you purchase games for the console from one particular shop or do you try different shops on the high street or online? If you purchase from the same shop, explain why. Discuss the USPs that attract you to this shop.

Functional skills

Working in a group to talk about this research will help you to develop your **English** skills in speaking, listening and making a range of contributions to discussions.

start-up business to evaluate potential customers by determining the likely customer base, or target customer. This involves defining the target customer by learning as much as possible about them to ensure they are potential customers. This allows the business to tailor any products or services to better suit the potential customer's needs and desires, and ensure marketing targets the right people.

Competitive edge

It is important to build a competitive edge into the foundation of the business. There are various ways to do this, including making a product or offering a service which is difficult for competitors to imitate; being more knowledgeable than competitors; offering a more efficient product than competitors; and being more adept at distributing the product or service. Other competitive edge factors include a better location or the offer of better customer service than that of any competitor.

It is essential that any small business holds on to its competitive edge by protecting its trade secrets. Another way of retaining a competitive edge is to react quickly, for example, if the business gets into difficulty, a plan will be needed to deal with it immediately. This may involve changing location, introducing a new product or service, or developing a better way to reach customers.

Balancing personal and business needs

Balancing personal and business needs is an important consideration when starting a new business. A business can suffer if home distractions are allowed to interfere with the daily work schedule, and vice versa. New business owners may find themselves thinking about work from the time they wake up until the time they go to sleep. Obviously there will be many occasions when the new business owner needs to spend more time either working or networking in order to help establish the business. However, they may need to take a step back and examine their priorities.

Activity: Work/life balance

It is recommended that in order to maintain a healthy lifestyle there is a need to strike a balance between work and personal activities. It is also important to allow a period of quiet time to reflect on life, and of course uninterrupted sleep is crucial.

1. In small groups, discuss this text. Do you agree with the premise?

2. Based on what you have learnt about work/life balance, write down any activities in your life that you will spend more/less time on. What changes will you make, and why?

3. Are there areas of your life where you are feeling stress? What could you do to help relieve stress in these areas?

Checking profitability

Before starting up any business it is essential to establish its **profitability**. Not only is this important for the personal finances of any owner but also if there is a need to approach outsiders such as banks, family or friends for financial backing. Therefore, a thorough appraisal of the business's potential financial requirements must be undertaken. Financial implications for a business may include the following:

- day-to-day operation costs
- start-up **capital**
- time needed to reach **break-even point**
- potential sales volume
- profit level required for the business to be successful and allow for growth
- the retail price of the product or service.

After establishing that the figures look optimistic, a business owner can then put together a business plan as well as a cash-flow projection, a **profit and loss account** and a balance sheet.

One of the main reasons small businesses fail in the early stages is that too much capital is used to buy **fixed assets**. Although certain equipment will be essential at the start, other purchases can be postponed until they become essential or when the business starts to become profitable. The higher the **fixed costs**, the longer it can take to reach the break-even point and therefore profitability.

Business trends

A business owner needs to be aware of changes or **trends** in the market before the competition finds out. Consumers' wants and needs are constantly changing and to ensure long-term success, businesses must be able to adapt to these changes. A business venture needs to take into account trends and environmental changes that could occur. In order to determine these trends, it is usual to look for patterns in data collected during the research process. Typically, these patterns show changes in political, environmental, social, technological, legislative and environmental factors (see the PESTLE analysis opposite). These trends typically include seasonal variations such as Christmas, Easter or summer holidays, random events such as the London Olympics or cyclical trends such as the World Cup; they can occur on a local, national or global level.

These trends offer substantial opportunities for the business world, but they can also be extremely

Key terms

Profitability – to earn a profit; the positive gain from a business operation after deducting all expenses.

Capital – cash or goods used as an investment in a business.

Break-even point – approximate sales volume required to cover costs, below which production would be unprofitable and above which it would be profitable.

Profit and loss account – an account compiled at the end of an accounting period to show gross and net profit or loss.

Fixed assets – a tangible long-term asset held for business use such as equipment and furniture.

Fixed costs – a cost such as rent and insurance, which does not depend on production or sales levels.

Trend – the general direction in which something tends to move.

challenging. Any new business will need to undertake a **situation analysis** which will be used to obtain up-to-date and accurate information to ensure a competitive advantage. If the analysis is the same as the competition, then the business may hold the same amount of market share. The situation analysis is used to audit a business and its external environment.

Key term

Situation analysis – assessment of the organisation's current and future strengths, weaknesses, and opportunities.

External influences

When starting a small business it is important to identify external influences that could impact on its viability and affect all aspects of planning. In particular, commercial, political, local, national and international influences should be considered. A PESTLE analysis is used to identify these external influences as shown in Figure 36.1.

PESTLE stands for political, economic, social, environmental, legal and technological issues that can have an effect on the business. Identifying PESTLE

influences is a practical way of summarising the external environment in which a business operates. However, a business will need to consider how to respond to these influences.

PESTLE analyses rely on reliable and up-to-date information. Two of the best sites for finding this information are:

*   National Statistics – a governmental organisation which provides accurate statistical information on businesses, the economy and society in the UK. Visit www.statistics.gov.uk.

*   The Bank of England – publishes a variety of useful statistical information. Visit www.bankofengland.co.uk/statistics.

Commercial

An external audit should consider the commercial environment in which the business intends to compete. The market and competitive environments are both key issues in the external audit. Before starting a business, an audit should be undertaken of the size, growth, trends and market share. It is also important to look at any new products introduced to the market and product positioning.

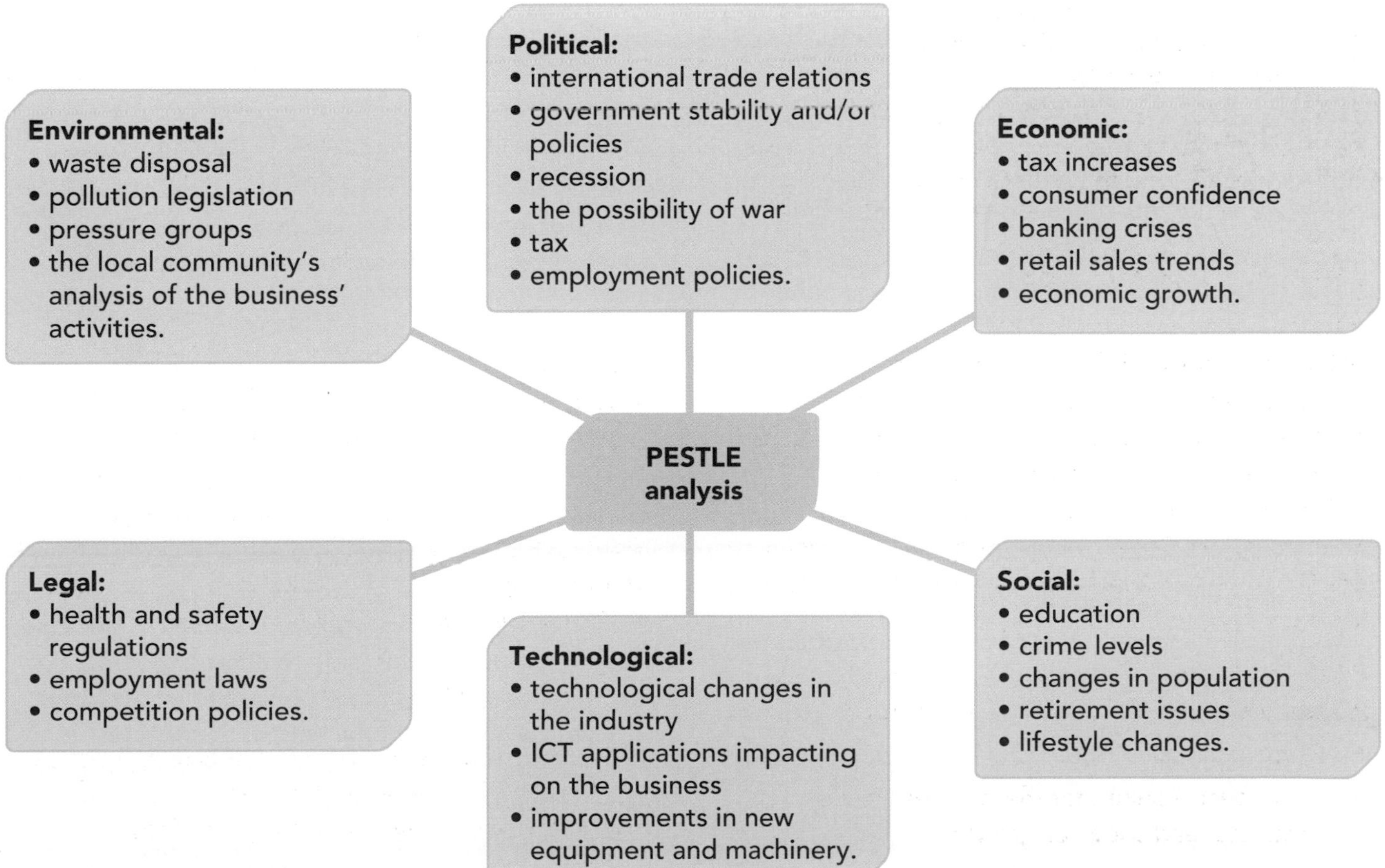

Political:
*   international trade relations
*   government stability and/or policies
*   recession
*   the possibility of war
*   tax
*   employment policies.

Environmental:
*   waste disposal
*   pollution legislation
*   pressure groups
*   the local community's analysis of the business' activities.

Economic:
*   tax increases
*   consumer confidence
*   banking crises
*   retail sales trends
*   economic growth.

PESTLE analysis

Legal:
*   health and safety regulations
*   employment laws
*   competition policies.

Technological:
*   technological changes in the industry
*   ICT applications impacting on the business
*   improvements in new equipment and machinery.

Social:
*   education
*   crime levels
*   changes in population
*   retirement issues
*   lifestyle changes.

Figure 36.1: PESTLE analysis

An audit of competitors should also be undertaken which would identify issues such as:

- who and how the competition conducts their business
- ascertain competitors' approximate size in terms of sales value and volume
- use published accounts (if available) to assess competitors' financial strength
- determine the extent to which competitors have diversified into a range of different products
- consider the channels of distribution, which they use
- evaluate the competitors' market standing with the customer and the extent to which each product range contributes to their reputation.

This information can be used to assess the likely objectives and strategies that the business will use in the future.

Political

Government policy can have a major impact on the operation of a business. For example, laws on competitive practice will influence the number of businesses operating in an industry and therefore the strength of competition. Health and safety legislation will affect work practices and production costs. Marketing tactics will be limited by consumer legislation. It is important to study the political environment within which business operates, particularly in countries where governments are unstable and therefore investment risks are high.

You may wish to divide factors into geographical relevance, such as local, national and international/global, which is known as LoNGPESTLE. LoNGPESTLE analysis considers the external environmental influences at the different levels that impact the business. These consider the following.

- **Local:**
  - Political influences: provision of services by the local council
  - Economic influences: local economic growth rates
  - Social influences: local population growth rates
  - Technological influences: local technological improvements such as broadband and digital TV
  - Legal influences: local planning permission and licences
  - Environmental influences: local waste disposal issues.

- **National:**
  - Political influences: government policies on subsidies
  - Economic influences: bank interest rates
  - Social influences: changes in the demography such as an aging population
  - Technological influences: countrywide technology such as online services
  - Legal influences: UK laws such as trade descriptions and retail opening hours
  - Environmental influences: changes in the weather.

- **International/global:**
  - Political influences: opening up of new markets making trade easier
  - Economic influences: economic growth overseas
  - Social influences: migration and foreign labour changes
  - Technological influences: technological breakthrough such as the Internet
  - Legal influences: international policies on the environment or human rights
  - Environmental influences: global or international climate changes.

Did you know?

The Second World War saw the nationalisation of many of the UK's services including the railways, the Bank of England and the coal reserves.

Self-esteem

There are many reasons why people choose to start their own business. One reason may be because they feel that becoming self-employed may offer enhanced pleasure and development opportunities, which raises their self-esteem.

A person may choose to work for themselves because of the challenge of being able to control the direction the business takes. They may be able to work closer to home or even from home; and, if the business is part time, they may be able to reduce the hours spent at work. There are other benefits such as possible reduction in income tax as a self-employed person can offset expenses and reduce the amount normally paid.

Reggae Reggae Sauce

BBC2's 'Dragons' Den' was the start of a successful career for Levi Roots and his *Reggae Reggae Sauce*. His family weren't keen for him to apply to go on the show, but Levi had confidence in his product and so, armed with his guitar and dressed in a smart suit, he sold the concept to both Peter Jones and Richard Farleigh managing to secure a £50,000 investment.

Levi sang his way through the show, and his unusual sales pitch and unique sauce have ensured that he has never looked back. *Reggae Reggae Sauce*, his Nana Miriam's recipe with its closely guarded secret ingredients, has become a huge success story. Sainsbury's even ran out on the first day it appeared on the shelves.

Levi is an inspiration for all would-be entrepreneurs. On the day of his 'Dragons' Den' appearance, Levi had £10 in his pocket – enough to get a taxi to the show. However, he also had self-confidence, belief and perseverance that all successful entrepreneurs seem to have.

What makes Levi Roots' story a success? A combination of a good product and a unique sales style which has struck a chord with the British people. He showed courage and creativity and a belief that his product was equally good as, if not better, than some products sold by larger brands.

Levi Roots' future seems set to be successful. He has already opened his own restaurant in Battersea, called the Papine Jerk Centre, presented an award at the MOBOs (music of black origin) and been asked to open supermarkets and charity fund-raising events.

Think about it!

1. Apart from the product, what do you think makes Levi Roots stand out from his competitors?
2. Name three entrepreneurial traits that Levi Roots has.
3. Why do you think that Levi Roots and *Reggae Reggae Sauce* have struck a chord with the British people?

Some people just do not want to work for a large corporation. They want to feel a sense of independence and therefore prefer to work for themselves rather than take orders and follow someone else's rules. People who work for themselves may also enjoy the sense of power gained from running their own business. They often regard the challenge as exciting and enjoy the sense of personal achievement when the business is successful.

1.2 Identifying target market

In order to ensure a successful business venture, it is essential to provide evidence that the product or service is likely to be bought by customers. The best way of identifying a target customer or market is to undertake market research.

Market research

Market research is concerned with gathering, recording and developing data. It is carried out to determine consumers' needs and wants before developing the product or service. It is a continual process and does not end with the launch of any one product or service. Once a business has started, market research needs to be ongoing in order to remain competitive and fulfil consumers' changing needs.

Did you know?

Primary data is new information that you have gathered which has not been published before. It is also known as field research because it involves going out into the 'field' to find it. Examples of primary data include surveys, interviews and observations.

Published research

Published research, also known as secondary or desk research, involves collecting information already researched by someone else. This information can be in the form of trade publications, academic journals and government statistics.

Sales forecasts

It is extremely important for any business to be aware of the potential sales that their product or service will generate in the **market place**. In order to estimate potential sales when starting up the business, it is always recommended to use primary research to

Activity: Research on the coffee industry

1. Find out about the coffee industry within a country of your choice. Use the Internet and other published research to find information. In particular, you should find out:
   - the market share of coffee producers
   - the value of the coffee industry.
2. Why do you think it is important for coffee producers to have knowledge of this data?
3. A coffee producer needs to find out more about the potential of coffee drinkers. What primary research methods are appropriate to find out about the habits of coffee drinkers? What are the advantages and disadvantages of each?
4. Why is it important for coffee producers to conduct both primary and secondary research?

Functional skills

Using the Internet to find information about the coffee industry will help you to develop your **ICT** skills in systems.

determine the forecast. The following questions could enable you to come up with some estimates of sales forecasts.

- Are the respondents likely to consider purchasing from your new business?
- How often will they purchase the product or service?
- How much do they anticipate paying for the product or service?
- Do the respondents' buying patterns change over the course of the year?

For most new businesses, sales tend to be slow and so estimates should be lower at first. Assuming the reputation of the business increases, the figures can be built up as time progresses.

Key term

Market place – the world of commercial activity where goods and services are bought and sold.

An understanding of market trends is also important for sales forecasts. Any prior information can reinforce primary research to discover the market trends in a business area. Secondary research is an effective method to assist in predicting trends and forecasting sales. It is particularly useful if a new business venture is based on an established market as there will be statistics and information widely available to help find recent trends as well as the size of the market. However, it is far more difficult to attain statistics on locally run, small businesses as they tend not publish their market statistics.

The number and strength of competitors in the market will also influence the potential sales. Forecasting potential sales is not easy to determine at first as it is difficult to estimate what the sales are likely to be. It becomes easier the longer the business is in existence as there will be historic trend information to help put together a reliable sales forecast.

Customers' actions and choices

Any retailer needs to understand why and what their customers buy, which is difficult to predict. Customers do not always give considered thought to what they purchase; instead they may buy on impulse. A business owner will need to anticipate customers' wants and needs. One famous academic researcher, Philip Kotler, has developed the Black Box Model to help to explain and understand what motivates consumers (see Figure 36.2).

A retailer needs to determine what motivates customers to purchase particular products and services to see how this will affect the business. The Black Box Model helps, as does primary research, which is used to gather information on why a customer would buy your particular product or service.

Competition

Every new business needs to determine both its **direct** and **indirect competitors**. The best way to do this is to visit the locality in which the business will be situated and identify what businesses are there. Other ways to find out about competitors include using an Internet search engine or online and paper-based directories. New businesses should also research how much market share their competitors have, how much marketing they undertake and whether the market is open to new competition.

Key terms

Direct competitors – competition between two or more businesses that offer essentially the same products and services.

Indirect competitors – competition among suppliers of different types of products and services that satisfy the same needs.

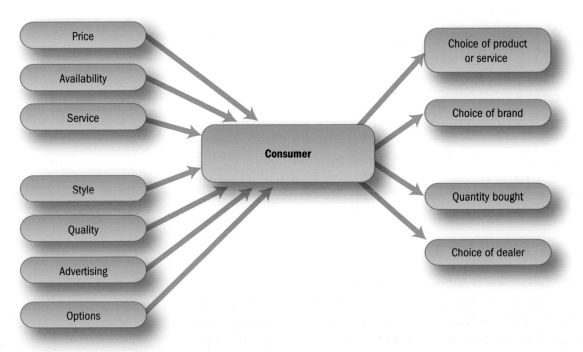

Figure 36.2: Kotler's Black Box Model

Strengths and weaknesses

When starting up, a retailer should understand strengths and weaknesses in the target market. Strengths are the capabilities, resources and skills that can be drawn upon to achieve the goals that have been set, whilst weaknesses are any lack of skills or deficiency in capabilities that may stop the ability to act on strategies to accomplish the goals. Strengths and weaknesses are internal factors, whilst opportunities and threats are external factors. A SWOT analysis helps a business to focus on key issues and should be the first stage of planning (see Figure 36.3). It is important that the SWOT analysis is specific and is applied to the competition.

Did you know?

The acronym SWOT stands for strengths, weaknesses, opportunities and threats and was first used by Albert Humphrey at Stanford University in California in the 1960s.

Figure 36.3: SWOT Analysis

Strength could be:

- expertise in a specialist area
- location of the business
- unique product/service.

Weakness could be:

- lack of business experience
- product/service similar to competitors
- no established reputation.

Activity: Garden nursery

1. You have been hired by a garden nursery to help with its marketing. Perform a SWOT analysis, taking into consideration the following issues.

   - The nursery is situated next to a large shopping centre and is a five-minute walk from the main railway and bus terminal.
   - There is competition from a local DIY centre which has a small gardening section, though it only sells a limited variety of plants and gardening furniture.
   - Due to a recession, local residents have less money to spend on their garden.
   - The area attracts a large proportion of retired people from the city.
   - The nursery has just lost a big contract with the local council.
   - The nursery has been awarded a merit in a national garden centre competition for good customer service.
   - Grants have been attained to ensure the nursery is fit to accommodate the disabled.
   - The on-site café has been outsourced and has a poor reputation for value and quality.

2. Discuss your findings with the group and make suggestions as to how the garden nursery can improve its overall performance.

Opportunity could be:

- no competition in the area
- a new market that has potential for larger profits
- a market vacated by unsuccessful and ineffective competition.

Threat could be:

- a new competitor emerging in the market
- competitors begin a price war
- competitor with better product/service in the same market.

Market trends

Market trends describe the movement of the financial market over time. These trends can be classified as long term, mid term or short term. Some are known as **cyclical trends** because they go around in a circle and come back again, for example, ice cream sales, which are more popular during the summer months. By being aware of market trends, manufacturers and retailers can plan accordingly.

Key term

Cyclical trend – a change that recurs on a regular basis.

Environmental issues

Business owners should be aware of any environmental issues that may affect the business. For example, if a business uses fire fighting equipment or cleaning solvents, it should ensure that they do not contain substances that can harm the ozone. The Department for Business Innovation and Skills (BIS) publishes leaflets that cover the relevant legislation. Furthermore, if you dispose, recover, transport (import or export) and produce waste you must be aware of the legal implications. This also applies to any packaging produced as well as the recycling of packaging waste as noted in the Producer Responsibility Obligations (Packaging Waste) Regulations 2005.

Assessment activity 36.1

1. Present an initial business idea in the form of a report and describe how you will identify your target market. The initial business idea must be suitable for self-employment. The presentation must cover:
   - a full description of your business idea **P1**
   - a full explanation of how to identify the target market
   - a full description of the target market. **P2**

2. Explain and justify the research methods used to determine the target market and why they were appropriate for your business idea. **M1**

Grading tips

1. You must present your initial business idea in a formal report using relevant criteria. ensure you include all of the following:
   - your chosen business type
   - your aims and objectives for the business
   - your unique selling point (USP)
   - reasons for the potential need or demand of the new business
   - details of the competitive edge you will have
   - how you intend to balance your personal and business needs
   - potential profitability

   - business trends
   - all external influences (PESTLE and LoNGPESTLE analysis)
   - how business planning will help you ensure your success. **P1**

2. You will need to follow the market research process to explain how to identify the target market. You should include all of the following.
   - Define your objectives.
   - Write a business brief.
   - Plan your use of primary and secondary research methods.
   - Identify a suitable sampling technique for your research.
   - Suggest an appropriate timeframe for your research.
   - Write a description of the target market. **P2**

3. You will need to complete the marketing research process begun in P1 and P2 and collect, analyse and evaluate the data. You will need to refer to the research results and explain how the methods you used allowed you to determine the key pieces of research information. You will also need to explain your chosen sampling technique including what it means and why you felt it was appropriate in your chosen circumstances. **M1**

2 Understand the skills and personal development needed to run the business successfully

2.1 Skills

Your own contribution

When starting a business, it is important for the owner to recognise skills they will be bringing to the business as well as those which need developing. A skills audit will help identify the skills needed for the business and the ones it already has. If you, the business owner, are lacking in skills, you may want to consider employing someone or taking on a partner who can fill the skill gap.

Activity: Starting your own business

1. You have been left £200,000 by an uncle, and are thinking about starting up a business. You know what business you would like to start and in what area you would like to locate it. However, this area is very expensive and you would not only need to move but you would also need to give up a secure, well-paid job.

   * Are you willing to risk the £200,000 on starting your business? Why, or why not?

   * When making your decision, what financial risks should you consider?

   * What do you think your chances are of succeeding?

   * What do you think are the advantages and disadvantages of running your own business rather than working for someone else?

2. Produce a PowerPoint presentation to give to the group, explaining your decision(s).

Functional skills

Presenting information in ways that are fit for purpose will help you to develop your **ICT** skills.

Technical and operational skills

Every business is unique in some way and so each requires a different combination of technical and operational skills to be successful. A new business owner will need to determine which skills are important to the venture.

Many products and services will require specialist skills to produce. A business owner may need to have a detailed knowledge of the trade as well as specific skills to enable them to produce the goods. Even if products are bought from a manufacturer, the business will need to have comprehensive product knowledge or employ someone who does to ensure the right level of customer service. The type of product and/or service knowledge required will be dependent on the business as well as the product or service itself.

Management

A successful manager needs to have three key skills.

* Human skills – managers are required to be able to lead, communicate and influence effectively everyone involved in the business including colleagues, employees, customers, shareholders and suppliers.

* Technical skills – managers are required to have the technical skills and knowledge to enable the product to be developed and produced.

* Conceptual skills – managers should have the ability to perceive and develop new concepts as well as be able to solve problems and make decisions.

More recently, there seems to be general agreement that there is a fourth skill required by managers – political skills. This involves the manager having the ability to build and develop the right relationships with the right people, or in other words, networking. This will in turn develop connections that may result in additional resources.

Records and checking performance of business

Businesses need to constantly monitor how well they are doing in order to take corrective measures should there be any problems. The process for recording and checking the performance of the business is usually set in steps, as shown in Figure 36.4.

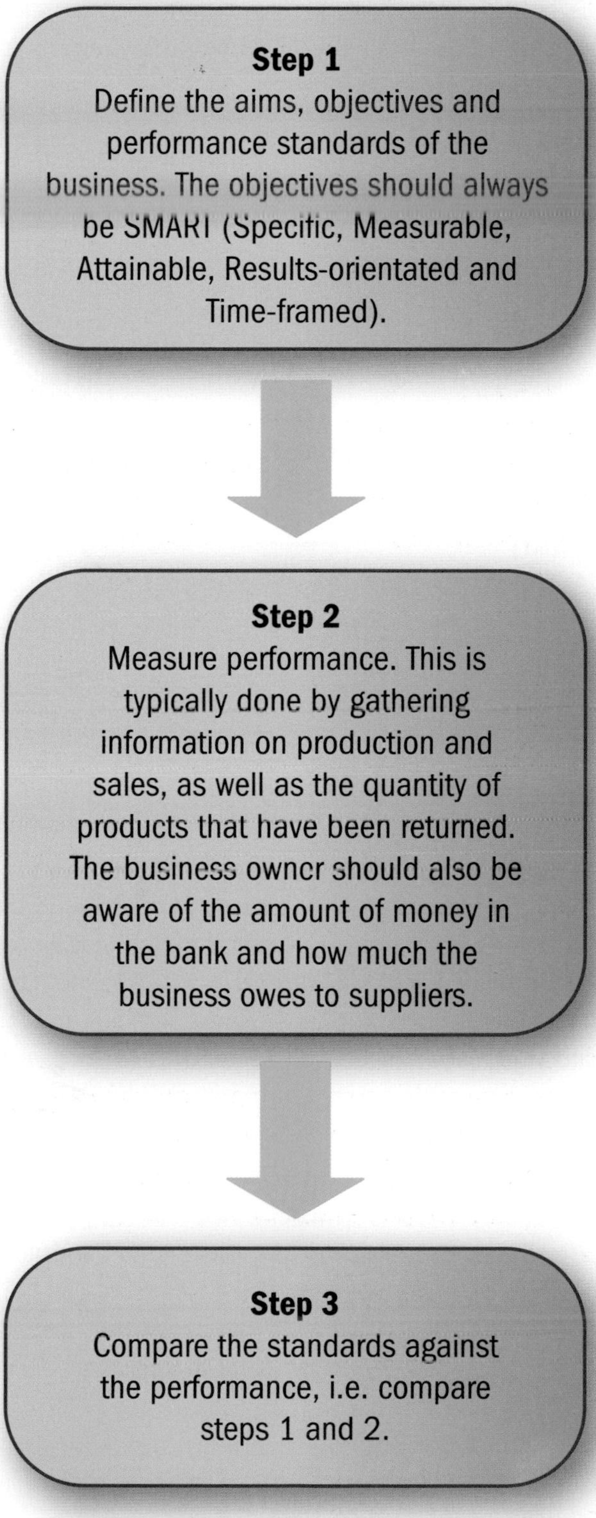

Step 1
Define the aims, objectives and performance standards of the business. The objectives should always be SMART (Specific, Measurable, Attainable, Results-orientated and Time-framed).

⬇

Step 2
Measure performance. This is typically done by gathering information on production and sales, as well as the quantity of products that have been returned. The business owner should also be aware of the amount of money in the bank and how much the business owes to suppliers.

⬇

Step 3
Compare the standards against the performance, i.e. compare steps 1 and 2.

Figure 36.4: Process for recording and checking a business performance

Personal selling

Personal selling skills are discussed in detail in Unit 29. Some of the key skills required are:

- to meet and greet customers
- to identify the customer's product needs
- to put across the attributes of the product or service.
- excellent product knowledge and to be able to communicate this effectively
- good listening skills
- to counter objections to the sale from the customer
- to effectively close the sale.

Activity: Good sales person

In small groups, discuss what makes a good sales person. Make a list of the skills you think sales people need, then answer the questions below.

1. What sort of knowledge and/or training do you think a sales person needs?
2. As a business owner, how would you motivate your sales people to sell effectively?

Functional skills

This discussion will help you to develop your **English** skills in speaking and listening.

Administration

Good administration skills are important to any business. Administration involves issues such as stock control, distribution and customer payment. A good administrator is well organised, logical and has good communication skills. Administrative skills involve a variety of different jobs and tasks including:

- using the telephone and email effectively
- preparing and printing documents
- meeting and assisting customers, visitors or employees
- accurately organising customer files
- preparing and dispatching invoices and other financial documents
- ensuring accurate and detailed research.

Previous experience

Before starting a business, an owner may have had prior experience working in a similar or related business; perhaps it was a hobby or an interest which was turned into a business venture. It is always useful to have had some relevant experience to bring to a new business as it may help the owner recognise and overcome some potential problems and ultimately succeed.

Strengths and weaknesses

It is important that business owners are aware of their strengths and weaknesses. Strengths that benefit the business should be built on. However, weaknesses must not be ignored; they should be addressed and turned into a strength where possible.

2.2 Development

Identification of skills gap/shortages

In order to identify skills gaps and shortages, an objective and accurate assessment needs to be done. The best way of establishing these gaps is to perform a personal skills audit. Once shortages are recognised, the owner can address how to fill these gaps. A personal development plan (see opposite) can be used to find out and address skill gaps and shortages.

Professional help

There are many organisations that offer professional help for small businesses. There are numerous ways of obtaining help and information.

- Most banks or building societies have a website that provides business start-up information (though this information could be biased towards their establishment).
- Business Link, a government-run organisation, which was set up specifically to help and support new businesses, offers a wide range of services and can be cost effective.
- Business consultants offer their experience for a fee. They can help with practical information and advice, cost-cutting ideas, suggestions on how to develop and expand the business and any other general business issues.

Training

There are many training providers available to suit each individual's needs from local colleges or training establishments to distance learning courses. Some distance learning providers offer training courses throughout the academic year and so could be more beneficial than a local college that has set schedules. Alternatively, a business consultant could be employed who can offer a more flexible training option tailored to individual skill needs.

Planning

Once the shortages are identified a personalised plan can be put together to address the skills gap. It is also important to consider the following.

- The cost implications of filling a skills gap can include determining whether it will be more beneficial for the owner to undertake training or perhaps employ someone who already has the skills.
- Accessibility may also be an issue when trying to fill skill gaps. Local colleges have a limited amount of courses or only offer courses during the day and therefore may not address a business' needs. Distance learning courses, business consultants or skilled employees who can help address skill gaps may be a consideration when accessibility is a problem.
- It is important to set time scales to help monitor skill development. Some skills need to be addressed more urgently than others and should therefore be a priority.

Activity: Personal development plan

Copy and complete the form below to help you assess your skills.

List the skills you think are essential to open your business.

What is your current skill situation?

What am I good at? (Strengths)	What am I not good at? (Weaknesses)
What do I need to work on?	What might stop me?

How will I compensate for those weaknesses and what would be the time scale?

Functional skills

Filling out a personal development plan will help you to develop your **English** skills in writing.

3 Know the legal and financial aspects that will affect the start-up of the business

3.1 Legal aspects

Legal status

There are many laws and regulations surrounding the conduct of new businesses. When starting up a business from scratch, an owner will have to decide on the company's legal status. The options include sole trader, partnership limited company and co-operative.

Sole trader

A sole trader is a business owned and controlled by one person, although they may employ workers. Individuals who provide a specialist service like builders or newsagents can be described as sole traders. As a sole trader the owner is personally liable for the businesses debts, and may have to pay them personally. This is called **unlimited liability.**

Advantages of a sole trader:

- not many legal restrictions on forming a business
- allows for a more personal service to the customer
- easier to maintain control, make decisions and implement changes quickly
- no need to share profits
- financial information is kept private.

Disadvantages of a sole trader:

- risk of unlimited liability
- business growth is limited by the amount of capital one person can raise
- long hours and difficulty in finding time off for holidays or illness
- no one to share the responsibility of the business with, which can be quite stressful and lonely.

Partnership

A partnership is a business owned by two or more people. It is usual for a contract called a 'deed of partnership' to be drawn up which states which type of partnership it is, how much capital each partner has contributed and dictates how the profits and the losses will be shared. Solicitors, doctors and dentists are examples of people who may go into partnership.

Advantages of a partnership:

- an increase in the levels of expertise available to the business

- a partner can introduce additional capital to the business
- any decisions can be shared
- decision making and implementation of change can be fast
- possible to offer a personal service to the customer
- cover available for holidays and sickness.

Disadvantages of a partnership:

- disputes between partners can cause problems
- growth restricted to the amount of capital the partners can raise
- partnership may need to be dissolved if one partner decides to leave the business
- partners have unlimited liability, unless they form a limited partnership.
- profits are shared.

Limited company

A **limited company** is owned by the **shareholders**.

Advantages of a limited company:

- capital can be introduced to the business which can help with growth
- shareholders benefit from **limited liability** for the debts of the business
- if something happens to one of the shareholders, the business still continues.

Disadvantages of a limited company:

- a percentage of the profits will be paid to the shareholders
- decision making and implementation of changes can be slow

Key terms

Unlimited liability – business owners are personally responsible for all the debts of the firm and their personal assets can be seized to pay company debts.

Limited company – a business that is owned by shareholders, all of whom have limited liability for the business debts.

Shareholders – individuals or organisations that own or hold a share in a business.

Limited liability – shareholders lose no more than the value of their shares if the business should fail.

- financial details of the business must be disclosed to a limited extent
- legal formalities for setting up are more complex; new company set-up packs are available for around £100–£150.

Co-operative

Co-operatives are owned and operated by members, who also use the services offered by this type of business. Members typically include management and employees of the business as well as customers. The members elect appropriate directors, have the authority to vote at meetings and share in any of the profits that the business makes.

There are benefits to this type of business as the members have a personal stake in its success and subsequently share in any profits. Any decisions affecting the business are conducted democratically and good working conditions are normal practice. However, disadvantages of this type of business include issues such as members being liable for any financial losses incurred and having a limited influence over business decisions.

Activity: New business

Antonia is a recently qualified portraiture photographer who wants to open her own studio. She feels that she is too inexperienced about the business world. Her friend Omar is an experienced wildlife photographer and has money he would like to invest in a business venture. Antonia is considering asking Omar to go into partnership with her.

1. In small groups, discuss what legal status option Antonia should choose.
2. Should she go into business with Omar? What would the advantages and disadvantages be for Antonia?

Legal liabilities

Depending on the type of business, owners will face different types of legal liability.

If the business is a sole trader or partnership, the owner(s) have unlimited liability for the business' debt and are personally responsible for all the debts of the firm. If the business fails and money is owed to **creditors**, the courts can seize personal assets of the

owner(s), such as the owner's home, car, savings and other valuable possessions, to pay off the debts.

Limited companies and co-operatives have limited liability. Shareholders or members are liable for any losses, but only for the amount they have invested. If a business should go bankrupt, the members do not lose any personal assets in order to clear the debts.

Trading terms and conditions

When a company starts out, it is important that it clearly sets out the business' trading terms and conditions, which should include information on pricing, payment terms, credit facilities, delivery options and so on. It is always recommended that the trading terms and conditions should be put in writing and agreed in writing by the customer. This will help protect the business from any disputes with customers.

If a business relies on buying certain products and services, it is important to read the terms and conditions of suppliers.

Trading standards

Trading standards protect the consumer from unscrupulous business traders. New business owners need to be aware of their legal obligations under the trading standards. Owners should also be aware of their legal obligations and rights when dealing with suppliers. A not-for-profit professional body, the Trading Standards Institute (TSI), 'helps safeguard the economic, environmental, health and social well-being of consumers' as well as offering advice and information on a range of related issues. The TSI has a comprehensive and informative website (www.tradingstandards.gov.uk) that offers numerous guidance leaflets on a range of matters including:

- rights of the consumer – standards that customers can expect from a business and what standards a business can expect from suppliers
- legislation relating to food – guidance given on the correct labelling, description and pricing required with regards to food products and services
- safety issues – legal safety guidelines which must be met by all products and services.

Key term

Creditor – a business or person the company owes money to.

Activity: Trading standards

Use the Internet to visit the Trading Standards Institute website (www.tradingstandards.gov. uk), click on the link *Advice* and then link to *Business guidance*. Choose two of the businesses below and make notes on the regulations you need to be aware of when setting up such a business:

- a small convenience shop that sells fireworks and alcohol
- a restaurant
- a travel agent
- selling products on the Internet
- an auction house selling antiques.

Functional skills

Researching and selecting information on trading standards will help you to develop your **ICT** skills.

Licences

Some businesses, such as pubs and clubs, nursing homes, cinemas, theatres, taxis and pet shops, require a licence before they can operate. Therefore, the first thing you need to do is find out whether your new business venture requires a licence and, if so, where you can obtain it. Some licences are obtained from local government departments whilst others are granted on a national basis.

Did you know?

If you intend to play copyright music in your business premises, then a licence from the PRS for Music is needed, whilst the playing of recorded music requires a licence from the music licensing company, PPL.

Record keeping

All businesses are required by law to keep financial and other records relating to it. There are a number of benefits to be gained from keeping records.

- Accurate records will save you time and therefore money.
- They ensure that bills are paid only once.
- They enable a business to keep up to date with how much it is owed and how much it owes.

Certain financial records are required by law to be retained for at least six years. The following are documents that must be kept by all businesses.

Cash book/spreadsheet

The final records of all money that goes into and out of a business should be recorded in a cash book or on a computer spreadsheet. These transactions are called cash flow. Completed cash-low records should include the following:

- cheque book stubs and cancelled cheques
- bank paying-in books and statements
- copies of own invoices and those of suppliers
- receipts and delivery notes
- receipts of all cash purchases
- remittance advice from customers
- copies of payments made or received using online banking.

Sales and purchase ledgers

A sales ledger (or spreadsheet) records all sales made by the business and money received for those sales. A purchase ledger (or spreadsheet) records all purchases made by the business.

Wages and petty cash books

A record of all wages, salaries and National Insurance contributions made by the business to its staff must be kept. Furthermore, a petty cash book should be used to record all small transactions paid for by cash.

Good accounting software computer packages are available which can save time. These packages can add, delete and amend any calculations as well as recalculating any running totals.

Accident records

All businesses are required to record any accidents or injuries that may occur in an accident book in accordance with the Reporting of Injuries, Diseases and Dangerous Occurrences Regulations (RIDDOR), 1995. Such records should be kept for at least three years.

Resolving problems

Most problems in the workplace can be avoided if there is effective communication between management and employees. In order to provide for any such problems, it is important that procedures are put in place, which can include the following.

- The development of effective staff associations and/or the building of trust with trade union representatives. Both offer employees the right to be heard when dealing with grievances and offer a solution to resolving many problems that arise.

- An appropriate and effective grievance procedure. This procedure, which is the law, should aim to assist employees and must be communicated to all members of staff in writing.

- Clear and effective disciplinary procedures which should clarify what employee behaviour is acceptable to the company. For example, employees found using personal email during the working day and against the wishes of the company may find themselves disciplined.

ACAS (Advisory, Conciliation and Arbitration Service) offers advice on grievance and disciplinary procedures. It publishes a code of practice which sets out principles of what the business owner and employees should do to achieve a reasonable standard of behaviour in any grievance and disciplinary cases.

Activity: Code of practice

Find out more information on the ACAS code of practice (www.acas.org.uk). Then read the following and answer the questions below.

Maura has worked as a nurse for the past five years in a private hospital. She belongs to the trade union UNISON. Recently, she seems to have lost interest in the job; her time keeping has become lax and her work is of a substandard quality. Her senior manager, with no prior warning, has just asked her to leave the job by the end of the week.

1. Should Maura have been offered counselling or extra training?

2. When it came to the dismissal procedure, was she given sufficient verbal and written warnings?

3. Should Maura bring an action against the senior manager and the hospital?

Write a short report stating your recommendations.

Functional skills

Writing a report will help you to develop your **English** skills in writing.

National/local laws

All businesses have a legal responsibility to comply with all legislation that affects their business. New business owners will need to determine which laws affect them and attempt to fulfil the requirements. A few key examples are listed below.

Paying employees

National Minimum Wage legislation requires that employees aged 22 years or over should be paid a minimum of £5.80 an hour; employees aged 18–21 years must be paid £4.83 an hour; whilst those aged 16–17 years are to be paid a minimum of £3.57 an hour. (Note: these figures were correct as of 1 October 2009; you will need to check for the latest information to confirm the minimum wage.) Furthermore, employers are required to supply itemised pay slips to employees and are responsible for making statutory payments to cover sickness, maternity, paternity and adoption leave and so on.

Hours of work, rest breaks and working week

Employee working hours are governed by the Working Time Regulations which cover:

- maximum average working week – no more than six days out of every seven (or 12 out of every 14)

- holiday entitlement – 5–6 weeks' holiday a year

- the right of employees to have a rest break during the working day – a 20-minute break if the shift lasts for more than six hours

- the right of rest days between working days

- hours when working at night.

Note that the regulations are slightly different for employees aged 16–17 years.

Discrimination

Legislation requires employers not to discriminate on the grounds of:

- gender
- age
- sexual orientation
- marital status
- race
- colour
- nationality
- ethnic origin
- religious beliefs
- pregnancy or childbirth.

It is also illegal to discriminate against job applicants and employees who are disabled under the Disability Discrimination Act 1995. This legislation covers failure to make reasonable adjustments to any recruitment practices as well as business premises and employees' jobs.

Activity: Discrimination

Use the Internet to learn about the Sex Discrimination Act 1975 and the Race Relations Act 1976. Prepare a two-minute PowerPoint presentation on either one of the two acts. At the end of the presentation be prepared to answer questions.

PLTS

Planning and carrying out research will help you to develop your skills as an **independent enquirer**.

VAT (value added tax)

If a business sells more than £68,000 of products and/or services, it needs to register for VAT. A business pays VAT on purchases and charges it on sales. It is important that the business accounts for VAT in any sales and purchases in order to claim back any overpayments from or pay any underpayments to **HM Revenue & Customs**.

Other laws

There are a number of other laws that you should be aware of when starting a new business. Some of the more common ones are as follows.

- Trade Description Acts 1968 and 1972 – these require businesses to give an accurate description of their products and services. Failure to do so can lead to prosecution.
- Sunday Trading Act 1994 – this Act was introduced in order to regulate the activities of shops opening on Sundays. Retailers that sell from large premises can only open for any six hours between 10am and

6pm. Smaller retailers, chemists, petrol stations and service stations are exempt from this legislation.

- Supply of Goods and Services Act 1982 – this requires that when a business supplies a particular service it must ensure reasonable care and skill within a reasonable time scale. It also requires that the customer is charged a realistic price when supplied with goods and/or services.
- Weights and Measures Act 1985 – this Act ensures that a business gives customers exactly the right amount as advertised.

Regulations and bylaws

Local government draws up local laws or bylaws, which are approved by central government. New business owners should check with local councils to see what local laws might affect them. Business websites must clearly display the company registration number, place of registration and registered office address. This information should also appear on order forms and in emails.

Furthermore, there are a number of regulations, which a business will need to abide by. Some of the more common ones are covered below:

Data Protection Act 1998

This governs the use of personal information by businesses and other organisations. The act requires that:

- the information to be contained in personal data shall be obtained and processed fairly and lawfully
- personal data shall be held only for one or more specified and lawful purposes
- personal data held for any purpose shall not be used or disclosed in any manner incompatible with that purpose, or those purposes
- personal data held for any purpose shall be adequate, relevant and not excessive in relation to that purpose
- personal data shall be accurate and, where necessary, kept up to date
- personal data held for any purpose shall not be kept for longer than is necessary for that purpose
- an individual shall be entitled at reasonable intervals and without delay or expense:
  - to be informed by any data user whether they hold personal data of which the individual is the subject

Key term

HM Revenue & Customs – the government department responsible for collecting taxes as well as paying tax credits and child benefit.

○ to access any such data held by a data user

○ where appropriate to have such data corrected or erased.

Activity: Data Protection Act 1998

Using the Internet, research the Data Protection Act and then answer the following questions.

1. Why was the Data Protection Act introduced?

2. Identify four ways that the Data Protection Act protects individuals from the misuse of personal data.

3. Other than name and address, state two other items of personal data that a business may hold about its employees.

4. Describe three things a business could do to ensure data is kept safe from unauthorised people.

5. State whether you think the following examples would be covered under the Data Protection Act:

- your address

- how many years you have lived at the address

- how many people live at the address

- your marital status (single, married, divorced etc.)

- work details such as tax, National Insurance etc.

Smoking

Smoking in all indoor public places is banned; this includes offices and any workplace, except if you work by yourself. The Department of Health takes the lead on smoking regulations in England; in Wales this is a matter for the Welsh Assembly Government and in Scotland it is the responsibility of the Scottish Executive. Business owners must remember to display No Smoking signs in any business premises.

Did you know?

One in three smokers is Chinese – and almost 25 per cent of all Chinese smoke. In 2008, Beijing introduced a ban on smoking in most public buildings.

The Consumer Protection (Distance Selling) Regulations 2000

These cover purchases made over the Internet, telephone and by mail order. The regulations require the selling firm to provide written details of orders to customers and gives them a cooling off period of seven days during which such orders can be cancelled.

The E-Commerce regulations 2002

These regulations are for businesses that sell or advertise over the Internet. Customers should be able to print out and store copies of contracts online.

The Privacy and Electronic Communications Regulations 2003

These regulations require that businesses which conduct direct marketing activities via the telephone consult the Telephone Preference Service (TPS) to ensure they are aware of all individuals who have registered to opt out of such an approach.

Health and safety

The Management of Health and Safety at Work Regulations 1998 ensure that businesses take responsibility for the safety of any employees or visitors. The regulations require that businesses undertake a risk assessment in order to make sure the premises are as safe as possible. Furthermore, the business must have a health and safety policy which states appropriate systems and procedures relating to the health and safety of all employees, customers and visitors to the premises.

Fire regulations

The Regulatory Reform (Fire Safety) Order 2005 requires a five-step fire risk assessment to be undertaken and steps implemented to prevent hazards. Businesses need to have adequate escape routes and equipment and all staff need good training in fire safety in the business premises.

Licensing

Appropriate licences are needed for any software a business plans to use and, if a business is planning to export controlled goods, such as antiques and works of art, it may need an export licence from the Department for Business Innovation and Skills (BIS), a United Kingdom government department.

Liabilities

All businesses need insurance cover. Some insurance is compulsory and these may include:

- employer's liability insurance which will protect a business from any legal damages claims if an employee injures themselves in the workplace; it typically covers claims for damages and court costs claimed against the business

- owner's liability insurance which covers any damage claims brought against the business by visitors to the premises
- motor insurance on any company vehicle to cover every person who drives it
- building insurance which will assist in the rebuilding of the business should it be damaged through a potential disaster such as a fire or an explosion
- contents Insurance which covers damage or theft of any stock, fixtures and fittings
- product liability insurance which will pay any claims made if a product sold by the business injures someone
- public liability insurance which will cover any claims for damages caused by any employee of the business.

Planning permission

A business that wants to build or extend its premises, or who wishes to change the use of a building, will need to seek permission from its local authority.

Contracts

Within two months of starting work employers must provide employees with a written statement of the main terms of the contract. This should include:

- the names of employer and employee
- job title or job description
- date of employment, the place of work and the address of the employer
- the amount of pay and how often payments will be made (e.g. monthly, weekly)
- hours of work
- holiday entitlement
- sick pay arrangements
- pension arrangements
- notice periods
- for temporary employees, the date employment will cease
- grievance and appeal procedures
- disciplinary rules, as covered by the Employment Act 2002.

Duties and responsibilities

It is every business owner's responsibility to ensure that no harm comes to any employee, customer or visitor. Some of the following legislation covers these responsibilities.

- Food Safety Act 1990 ensures that any business dealing with food takes all reasonable safety measures in the manufacturing, transportation, storage, preparation and selling of food items.
- Environmental Protection Act 1990 requires that businesses are responsible for the control of pollution, noise and any disposal of waste that could harm or contribute to the damage of the environment.
- Consumer Protection Act 1987 covers issues such as flammable and potentially poisonous products. The law requires that clear warnings are placed on these items. If any of these products cause death or injury, the manufacturer is liable for any claims of damage.
- The Control of Substances Hazardous to Health (COSHH) Regulations 1994 requires that businesses take reasonable precautions when disposing of dangerous chemicals. All employees of the business must be aware of the risks involved when disposing of these chemicals and should be informed how to prevent any accidents.
- Sale of Goods Act 1979 states that goods must be as described, fit for purpose and of satisfactory quality (i.e. not inherently faulty at the time of sale). Things businesses must remember:
  - It is the seller, not the manufacturer, who is responsible if goods do not conform to contract although it is the purchaser's responsibility to prove that the goods did not conform to contract.
  - If goods do not conform to contract at the time of sale, purchasers can request their money back within a reasonable time; and, for up to six years after purchase, purchasers can demand damages (which a court would equate to the cost of repair or replacement).
  - If repair and replacement are not possible or too costly, then the consumer can seek a partial refund if they have had some benefit from the product, or a full refund if the fault(s) have meant they have enjoyed no benefit.

Regulatory bodies

The UK government has set up a variety of independent regulatory bodies to monitor standards in industry.

- The **Food Standards Agency** is a regulatory body responsible for setting the standards required in the process of food preparation and the delivery of foods in order to protect consumers' health.

- The **Gambling Commission** is responsible for regulating casinos, lottery and bingo companies and any other form of gambling activity.
- The **Office of Fair Trading (OFT)** monitors business activities to endorse fairness and competition relating to the consumer.
- The **Office for Standards in Education, Children's Services and Skills (OFSTED)** regulates the provision of education and training for learners of all ages except those in higher education institutes and universities
- The **Office of Communications (Ofcom)** regulates media activities and communications industries.

Sources of advice

Department for Business Innovation and Skills (BIS)
The UK government established the Department for Business Innovation and Skills (www.bis.gov.uk) to help 'create the conditions for business success'. It provides comprehensive advice, information and support for businesses.

Local Enterprise Agencies
The primary responsibility of the Local Enterprise Agencies is to act as a partnership between the private sector and local authorities. The agencies can be found on the Business Link website (www.businesslink.gov.uk). These Local Enterprise Agencies also offer consultancy and training services to local businesses.

Shell live WIRE
Shell UK set up this programme with the key objective of assisting young entrepreneurs aged between 16 and 30 years to start up their own business (www.shell-livewire.org). Through a network of advisers and coordinators, the online community supports and guides young people in the early stages of their business start-up.

Other websites
The Internet is full of websites offering advice and support to businesses, for example, the NFEA (www.nfea.com), which is a national enterprise network providing a variety of services to new and emerging businesses. Other recommended websites include:

- www.better-business.co.uk
- www.smallbusiness.co.uk

Bank websites also offer advice and information for small businesses.

3.2 Financial aspects

A new business is more likely to fail if it does not put in place good financial planning. One key consideration of any new business owner will be to keep the start-up costs as low as possible.

Personal survival budget

Start-up businesses will need a personal survival budget to ensure that the owner has enough money to live whilst building and growing the business. Table 36.1 (overleaf) exemplifies one of the easiest methods of planning and implementing a personal survival budget. This personal survival budget should be compared with the cash-flow forecast to give an indication as to whether the business will generate enough income for financial survival.

Cost of premises

Choosing appropriate premises is crucial to the success of a business as is the cost of the premises. Many business owners decide to rent their premises. However, when renting or leasing they need to check that there are no hidden charges (e.g. service charges) that have not been budgeted for. Other things to consider include rates and insurance as these can add significantly to overheads. It is a good idea to set a monthly/annual premises budget.

Figure 36.5 (overleaf) outlines what needs to be considered when looking to secure an appropriate premises to conduct business.

The more a premises meets the criteria, the more likely it is to be comparatively expensive. Therefore, it is always worth attempting to balance the financial constraints of the business premises against that of the actual business requirements.

Activity: Premises

You are going to open up a small shop selling convenience foods. Take all factors into consideration, especially costs, then write a short report on where you intend to locate your premises. State the reasons why.

PLTS

Reviewing the options to write a report will help you to develop your skills as a **reflective learner**.

Table 36.1: How to calculate a personal survival budget; the estimated other income total should be deducted from the estimated annual expenditure total to give the amount of money required from the business in order to survive

Estimated annual expenditure	£s	Estimated other income	£s
Mortgage/Rent/Lease		Other earned income	
Council tax		Partner's income	
Utilities		Benefits received	
Food		Other	
Clothing		Other	
Savings/Pension		Other	
Motor expenses		Other	
Loan repayments		Other	
Telephone			
Entertainment			
Total (£)		Total (£)	

Are there the necessary amenities at the premises?

Where are the premises located? Are they close to any potential customers to the business?

Are the premises located close to any of your competitors?

What is the transport infrastructure in the area? Can your potential customer find/access the location easily?

Appropriate business premises

Can you afford to purchase, rent or lease the premises?

Are the premises located in an up-and-coming area or is it declining?

Can your employees, customers and supply and delivery vehicles park close to the premises?

Do the premises offer enough storage space for your immediate and long-term needs?

Can the premises be adapted for any future expansion needs?

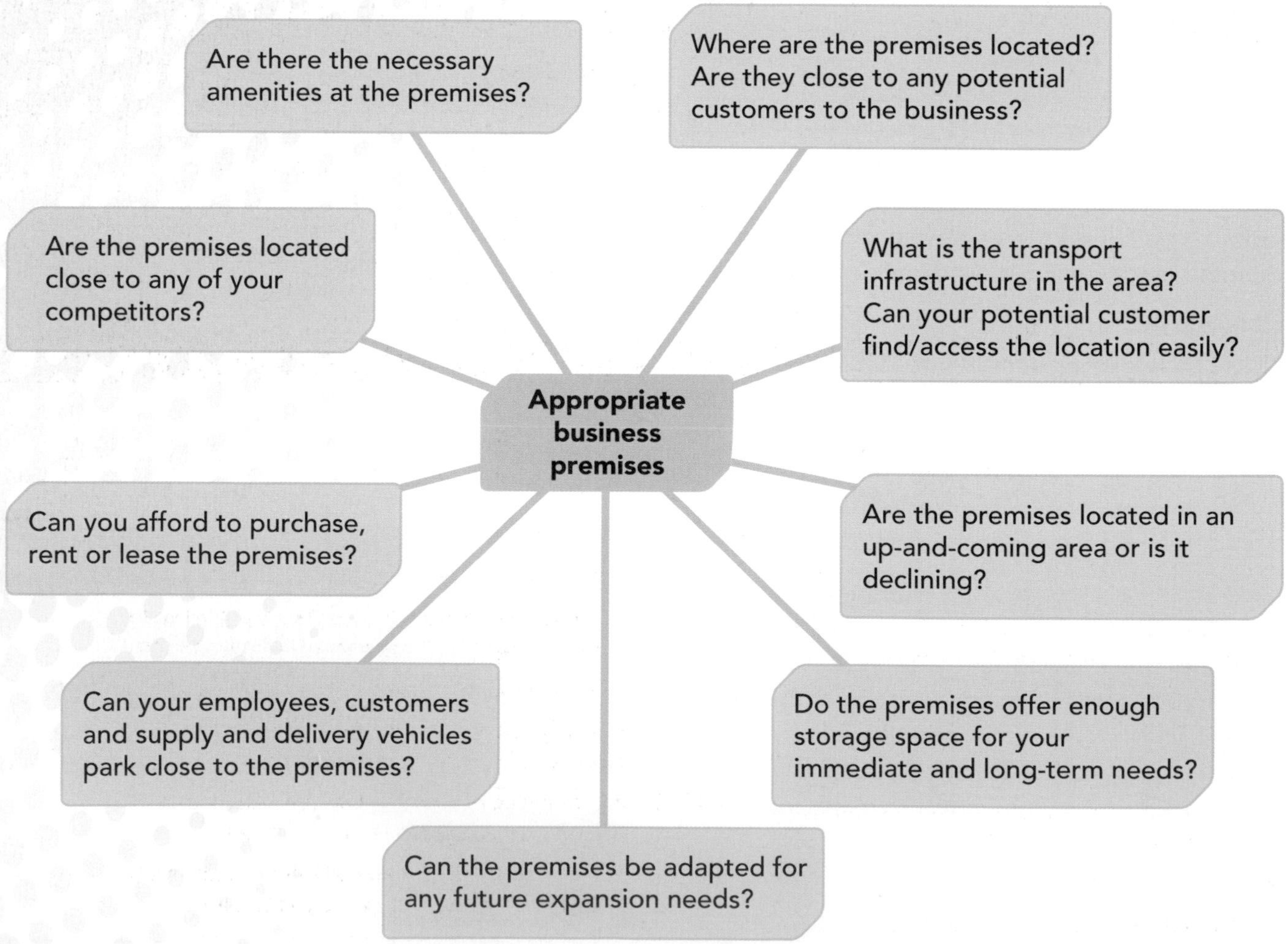

Figure 36.5: Factors to consider when choosing a business premises

Cost of equipment and supplies

Any equipment or supplies that a business needs to purchase will typically end up being a substantial financial cost and must be decided upon before putting together a cash-flow forecast. In order to determine what equipment is needed and how much it will cost, a capital-needs breakdown should be produced (see Table 36.2). The same type of breakdown should be done for any supplies needed to start up the business.

Employing staff

There are many running costs involved in a business; these will be discussed in the section dealing with cash-flow forecasting. However, one of the major expenses incurred by any business is the employment of staff. The law requires that businesses comply with the current minimum wage legislation and make National Insurance contributions for each employee.

Did you know?

Many businesses opt to contribute to an employee's pension scheme even though this is NOT a legal requirement.

Table 36.2: A capital-needs breakdown

Shop fittings*		£15,000		
Equipment*		£2,500		
Total		**£17,500**		
Comprising	**Shop fittings***		**Equipment****	
	Storage and shelf space	£4,150	Tills	£1,000
	Seating	£1,950	Lighting	£750
	Cupboards	£1,500	Scanning equipment	£750
	Desks	£2,900		
	Signage	£2,250		
	Counter	£2,250		
Totals		**£15,000**		**£2,500**

Case study: Devlin Builders & Maintenance

Devlin was a builder with a very good reputation. He was good at his job and had customers who used his services regularly. He employed a couple of workers to help him with his building contracts. Unfortunately, he did not get enough cash into his business quickly enough as he was always doing odd jobs for friends and family. He was so busy, that he did not follow up his work with invoices for the jobs he performed. Eventually, his business bank account ran out of money and Devlin was unable to:

- pay his workers
- pay the lease on his building yard

- make the repayments on his bank loan
- pay his suppliers.

As a consequence, Devlin lost his business, even though it should have been making a good profit.

In small groups, discuss the following questions.

1. Identify the key mistakes Devlin made. Why do you think he made these mistakes?

2. Explain how you think Devlin could have avoided these problems.

3. What do you think about Devlin's experiences? Would you make the same mistakes?

Pricing policy

Products or services need to be priced correctly or the business may not succeed. There are a number of ways to determine a satisfactory price.

- **Cost-plus pricing** – the business adds up the cost of the item with the overheads, then marks up the product/service for the profit. The problem is that this strategy does not consider the customer and it is difficult to calculate the cost of providing a service.

- **Penetration pricing** – the business charges low prices in order to obtain a market share. Once it has achieved an acceptable share of the market, it increases the price.

- **Premium pricing** – the business will price unique products/services higher. This strategy is used when the business has a significant competitive advantage.

- **Price skimming** – this method is used by businesses that have a competitive advantage which is not sustainable. The high price attracts new competitors into the market, which results in prices being lowered due to increased supply.

- **Economy pricing** – a business sells its products/ services at a low price. All business activities are kept at a minimum, including marketing and manufacturing. Examples include supermarket own brands.

- **Psychological pricing** – this strategy is used by businesses that want the consumer to believe they are getting a product/service much cheaper than it actually is. An example of this method would be a product priced at 99p rather than £1.00.

- **Promotional pricing** – this method is used when a product/service has been on the market for some time and demand is beginning to fall. Prices are reduced temporarily in the hope of stimulating renewed interest in it. There are many examples of promotional pricing including approaches such as BOGOF (buy one get one free).

- **Value pricing** – this approach is used when external factors, such as increased competition in the market or a recession, force a business to provide value products and services in order to retain sales. Cafes and restaurants often use this strategy in order to attract customers, for example, two meals for the price of one or cheap lunchtime meals.

Activity: Pricing policy

In small groups, discuss what would be the pricing strategies of the following:

- Tesco launching its own brand of washing powder
- Pizza Hut introducing a new range of value meals
- a double-glazing firm offering two replacement windows for the price of one
- Sony launching a new mobile phone with innovative technology.

Cash-flow forecasting

Small business owners will be expected to prepare a cash-flow forecast as part of their business planning. This will involve trying to plan when costs will occur as well as estimated revenue over the next 12 months. A new business will have to base its forecast on market research undertaken prior to starting up whilst an established business will base it on what has happened to the firm in previous years (see Unit 5 Book 1 for detailed discussion on cash flow).

One of the key contributory factors of a business failing is that of ineffective cash planning. Cash-flow forecasting should not be confused with profit. Profit refers to the difference between the total revenue (TR) and total cost (TC) over a period of time. Figure 36.6 opposite shows the cash-flow forcast for January to April for Devlin Builders.

This is the opening balance in the bank at the start of the year

The Totals column summarises all of the months shown on the forecast

Balance B/F is the same figure as the Balance C/F for the previous month

Balance C/F is Total cash available minus Total payments

Balance C/F is Total cash available minus Total payments

	January £	February £	March £	April £		Totals £
Balance B/F	0	−645	367	690		412
Income						
Owners capital	6,000					6,000
Total receipts	1,400					1,400
Cash sales	3,000	4,000	3,000	3,500		13,500
Credit sales				700		700
Rent received	550	550	550	550		2,200
Total receipts	10,950	4,550	3,550	4,750		**23,800**
Total cash available	10,950	3,905	3,917	5,440		**23,800**
Expenses						
Initial stock purchases	3,000					3,000
Cash purchases	700	600	300	400		2,000
Credit purchases				400		400
Gas and electricity	155	155	155	155		620
Fixtures and fittings	2,500					2,500
Equipment	2,250					2,250
Drawings	1,300	1,300	1,300	1,300		5,200
Advertising	250	40	30	50		370
Insurance	80	80	80	80		320
Rent and rates	600	600	600	600		2,400
Wages	700	700	700	700		2,800
Overdraft interest	0	3	2	0		5
Loan repayments	60	60	60	60		240
Total payments	11,595	3,538	3,227	3,745		**22,105**
Balance C/F	−645	367	690	1,695		1,695

Total payments is all the Expense items added together

Balance C/F is Total cash available minus Total payments

These two figures should be the same; this shows the forecast balances for the time period

Figure 36.6: Devlin Builders & Maintenance, cash-flow forecast, January to April

Profit and loss budgets/accounts

Once a cash-flow forecast has been constructed, a forecasted profit and loss account and **balance sheet** for the company can be produced. These will help to show the business' projected levels of profits.

Worked example: Profit and loss account and balance sheet

In order to complete a profit and loss account and balance sheet for Devlin Builders for January to April, we need a little more information.

- As a rough estimate, it is anticipated that Devlin will end this period with stock levels of £1,000.
- Any equipment will be depreciated at 8 per cent, while fixture and fittings will depreciate at 10 per cent.

It is now possible to construct the profit and loss account using the figures in the Totals column of the cash-flow forecast in Figure 36.6.

DEVLIN BUILDERS & MAINTENANCE			
Forecasted Profit and Loss Account for period January to April			
	£	£	£
Sales			13,500
Less sales returns			0
Net sales (or Turnover)			13,500
Less Cost of goods sold			
Opening stock		3,000	
Purchases	2,000		
Less Purchase returns	0		
Net purchases		2,000	
		5,000	
Less Closing stock		1,000	
Cost of goods sold			6,000
GROSS PROFIT			7,500
			2,200
			9,700
Less Expenses			
Administration			
Rent and rates		2,400	
Wages and salaries		2,800	
Loan repayments and overdraft interest		245	
Insurance		320	
Advertising		370	
Gas and electricity		620	
Depreciation			
Buildings		0	
Equipment		180	
Fixtures and fittings		250	7,185
NET PROFIT			2,515

Total for cash sales

The figure for initial stock purchases

The figure for cash purchases

Devlin's estimated stock value

Total for rent received

All taken from expenses. Notice we do not include drawings or purchases of capital items – these appear on the balance sheet

£2,250 × 8%

£2,500 × 10%

Carrying the net profit forward, it is now possible to produce a forecasted balance sheet for Devlin.

DEVLIN BUILDERS & MAINTENANCE			
Forecasted Balance Sheet for period January to April			
	Cost	Accumulated depreciation	Net book value
	£	£	£
Fixed assets			
Buildings	0	0	0
Equipment	2,250	180	2,070
Fixtures and fittings	2,500	250	2,250
	4,750	430	4,320
Current assets			
Stock		1,000	
Debtors		0	
Bank		1,695	
Cash		0	
		2,695	
Less Liabilities			
Creditors	0		
Overdraft	0		
		0	
Working capital			2,695
			7,015
Less Long-term liabilities			
Bank loan			1,400
NET ASSETS			5,615
Financed by			
Capital			
Opening capital			6,000
Add Net profit			2,515
			8,515
Less Drawings			7,800
			715

Devlin's estimated stock value

This comes from the Net profit line in the profit and loss account

This is the amount the owner pays him or herself

Key terms

Gross profit – total revenue of a business minus the cost of goods it sold.

Net profit – income after all expenses and taxes have been deducted.

Activity: Profit and loss

Table 36.3 shows the final position of a pizza delivery service at the end of the financial year.

Table 36.3

Item	Cost	Sales per week (average)
Maintenance	£12 per week	
Overalls	£18 each	
Pizza boxes	£1 each	
Delivery charges	£3 per delivery	
Pizzas:		
Margherita	£4.50	65
Hawaiian	£4.75	40
Pepperoni Feast	£4.75	35
Vegetable Supreme	£4.25	25
Chicken Supreme	£4.50	22
Farmhouse	£4.25	18

Other information to be aware of: each pizza cost £2.20 (on average) to make and the maintenance cost for the kitchen rose to £12 from £8 halfway through the year. Furthermore, the rise in petrol means that the owner had to increase the delivery charges mid-way through the year from £2 per delivery to £3.

1. Use the information above to complete the following:

    * a profit and loss account for the trading period January to December
    * average mark up for each pizza
    * gross profit
    * net profit.

2. Write a short report stating how you think the pizza delivery business is doing financially.

Functional skills

Bringing the information together for the profit and loss activity will help you to develop your **ICT** skills in presenting and communicating information.

Sources of finance

Whatever the business, it will need some level of financial consideration when starting up. There are different sources of finance available to suit each business' needs.

Sources not requiring creditors

Own savings – the advantages of using your own money to finance a business include:

* no interest charges incurred from an external source
* other individuals, banks or building societies are more likely to invest in your business
* ready access to finances.

A disadvantage could be that you will lose any interest offered by financial institutions on the money.

Grants – in the UK and Europe there are numerous organisations which offer grants to businesses. Local councils, enterprise agencies and economic development units can also be approached. However, the amount offered by these organisations largely depends on what the money is needed for. Some of these grants are not available to start-up businesses but can provide some sort of financial assistance as long as the business meets the required criteria. The following organisations offer grants.

* Grant for Business Investment (GBI) – a national support scheme that offers grants to businesses in assisted areas to ensure sustainable investment. Its aim is to help businesses to expand, rationalise, modernise or diversify.

* Grant for Research and Development – this initiative offers funding to SMEs for the development of innovative technological products and processes. In order for a business to obtain a grant of up to £20,000, it must have fewer than ten employees and the purpose of the grant must not last more than 12 months. Larger businesses can also apply for funding for assistance in research and development and any proposed project of strategic importance relating to technology or industrial sectors. For more information contact www.businesslink.gov.uk.

- EU convergence region funding – the European Union (EU) offers funding to assist in setting up projects that will support the creation of employment and increase the economic growth in disadvantaged areas. Cornwall, Isles of Scilly, West Wales and the Valleys are deemed disadvantaged areas and are supported by this initiative. For further details visit the European Commission's website www.ec.europa.eu.

- The Prince's Trust – this programme offers practical help that may include sponsorship, training, mentoring and some financial assistance for people aged 18–30 years. In order to meet the criteria, anyone applying for funding must be unemployed or working fewer than 16 hours a week. For young people who wish to start up in business but have been unable to attain financial help from other sources, this programme may help by offering grants of up to £250 to be used to test marketing and low interest loans of up to £5,000. It also has specialists that can give support in the area of marketing and business advice as well as volunteer business mentors that will help with any guidance required. Visit www.princes-trust.org.uk for more information.

Sources from creditors

Bank loans – these are available for a few thousand pounds up to hundreds of thousands of pounds, depending on the project proposed and the amount of security available to back the loan. Unlike loans for consumer goods where you can often borrow the full amount of the purchase price, banks may not always lend more than you have put in yourself when setting up a new business venture. You need to convince banks that they will get their money back. Loans are normally granted for an extended period for the purchase of capital items. As with any form of loan, there are interest payments to be made and these can be quite expensive.

Overdrafts – banks are quite aware that businesses are not always paid straight away from sales, for example, a plumber or an electrician will not get paid until they have finished the job and sent out an invoice. Subsequently, there may be times when the business is waiting for money to come in from jobs already done or products sold. Some businesses will choose to arrange an **overdraft** with a bank. The key difference between an overdraft and a loan is that the business only gets charged interest on the amount used – not the whole amount (if not used by the business). However, there are some disadvantages to having an overdraft facility. The interest rate on an overdraft can be quite high and you must agree not to go above your overdraft limit or the bank may refuse to pay cheques to creditors and will charge the business quite heavily for exceeding the limit.

Key term

Overdraft – an agreement with a bank to allow the business to spend money it does not have at that moment.

Activity: Overdraft

You own a small garage and have an overdraft facility with your bank for £15,000. You have used this facility regularly over the past 12 months and, on average, have an overdraft of approximately £11,000 per month. The interest rate on the overdraft is set at 10%.

1. How much interest does your business pay over that 12-month period? (Use simple interest formula:
   $I = p \times r \times t$ where I = the interest, p = the principle (the amount borrowed), r = the rate and t = the time period).

2. The Bank of England has changed the interest rate to 14%. What effect does this have on the business' finances if you continue to use the overdraft facility in the same way over the next 12 months?

Trade credit – this is a period of time, usually 28 days, given to businesses to pay for products that they have received. Sometimes businesses may not have to pay for six months or even 12 months after receiving the products.

Credit card – this is similar to trade credit; there is a certain period of time to either pay the full amount or a minimum amount. Many businesses have a company credit card that can be a useful way of managing expenses and if paid off in full can be a valuable and cheap source of short-term finance.

Leasing – by opting to lease equipment or machinery, a business pays for the use of the product but does not actually own it. Leasing can be beneficial to businesses for the following reasons.

- It can be cheaper than purchasing the equipment.
- Leases tend to be flexible. Equipment may only be needed for a short time and so it would not be economically viable to purchase it outright.
- All maintenance costs are the responsibility of the owner of the equipment or vehicles.
- Payment is usually fixed and allows the business to plan more effectively.

Mortgages – a mortgage is a large loan, usually given for the purchase of property. A typical mortgage will last 25–30 years and is always secured on the property that is being purchased.

Venture capital – this is different from other sources of finance in that a venture capitalist will usually purchase shares in the business rather than simply loaning the money. By purchasing a stake in the business, the venture capitalist will want to ensure the business makes a profit. Venture capitalists are becoming an increasingly important source of finance for supporting new business that may be considered risky by traditional lenders such as banks. Venture capitalists are always on the look out for businesses with potential and are prepared to offer finance to help the business grow.

Borrowing – borrowing money from personal sources or from family to finance a business is called boot strapping the business. This usually involves personal investment by the business owners, their family and friends and/or the owners foregoing salary. It is wise for every business owner to have at least some personal funds at risk since that shows other potential investors that you are committed to the success of the business.

Sponsorship – with a small business, finances may be in short supply and so one option is to generate publicity through a sponsorship option. This could include sponsoring a local football team or business competition. It could generate considerable publicity for quite a small investment as long as you research who your target audience is going to be. Sponsorship is extremely popular with big businesses, especially in the sport and leisure industry. Consideration should be given to what the business wants to achieve, for example, do you want to build brand awareness and therefore need an opportunity to display your logo, or perhaps you just want the chance to showcase your product/service. If successful, the business will benefit significantly from the publicity.

Activity: Raising funds

Jacinda owns a sandwich bar that also delivers snacks, sandwiches etc. to local offices and shops. The business has been very successful and, because of the excellent service offered as well as the good quality food, there has been an increased demand for the delivery service. Jacinda would like to increase the number of motorbikes and bicycles used to deliver the food to offices in the city centre. She would like your advice on the most appropriate way of financing the purchase of two motorbikes and two bicycles.

Prepare a report advising Jacinda of her options. What sources of finance are most appropriate for her needs and why?

Record keeping

Up-to-date, logical and meticulous financial record keeping is an essential factor for any business. It is important to make all employees aware of the significance of good financial record keeping. It may be a good idea to employ an accountant who can help in dealing with HM Revenue & Customs and ensure that all financial records are in acceptable order.

Assessment activity 36.2

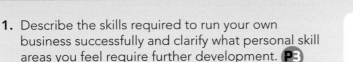

1. Describe the skills required to run your own business successfully and clarify what personal skill areas you feel require further development. **P3**

2. Describe the legal aspects that will affect the start-up of a business.

3. Explain the different financial aspects that will affect the start-up of a business and the impact they will have. **P4**

4. Analyse the skills development needed to run your selected business successfully.

5. Elaborate on your findings for P3 by giving a detailed explanation of each skill gap you have identified and how you will address these gaps. **M2**

Grading tips

1. You need to complete a personal skills audit using the method outlined in this unit. You must be realistic and offer evidence about your skills. You will be graded according to how honest and realistic you have been in your analysis. **P3**

2. You should describe the legal and financial aspects that will affect the start-up of the business. You may need to consult with

specialists (discuss this with your tutor) and will need to address aspects such as the legal status of the business and the form of trading it will undertake together with specific relevant legal and financial issues. You should presume that your ideas will become a reality and therefore consider these areas accordingly. **P4**

3. Analysing means breaking down and examining each part in detail. You should take each skill or ability you lack in turn and then include the following details for each:

   • why it is necessary to the success of your chosen business

   • the time frames you have set for addressing the skill requirement

   • explanation of how the action plan you have formulated will address this gap

   • explanation of how gaining this skill will help to improve the performance of your chosen business

   • how you propose to check to ensure that the skill gap has been filled successfully. **M2**

PLTS

Planning and communicating your skill gaps will help you to develop your skills as an **effective participator**.

4 Be able to produce an outline business start-up proposal

4.1 Business proposal

A business proposal is a tool that helps give an indication of a business' future. It helps the business owner to focus on key points, allocate resources and prepare for opportunities as well as problems. There are many different business proposal (or plan) templates.

Models

The models that have been described throughout this unit can be used when putting together a business proposal. They include:

- PESTLE and LoNGPESTLE analysis
- SWOT analysis
- personal skills audit.

All the information and ideas regarding the start-up business should be reviewed with the reasons and motivation for the business venture being set out. The proposal should set out the targets and goals of the business. For these aims and objectives, it is a good idea to use the SMART model.

Purpose of plan

Approximately 40 per cent of all new businesses fail within the first three years. Therefore, to avoid any difficulties and to ensure the success of a business, you must plan carefully. Of course, a business plan is not necessarily a guarantee of success, but it does help to serve some key purposes.

- It helps identify potential problems and strategies for overcoming these problems.
- It flags issues such as the availability of finances and how much is needed to start the business.
- It helps identify sales targets and makes owners consider ways first to break even and then make a profit.
- It will indicate to a bank manager or other financial organisations the seriousness of the business idea. This could be the make or break of a business, because without additional financial support the business may not get off the ground.

Components

Type of business

This section should include not only describe the type of business, but also take into consideration its aims and objectives. It should also include the business's USPs, the expected levels of demand and how the business plans to maintain a competitive advantage as well as a PESTLE and LoNGPESTLE analysis for the business.

Market

This section should include:

- the market research objectives, brief and subsequent proposal

- the market research plan which should propose both primary and secondary methods)
- a data collection summary
- an analysis and evaluation of the data collected. Details should include: market trends, cash-flow forecast, customer buying behaviour, an analysis of the competition and a SWOT analysis.

Human resources

This section should include:

- a skill gap analysis
- details of which methods will be used to address the identified skill gaps
- an action plan which includes details on realistic and achievable time scales and estimated costs for addressing the skill gaps
- details relating to any additional employees or partners which may be needed to start the business
- information covering employment contracts
- overview of the plan to pay employees, taking into consideration legislation such as the National Minimum Wage Regulations
- details relating to employees' working hours, taking into consideration legislation such as the Working Time Regulations
- details of policies relating to resolving grievances and other such problems
- an outline of the business's discrimination policy.

Physical resources

This section should include the legal status chosen for the business, along with the reasons for the choice including details of the legal liability position of the business. The section should also include:

- information relating to trading terms and conditions
- how the business will address trading standards responsibilities
- details of any licences required for the business and where they would be obtained from
- details of all records needed for the chosen business
- information concerning the key local and national legislation you will need to adhere to for your business.

Financial resources

This section should include:

- a personal survival budget
- details of costs relating to the business' premises
- details concerning the selection of suppliers and justification for these choices
- details of the sources of finance chosen for the business.

Financial and profit forecasts

This section should include:

- the capital needs budget
- details of the main running costs of the business
- the pricing policy with justification along with some sample prices

- a forecast profit and loss account and balance sheet
- a break-even analysis for the business.

Growth and development

This section should include details relating to the prediction for the future growth and development of the business. The long-term strategy for the business should be looked at and consideration given to whether there is a capacity for expansion and what form this may take in the future.

Contingencies

Businesses typically face some sort of difficult trading times, such as recession or increase in competition; therefore it is important to include details of any financial contingency plan. Refer to the sources of finance section for possible sources of additional finance should they be required in the future.

Assessment activity 36.3   P5 M3 D1   BTEC

You will be presenting a business plan to a bank manager, who could provide potential funding for your business venture.

1. Produce a written outline business plan in a formal report format. You will then be given a short interview where you will give a short presentation of your business. **P5**

2. Describe the systems that must be in place to address the legal and financial issues summarised in P5.

3. Summarise how these systems will be embedded in the overall business plan. **M3**

4. Present a comprehensive business proposal that addresses all relevant aspects for a business start-up. **D1**

Grading tips

1. Your outline business plan should follow a formal report format and can be developed into a comprehensive document. It should reflect legal and financial aspects relating to

the start-up of a new business. The report should be supported by an oral discussion, which may be undertaken with a specialist such as a bank manager. **P5**

2. You will need to consider the impact that the legal and financial aspects will have on the start-up business. You will be required to describe systems that should be put in place to address these aspects, such as recording systems for tax and VAT liabilities. You could include a summary of how these systems will be embedded in the overall business plan. **M3**

3. You will need to draw all your evidence together into a comprehensive business proposal that addresses all relevant aspects of business start-up. You will need to present all the evidence in a fluent proposal. You should discuss the draft with your tutor and/or business mentor and take advice on any improvements and revisions before presenting the final version. **D1**

PLTS

Working together and taking advice for any improvements in this activity will help you to develop your skills as a **team worker**.

Just checking

1. What advantages might persuade you to become a franchisee rather than starting a business from scratch?
2. You are going to set up a mobile cleaning business concentrating on office and factory cleaning services. Prepare a SWOT analysis for your business.
3. Give three reasons why it is important for a new business to understand its target market.
4. Which personal skills do you think are important for any new business owner? Why?
5. During a recession, which pricing methods might prove successful for a new double-glazing business? Why?
6. Why is it important for a start-up business to do a cash-flow forecast?
7. What legislation should an Internet start-up business be most aware of?
8. Name three different ways a new business may be able to obtain finance.
9. Why is it important for a start-up business to have a personal survival budget?
10. The process for records and checking the performance of the business is usually set in stages. How many stages are there and what is the significance of each stage?

edexcel

Assignment tips

1. One useful tool for gathering this customer information is to use a questionnaire. You can find useful guidelines on how to design a questionnaire on the Market Research Society website (www.mrs.org.uk) under Frequently Asked Questions. The site also includes sources of free statistical and demographical information. The Office for National Statistics (www.statistics.gov.uk) website contains a wealth of statistical information about the UK.

2. One way of illustrating your work would be to put together a cash-flow forecast. If you produce a forecast, remember to allow for seasonal trends. Rather than putting together your projected annual sales figures and dividing by 12 to get a monthly figure, you should consider what effect seasonal trends might have.

3. Remember to write clear and realistic objectives as this will help you when you come to write other sections of the marketing plan – when in doubt, you can always look back and remind yourself what your business objectives are and what you are trying to achieve, and why.

4. It is useful to know that some banks offer a special franchise funding facility. This may make getting a loan much easier than going to the bank with just your business idea and plan. Banks with special franchise financing sections include:

   • NatWest (www.natwest.com)

   • Royal Bank of Scotland (www.rbs.co.uk)

   • Lloyds TSB (www.lloydstsb.com)

   • HSBC (www.hsbc.co.uk).

37 Understanding business ethics

The word 'ethics' comes from the Greek word 'ethikos', meaning 'character'. One way to think about business ethics is to consider the ethics of people you might know. For instance, if you were asked about people who live in your area, you might describe someone well known for doing good things (being nice) or someone it might be better to stay away from (a 'dodgy' character) etc. Individuals have different standards of ethics and so do businesses. Ethical behaviour is good behaviour; it measures up to standards and no one suffers from it.

Businesses exist to create profit, but where should we draw the line? This unit will help to make you aware of many of the ethical issues and questions that businesses must face. You will begin by learning how important ethics is in the business world and move on to understanding the different ways businesses can operate ethically. Finally, you will look at how ethical concerns of the community also affect businesses.

Learning outcome

On completion of this unit, you should:

1. understand the meaning and importance of ethics in the business world
2. understand the implications of businesses operating ethically
3. know the social implications of business ethics
4. understand ethical concerns facing different communities.

Assessment and grading criteria

This table shows you what you must do in order to achieve a **pass**, **merit** or **distinction** grade, and where you can find activities in this book to help you.

To achieve a **pass** grade the evidence must show that the learner is able to:	To achieve a **merit** grade the evidence must show that, in addition to the pass criteria, the learner is able to:	To achieve a **distinction** grade the evidence must show that, in addition to the pass and merit criteria, the learner is able to:
P1 explain the ethical issues a business needs to consider in its operational activities **See Assessment activity 37.1, page 256**	**M1** assess how a selected business could improve the ethics of their operations **See Assessment activity 37.1, page 256**	**D1** evaluate the impact of a selected business's ethical behaviour on stakeholders and the business **See Assessment activity 37.2, page 264**
P2 explain the implications for the business and stakeholders of a business operating ethically **See Assessment activity 37.2, page 264**		
P3 describe the social implications of business ethics facing a selected business in its different areas of activity **See Assessment activity 37.3, page 269**	**M2** assess the social implications of business ethics facing a selected business in its different areas of activity **See Assessment activity 37.3, page 269**	
P4 examine the ethical concerns of the communities in which a selected business operates **See Assessment activity 37.4, page 277**	**M3** explain the ethical concerns of the communities in which a selected business operates and suggest measures that could be taken to improve corporate responsibility **See Assessment activity 37.4, page 277**	

How you will be assessed

In this unit, you will take an in-depth look at the ethical issues surrounding the work of one or more businesses. You will consider the ways in which business practices are affected by ethical considerations, how different stakeholders may influence business decisions and how a business's ethical standards affect the community.

Your assessment work may be presented in a variety of forms, from written reports through to oral presentations.

Michael, 19, BTEC student

Before I started this unit, I thought that a business being ethical was just about fair trade and how a business operated internationally. Child labour and the exploitation of workers make the headlines in the national papers, but I learnt that there is a lot more to business ethics, both locally and internationally. With this unit, I soon realised that business ethics cover a broad range of different things.

In my class, we looked at two situations to help us understand ethics. The first one was about a lady who was stuck miles away from her home with a broken down car and was forced to call out a garage to tow her car in for repair. The second situation was about a wealthy man who had a car problem and called his own local garage. We discussed which one had the best service. It was really interesting.

Being ethical is in a business's best interest. I enjoyed studying this unit and think it will make me a better employee when I start working full time.

1. How can a business benefit from an ethical position?

2. Why should it concern teenagers in Britain if people in other countries have to work in shocking conditions to produce cheap clothing?

3. What are you looking forward to learning about most in this unit?

1 Understand the meaning and importance of ethics in the business world

A balancing act

It is estimated that 7.5 million hectares of rainforest are being cut down for profit each year – an area the same as 20 football pitches every minute. However, there is an area of rainforest the size of Western Europe remaining in South America. So, although this is likely to increase the level of greenhouse gas carbon dioxide in the atmosphere, it is a minor effect when compared to burning fossil fuels for industry and transport.

In pairs or small groups, discuss why this is an 'ethical' issue for business. Create a joint statement saying what you think could or should be done about it.

1.1 Operational activities

Business operations refer to what a business actually does. So, a factory making clothing contains machines and has people running them; it makes and receives deliveries; materials are moved about; people travel to and from the factory.

Operational management is about controlling how a business works, so that it achieves the aims and objectives set by strategic management. Wherever a business operates, there are effects – some good, some not so good.

What is business ethics?

An organisation works to achieve corporate aims. Aims are dictated by the kind of organisation itself. A public service organisation, for instance, must deliver government services such as social services; a private business seeks profit for the benefit of its owners. Business managers in these organisations are paid to make decisions that will help the business to achieve its aims and objectives. These decisions can be related to staff, financial investment, marketing strategy, products or location.

Operational activities refer to anything a business does in order to achieve its aims. Marks & Spencer, Asda, Tesco and Sainsbury's each have retail outlets all over the UK. This is an aspect of these businesses: operating in order to sell. Their other operational activities include buying, storing, delivering, advertising and so on.

Issues connected to ethics in business arise because some businesses make poor operational or strategic decisions. These decisions can hurt local people, the staff and the customers. Other businesses simply make mistakes. Sometimes, individuals within businesses act selfishly or incompetently – whatever the reasons, business ethics is now a vital part of management.

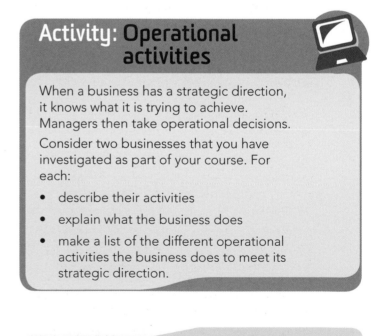

Activity: Operational activities

When a business has a strategic direction, it knows what it is trying to achieve. Managers then take operational decisions.

Consider two businesses that you have investigated as part of your course. For each:

- describe their activities
- explain what the business does
- make a list of the different operational activities the business does to meet its strategic direction.

Key term

Operational activities – the day-to-day actions taken by a firm to achieve its primary purpose.

Definitions of business ethics

Ethics are to do with what is 'right' and 'wrong'. Ethics plays an increasingly important role in business today. When a particular business seeks to achieve its aims, is it right that it might do so by paying low wages? Is it right that our planet is damaged through business activities? A business is part of society and, just as society requires a certain standard of behaviour from individuals; it also expects businesses to abide by similar standards.

Business ethics is therefore the application of **ethical values** to business behaviour. It applies to all aspects of business conduct – from boardroom strategies and how companies treat their suppliers to sales techniques and accounting practices. Ethics goes beyond the legal requirements for a company and is therefore a matter of choice. Business ethics applies to the conduct both of individuals and to the organisation as a whole. It is about how a company does its business and how its activities affect all of its **stakeholders** (see page 256).

Ethical behaviour within a particular business is different from an ethical business. An ethical business sets out from the beginning to work ethically and ethics form a part of its strategic aims.

Key terms

Ethical values – the standards that are held and are set by a business or individuals that control their behaviour.

Stakeholder – individual or group with any sort of interest in the activities of a business.

Case study: The Body Shop

The Body Shop presents a very clear and identifiable corporate culture. The Body Shop corporate culture comes from the philosophy of the founder of the business, the late Dame Anita Roddick. This culture is based on five core 'values':

'1. *Against animal testing – We consider testing products or ingredients on animals to be morally and scientifically indefensible and should be banned. So we don't test our cosmetic products or ingredients on animals, nor do we commission others to do so on our behalf. We never have and we never will.*

2. *Support community trade – A fair price for a fantastic product or ingredient, from a disadvantaged or small-scale supplier. When we purchased our first Community Trade product we became a pioneer of fair trade in the cosmetics industry. That was in 1987; now we have 15,000 people, in 31 communities, across 24 countries supplying ingredients for over 1,000 of our products.*

3. *Activate self-esteem – We promise only to create products that do exactly what they say on the label and communicate honestly and clearly, without confusing jargon and misleading product claims. So you can make your own mind up. Our motto? Know your mind, love your body.*

4. *Defend human rights – We strive to ensure that we have rigorous systems in place so that we only source from suppliers that commit to our ethical trade standards where working conditions are safe and hygienic, child labour is not used, living*

The Body Shop has clearly defined ethical values

wages are paid, working hours are not excessive and no discrimination is practised.

5. *Protect the planet – We promote the use of renewable resources and sustainable raw ingredients, supporting sustainable wood through the use of the Forest Stewardship Council certified wood products. We actively strive to minimise waste and the unnecessary use of excess packaging on our products. We are constantly seeking new ways to improve our business practices and reduce our carbon footprint.'*

1. What impact do The Body Shop's core values have on its stakeholders?

2. What are the benefits of its application of ethical values for The Body Shop? Are there any disadvantages?

3. Find out about the work of the Forest Stewardship Council.

Ethical activities

An ethical business has a broad agenda and focuses on making a positive contribution to the community. An ethical bank such as the Co-operative Bank, states that it seeks to make the world a better place by taking a different approach to banking. In the case of this type of business, ethics becomes at least as high a priority as profitability.

Values of businesses

So what is meant by 'values'? Individuals' values can come from religion or from culture. In mathematics, a value is a number, a quantity. In economics, a value is a measure of what something is worth. (The school or college building you are in has a monetary value.) However, personal values are not written down anywhere because they are, in fact, a state of mind.

Parents and carers might try to ensure children are brought up with a good set of personal values. This might mean, for example, the children will feel instinctively that they should care for others and try to behave in a certain manner. The things they will hold to be important – their personal values – will consciously or unconsciously determine how they behave.

Personal values affect the way people behave, both at work and in their private life. In a business context too, the values held by certain key individuals are often translated into specific corporate behaviour – as was seen by Anita Roddick.

What is professional ethics?

Professional ethics relates to how people behave in relation to their chosen careers. Doctors, lawyers, accountants, engineers and other professionals are expected to behave in certain ways or follow specific codes of conduct. This helps to guard against their actions bringing their profession into disrepute.

Living up to professional ethics can lead to dilemmas in the workplace. An example of this would be the professional duty to 'whistleblow' (see page 276) which conflicts with a sense of loyalty to a company.

Professionals are governed by the rules of conduct laid down by their own professional institutes. Failing to comply with these can result in these professionals losing the right to practise.

Individual ethical behaviour

Once a business grows beyond a particular individual it becomes a corporation with a legal personality all of its own, the corporate identity. However, all corporations consist of individual personalities. No matter what ethical principles a corporation might claim to possess, if individuals within the business take unethical decisions, these may have negative effects.

We will see in the following pages that many corporations take a firm ethical stance on many issues. It is the responsibility of managers to make sure that individual members of staff act in an ethical manner.

Activity: ICA ethical statement

Read the following statement from The Institute of Chartered Accountants in England and Wales, then answer the questions below.

> 'Chartered Accountants are expected to demonstrate the highest standards of professional conduct and to take into consideration the public interest. Ethical behaviour by Chartered Accountants plays a vital role in ensuring public trust in financial reporting and business practices and upholding the reputation of the accountancy profession.'

1. An accountant is asked by a client to hide some income so that he avoids taxation. This is an ethical dilemma for a Chartered Accountant. Why?

2. An accountant has responsibilities to employers, staff and the wider public, and to other professionals. Can you think of a way in which the values of an accountant might be in conflict?

3. Why do you think that Chartered Accountants play a 'vital role in ensuring public trust in financial reporting and business practices'?

Activity: Individual ethics

You are the manager of a medium-sized building firm and have just received a call from a member of the public, accusing one of your drivers of dumping building rubble near a public park.

1. What stance would you take?

2. How would you ensure that all staff acted in an ethically correct way?

1.2 Ethical issues

Corporate governance

When a business corporation is brought into existence, the question, 'Who makes decisions?' often arises. A limited company consists of a board of directors who are responsible for overarching strategic direction (hence the term 'directors'). Answerable to the board are usually a number of operational managers at various levels.

The 'governance' of a medium to large business is important. How do directors know what managers are doing? In the case of public limited companies (PLCs), how are shareholders consulted about policy, performance and decisions? Of course, there are rules about shareholders' rights. Nevertheless, the specific means by which individual businesses consult and control the various decision makers within the corporation are crucial.

Corporate social responsibility (CSR)

At the start of the unit, we suggested that you can compare the ethical position of a business to that of a human being. Some people care about others; some people are very selfish; the same can be said about corporations. **Corporate social responsibility** refers to the extent that a business considers what it does in relation to the wider world.

All businesses are expected to think about what they do. The UK government encourages CSR, as seen in the following passage from the government's gateway web:

'The government sees CSR as the business contribution to our sustainable development goals. Essentially, it is about how a business takes account of its economic, social and environmental impacts in the way it operates – maximising the benefits and minimising the downsides. Specifically, we see CSR as the voluntary actions that business can take, over and above compliance with minimum legal requirements, to address both its own competitive interests and the interests of wider society.'

Key terms

Corporate governance – the people and procedures for taking the major decisions within a business.

Corporate social responsibility (CSR) – the policy of a business towards all stakeholders that takes their interests into account.

Case study: Tesco and Dairy Crest

Read both of these **corporate governance** statements. One is from a national supermarket and the other from a national food producer. Then, answer the questions below.

Tesco

'We are committed to the highest standards of Corporate Governance. We recognise that good governance helps the business to deliver our strategy and safeguard shareholders' long-term interests. We believe that the revised Combined Code provides a useful guide from which to review Corporate Governance within the group. This statement describes the board's approach to Corporate Governance.'

Dairy Crest

'The company's Corporate Governance procedures have met the requirements of section 1 of the Combined Code on Corporate Governance ("the Code"), with the one exception that no meetings were requested or held between shareholders and the Chairman and the senior independent non-executive director during the year. However, the Board considers that arrangements are in place to ensure a balanced understanding of the issues and concerns of major shareholders.'

1. Explain what is meant by 'corporate governance'.

2. Work with a partner and investigate the Financial Services Authority's website (www.fsa.gov.uk). Draft a statement that summarises section 1 of the Combined Code on Corporate Governance. Why is this important to businesses like Tesco and Dairy Crest?

3. 'Anyone can be unethical in a business. Governance is not relevant'. Do you agree with this statement? Justify your response.

Case study: Ryanair

In 2007 budget airline Ryanair's boss Michael O'Leary rejected criticism from a government minister, arguing that his airline was 'the greenest in Europe'.

In an interview, Minister Ian Pearson said: 'When it comes to climate change, Ryanair is not just the unacceptable face of capitalism; it is also the irresponsible face of capitalism.' He also attacked British Airways, saying it was 'only just playing ball' on environmental regulations.

O'Leary defended his company and the industry as a whole, saying: 'What [Pearson] should be attacking is the power generation stations and the road transport industry, who between them account for over 50 per cent of emissions.'

1. What is the ethical issue Ryanair faces in this case? Why is it an ethical issue?

2. Do you think that Ryanair shows a lack of CSR in the case above? Justify your answer.

3. What do you think of the debate about budget airlines? Do you think cheap flights should be restricted?

Environment

The Ryanair case study is not only a corporate social responsibility issue, it is also an environmental and therefore an ethical issue. The emissions coming from aircraft are believed to have a bad effect on the Earth's atmosphere, leading to **global warming**, which affects us all.

It is now widely felt that most of the global warming that has taken place over the last 50 years has been

What is the size of your carbon footprint?

Key term

Global warming – the gradual warming of the planet's surface caused by carbon dioxide build up in our atmosphere. It has the effect of changing the climate in the long term.

caused by human activity. The emissions of carbon dioxide into the Earth's atmosphere – caused by petrol engines, oil burning and coal burning among other industrial activities – have caused a 'greenhouse effect' that effectively warms the Earth's surface. The gas forms a barrier that prevents the Sun's rays from bouncing back away from the Earth and out into the atmosphere.

Some facts regarding global warming include the following.

- Since the start of the twentieth century, the Earth's average surface temperature has increased by 0.6°C (1.1°F).

- The twentieth century saw temperature increases greater than in the previous 400–600 years.

- Seven of the warmest years in the twentieth century were in the 1990s.

Some effects of global warming include the following.

- Mountain glaciers all over the world are receding (melting).

- The Arctic ice pack has lost about 40 per cent of its thickness in the last 40 years.

- Global sea levels have risen three times faster over the last 100 years than over the previous 3,000 years.
- Plants and animals are changing their range of behaviours in response to climate change.
- The climate is changing and we don't understand how.

Source: www.greenfacts.org

Sustainability

While there is no universal agreement on this, the evidence is strong that our planet cannot sustain (keep up) for too long increasing levels of industrial development – particularly development that uses carbon dioxide-producing technology (e.g. engines and oil burning). This is the 'sustainability' question and is something that affects us all.

The Antarctic ice pack is receding as a result of global warming

Did you know?

One billion people in our world depend on forests for some essentials like food, fuel and fresh water.

Case study: The Go-Ahead Group

The Go-Ahead Group of transport companies recognises that its activities affect the environment and acknowledges that it should take reasonable measures to look after the environment for both the present and future generations. Therefore, the Go-Ahead Group aims to minimise the effects of its activities within its financial, technical and operational constraints to ensure ongoing improvement in environmental performance, in addition to compliance with all statutory duties and regulatory requirements.

The Group Environment Manager will provide assistance and advice to operating companies where appropriate and particular attention should be given to the following areas recognised as being the primary environmental issues relating to our activities.

Pollution of air, water and land – Actual and potential sources of pollution should be identified and all appropriate measures taken to reduce or prevent pollution. Particular regard should be given to vehicle exhaust emissions with purchasing, maintenance, operational and technical solutions evaluated within the decision making process.

Generation and disposal of waste – All feasible waste minimisation and recycling initiatives to reduce the amount of waste generated should be established and implemented.

The use of natural resources – The most environmentally sensitive resources used should be identified. Environmental considerations should be incorporated within the purchasing processes for these materials, and the use of such materials monitored with appropriate measures implemented to ensure efficiency.

Nuisance – A degree of nuisance, particularly noise, is an inevitable consequence of the group's activities. However, it must be ensured that nuisance caused by operations is kept to a minimum and any complaints received are dealt with promptly and sympathetically within the operational constraints that apply.

Source: Adapted from Go-Ahead PLC's 'Environment Report', www.go-ahead.com

1. How does the Go-Ahead policy outlined here show concern for 'sustainability?'

2. What other ethical issues are shown in the statement?

3. Why does a PLC like the Go-Ahead Group consider CSR to be important?

Human rights

When we talk about business ethics, we are considering the actions taken on behalf of organisations and asking the general question: 'Is this for the good or the bad?' In other words, are the actions of business hurting us collectively and/or individually?

Many of the questions that we deal with in business ethics relate to major questions affecting us all, such as the environmental ones. There are also some issues that relate to fundamental human rights that we all have as individuals. Later in this unit (page 274) we will see that this is a worldwide concern.

Human rights revolve around some very important questions, many having to do with discrimination. For instance, it is illegal in the UK to treat people differently on the grounds of race, gender, religion, sexual orientation or disability. This is basic human rights. Other human rights are also built into our legal system. We are entitled to a contract of employment, to work part time, to be able to join a union and to have a hearing against wrongful dismissal.

Activity: Rights

1. In pairs, go to the website www.yourrights.org.uk. List as many rights of employees as you can find.
2. From your list, select three issues and describe how they can become ethical issues for employers.

Functional skills

Using websites to research information on employee rights and business ethics will help you to develop your **ICT** skills.

Corruption

Corruption arises in many forms and can be a major public concern. A person or a business corporation is corrupt if they use influence or unfair means to gain business or personal advantage. Local councils may employ a lot of building companies to carry out construction work in their areas (for example, to build roads, bridges, houses and offices). There is a lot of money to be made from local council contracts and

it is only fair that when a local council has a building project to complete, the contract is openly and fairly made available to all firms. Competition should be based on price, quality and ability to do the job and so on. However, what if one of the officers or councillors were related to a builder and this builder were given the job? What if one particular builder paid cash to an officer or a councillor to secure the work? These are examples of serious corruption and of how a process that is meant to guarantee fairness has been corrupted.

Trading fairly

Fair trade is where:

- business is carried on in an open manner
- competition takes place on grounds that are equal for all parties
- consumers can feel secure that the goods and services they are buying are going to be of satisfactory quality.

Legal and regulatory compliance

There are several areas of law that businesses must follow. These are designed to protect a business's consumers, its employees and others in the wider environment.

Did you know?

Wheel clampers can fine car owners who park illegally almost anything they like and have been known to fine people up to £670. Wheel clampers, however, do have to be licensed by the SIA (Security Industry Authority).

Consumer law

When a consumer makes a decision to buy something there is an element of trust and of risk involved. An unethical trader could potentially give a false description of something or overcharge for a product. Businesses are therefore subject to the law.

It is illegal to give a false description of something, or to mislead consumers. This body of law is known as

Key term

Corruption – not following fair and equal procedures to make decisions; attempting to persuade by using cash or opportunity.

Case study: The Office of Fair Trading (OFT) at work

The Office of Fair Trading (www.oft.gov.uk) exists 'to make markets work well for consumers. Markets work well when there is vigorous competition between fair-dealing businesses. When markets work well, good businesses flourish.'

The Director General of Fair Trading once said: 'Consumers have a basic right to goods of satisfactory quality that are fit for their purpose, match their description and are installed properly. The OFT and trading standards services will act against suppliers who breach these rights.'

With that in mind, Mr X, a door supplier, has been stopped by the OFT from supplying and installing poor quality goods. The OFT received a number of complaints from consumers that the company:

- supplied doors and fittings that were unsatisfactory in quality

- supplied doors not fit for their purpose

- supplied goods that did not match their description

- failed to deliver and/or fit goods within the agreed time or at all

- fitted goods without reasonable care and skill.

Mr X, in writing, has agreed under the Stop Now Regulations to stop breaching the Supply of Goods and Services Act 1982. Mr X also provided assurances under the provisions of Part III of the Fair Trading Act 1973.

1. In your own words, describe how this door company was trading unfairly. Was it in the business' interests to do so?

2. Do you think it is necessary for the government to step in and protect consumers like this? Justify your answer.

3. What might be the implications if the government were to abolish the OFT?

'consumer protection' law. Consumers have rights, and businesses must respect these. The well-known Acts of Parliament in this area are:

- the Consumer Protection Act 1987
- the Sale of Goods Act 1979
- the Trades Description Act 1968.

These Acts give ministers the right to make future regulations that further control what businesses can do.

New regulations came into effect in May 2008 which give consumers much greater protection from unfair trading practices. The regulations replaced several older pieces of consumer legislation including most of the Trades Description Act 1968. Trades have a duty not to trade unfairly with consumers. The Consumer Protection from Unfair Trading Regulations 2008 introduced new rules for 'business to consumer' sales.

At a local level, all businesses must comply with trading standards. Trading Standards officers exist to ensure consumers are given protection against **rogue traders**, whether they are selling goods or offering services.

Protecting employees

Just as a consumer accepts an element of risk when buying, an employee places trust in an employer. The UK government has taken steps to establish laws, known as employment laws, which protect people employed by business. Businesses are required by law to treat employees fairly and without discrimination. The Sex Discrimination Act 1975, the Equal Pay Act 1970 and the Employment Protection Act 1975 all place businesses under an obligation to deal with staff in a fair and open way.

Since 1995 it has been against the law to treat anyone with disabilities less favourably than anyone else, unless there is justification that the individual is less suitable for a task because of their disability. In 2003 the Employment Equality (Sexual Orientation) Act gave gay employees the protection of discrimination law. Since 2006 it has been illegal to discriminate against an employee because of their age.

Activity: Trading standards

The Trading Standards Institute offers a useful list of government laws applying in England and Wales. Visit ts website at www.tradingstandards.gov.uk and find more information about the issues covered in the list of government laws.

Create a summary of those Acts that try to protect the consumer.

Key term

Rogue trader – a trader operating as a legitimate business without the necessary skills and abilities to do the job.

Employees are also offered protection under health and safety laws and regulations. Employers have a duty of care to monitor the health and safety of their staff to ensure that they do not carry out jobs that have too much risk or danger.

All of these Acts of Parliament are enforceable by the courts or by government agencies. Regulations are made as a result of each Act, and these control what businesses can lawfully do. The effect of the law, therefore, is to regulate (modify or moderate) business activity.

The wider environment

An unethical business could, if left unregulated, cause immense damage to the environment around it.

At the local level, businesses are held responsible for what they do. It is unlawful for a business to:

- dump rubbish
- pollute waterways
- build without authority from planners.

Polluting the atmosphere is now a major ethical issue

Did you know?

The government has an agency called the Environment Agency (see www.environment-agency.gov.uk), which is responsible for enforcing environment regulations.

Case study: Air pollution prevention

An international company was fined £35,500 for four offences of breaching the Pollution Prevention and Control (PPC) regulations. The company was also ordered to pay £30,000 in costs to the Environment Agency.

When the company built the plant, an automatic process shutdown system was not installed – even though it was stipulated as a condition in the pollution control regulations in the permit. This would automatically have shut down the plant in the event of equipment failure. An abatement plant was put in place to reduce potentially harmful substances such as oxides of nitrogen (NO_2) to safe levels.

Because there were no such safety measures, the permitted level of emissions were grossly exceeded over several months. There is no evidence to suggest that environmental harm or harm to human health occurred because of the incident. However, there was potential for environmental harm and harm to nearby residents if such releases were allowed to continue for a prolonged period.

On top of the excessive releases caused by the failure to install an automatic shutdown system, there was also a failure of the oven seals in another part of

the same process. This caused the escape of oven gases resulting in elevated levels of NO_2 within the perimeter of the company's premises. The company failed to notify the Environment Agency that there had been a detection of escaped NO_2. Nor did it notify the Environment Agency that there had been a malfunction, breakdown or failure of the plant or techniques that either caused or could have caused pollution.

A local Environment Agency officer said: 'In each of the failures by the defendant to comply with the terms of the permit, its conduct fell way below the standards required of it and expected of a company of this size and experience working in this industry.'

Source: Adapted from an article at www.environment-agency.gov.uk

1. Based on the text, what do you feel were 'the standards required' of the business concerned?

2. Who were these standards designed to protect?

3. Analyse the overall work of the Environment Agency. In your view, in what ways does it affect the ethical behaviour of businesses?

Business practices

The law covers the main ethical issues that can affect many key stakeholders in a business, including consumers, staff and the immediate neighbourhood, but there is still a potential for actual business practices to fall short of legal requirements. If this were not the case, perhaps there would be no need for regulations.

Businesses exist to achieve their aims and objectives. Every business manager has a degree of pressure to meet targets (see pages 256–9 covering stakeholders). Managers themselves are employees and have senior management as well as shareholders (see page 256) to consider. These pressures can sometimes result in neglect or **malpractice**. A business manager may neglect to comply fully with health and safety regulations, because to do so would cause delay. An accident caused as a result of this will have serious consequences for the business.

Key term

Malpractice – any occasion when someone does not follow accepted normal practice (usually to gain advantage).

Things can become more serious and sinister when a business uses malpractice to achieve objectives. This could be through corruption or illegal activity. Ethical business behaviour is promoted by company policies, governmental policies and public concern about things affecting us all.

Working conditions

When people start working for a business organisation, they are entitled to a set of minimum working conditions, which are not just about wages and salaries. They also cover aspects of work such as

Activity: Ethical issues

To illustrate the difference between an ethical issue caused through a mistake and one caused through malpractice, investigate the following cases and prepare a presentation which compares and contrasts both of them.

- Enron – Enron executives bribed tax officials in order to fabricate accounts.
- Cadbury – Cadbury withdrew a million chocolate bars which may have been contaminated with a rare strain of salmonella.

Functional skills

Putting together a presentation for this activity will help you to develop your **English** skills in writing and speaking.

hours, holiday entitlement, privacy, harassment and discrimination. It is up to employers to create working conditions that are fair, just and open. Trade unions have the traditional role of defending worker rights against bad employers.

Individual ethical responsibilities

At the start of the unit, we saw that individuals as well as businesses have ethical responsibilities. Individual ethics determine our basic values and standards of behaviour. Management is responsible for staff working in a business. The human resources (HR) function tries to employ the right people who will carry out their job roles well. It is up to HR specialists, as well as line managers across a business, to make sure that staff follow the ethical guidelines of a firm. However, it is up to individuals to follow their own ethical principles at all times.

Assessment activity 37.1

P1 M1 · BTEC

You work for a firm which manufactures UPVC windows, doors and conservatories. Directors have recently commissioned a new website for the company and want to make sure that a 'Corporate Social Responsibility' section is included on the site. You have been given the important task of gathering background information for this purpose.

1. Explain the general ethical issues a particular business of this sort needs to consider in its operational activities. **P1**

2. Assess how this firm could improve the ethics of its operations. **M1**

Grading tips

1. You could take a local firm and, after investigating its basic operations, outline at least three ethical concerns. Note: this does not mean that the business should be doing something wrong, just that these things are 'concerns' for it. **P1**

2. This requires careful consideration. Think about the issues you have described for P1 and assess how/if the business could deal with them better. **M1**

PLTS

Exploring ethical issues to complete this activity will help you to develop your skills as an **independent enquirer**.

2 Understand the implications of businesses operating ethically

2.1 Stakeholders

All businesses have a number of **stakeholder** groups, each with different interests in what the business does. Business owners – perhaps the key stakeholders – want good financial performance from their investments. Business managers know it is their first responsibility to deliver good financial results.

However, while it was always acknowledged that businesses exist in a diverse social, economic and political environment, today it is also accepted that a business should be managed with the interests of all stakeholders in mind. It has become a fashionable thing for business to try to be the friend of all stakeholders.

Shareholders

Shares in UK businesses might be held by private individuals or institutions holding blocks of company shares as investments for pension funds or mortgage endowments. If a business is performing very well, then it is likely that the share value – and therefore the value of the business – will rise. The big question is, what

decisions will help the business to prosper – those that sacrifice short-term profit for long-term security?

Employees

Ordinary citizens benefit from business activity whilst at the same time providing a labour force for business leaders to create wealth. One of the basic tensions and difficulties involved in our kind of economy is that labour is a major cost of business. In the past in the UK, owners of firms could be ruthless – even employing children to work in mines and factories. Workers could be exploited and made to work long hours, then be made redundant when they were no longer needed. Nowadays it is expected that employers will provide satisfactory working conditions and that workers – who, after all, are the ones directly adding value to provide products or services – will be kept safe from danger. It is illegal to employ children and there is a minimum wage.

In modern business, the needs and fears of employees are expected to be taken into account by managers. Some modern businesses try to treat staff not just with fairness; they give them first-class working conditions and benefits so that they are a world-class employer.

Customers, suppliers and competitors

If you have a favourite takeaway near you it becomes quite an important issue if the business is suddenly sold. If you are a regular customer of any business, it can be assumed that you are satisfied with the service received. You are naturally a stakeholder because the business is serving your needs and you hope that you can continue to be satisfied.

In many industrial markets, this relationship between customers, suppliers and competitors can be very important. The existence of some businesses can be affected by the success or performance of another. If one significant firm fails or takes dramatic decisions about strategy, there can be a whole network of other related firms, especially suppliers, which are affected. The decisions of one can have a major impact on the others, even if they are competitors.

Activity: Northern Rock

Research the 2007 collapse of Northern Rock. Write a clear set of notes describing the ways in which at least three different stakeholder groups were affected.

Functional skills

Using websites to research information on stakeholder groups will help you to develop your **ICT** skills.

Citizens

Business activity occurs within a community. So it is important that the local population is considered in major business decisions. Many firms adopt a specific company mission to do 'good work' in the community (such as Proctor & Gamble). This is in part why public relations is such a key feature of business.

Many businesses have national importance and their activities are very significant to members of communities. Tesco, for instance, is a powerful presence in any community. It can have a considerable impact on traffic, new buildings, employment and established businesses.

Sometimes a business or a governmental agency takes a particular strategic decision that will have an effect on the natural environment. For example, a business park is developed. Some derelict land might be used beneficially, with jobs created and building firms getting work. These are good things for those who benefit – the winners.

However, in the background there are other consequences: green land is lost, wildlife loses its habitat and some plant species are lost. The natural environment – plants, trees, wildlife – can suffer as soon as human beings intervene, and are the losers.

Finally, it is important to remember that the whole world is a global community. We all have a 'stake' in the health and well-being of our planet. When natural disasters occur, such as the 2010 Haitian earthquake or the 2005 Hurricane Katrina, business concerns are placed in perspective. The world seems – temporarily at least – to come together as one. We can quickly realise through such 'wake up calls' how much we all have in common.

Did you know?

The UK has committed 26.7 per cent of its Gross Domestic Product (GDP) to bail out our failing banks. This is taxpayer's money and puts us in second place behind the Netherlands and a whisker ahead of Spain.

Bankers, stock markets and financial commentators

Public companies are listed on the **Stock Exchange** and attract investment from wealthy individuals and professional investors such as insurance companies or pension funds. These groups and individuals constantly monitor the performance of companies and entire markets. They will sell shares in companies that are expected to do less well (because their value might fall) and buy shares in companies that are expected to do better (because their value will go up).

Financial commentators can have a big influence on what people or investment professionals will do. Expert opinion of the banks, markets and commentators can sway the stock markets one way or another.

Key term

Stock Exchange – the market place where company shares are bought and sold.

Competition inquiry

The Competition Commission is investigating whether Britain has become a 'supermarket state', with thousands of local specialist stores being killed off by big supermarkets moving into the convenience store sector. Critics believe this could eventually limit choice and push up prices for customers.

An 'emerging thinking' report in 2006 gave the first indications of whether the commission would attempt to break the power of the 'Big Four' supermarkets (Tesco, Sainsbury's, Asda and Morrison) by promoting fairer pricing. The 'Big Four' are believed to have spent tens of millions of pounds on lawyers and consultants to fight accusations that their dominance is hurting consumers.

Tesco has even set up a special website to try to refute some of the claims made by suppliers, MPs and members of the public in written responses to the Competition Commission inquiry. Tesco is the focus of concerns about supermarket power, because it takes £1 in every £8 spent in the high street.

The investigation also looked at the expansion of Asda, Sainsbury's and Morrisons. The commission has the power to impose planning restrictions on all four supermarkets, and could force them to sell land they have earmarked for new stores. It could also outlaw the practice of 'price flexing', where supermarkets sell staple items such as bread, baked beans and bananas at below cost-price in certain areas of the country to entice customers away from rivals.

In submissions to the Competition Commission, an independent body, some food suppliers and farmers said they were afraid of the supermarkets, which use their power to drive prices down to unsustainable levels.

Consumer groups have also complained about the supermarket practice of holding areas of land for development, supposedly to prevent rival supermarkets from building near their existing stores.

Source: www.telegraph.co.uk, 25 January 2007

Think about it!

1. According to the article, what ethical concerns face local communities as a result of the big supermarkets? Do you feel they are justified concerns?

2. What CSR measures would you suggest for the big supermarkets to adopt?

3. Carry out some research into the question of supermarkets and land acquisition. What are the justifications for companies like Tesco in relation to buying up land in and around towns and cities?

Conflicts of interest between stakeholder groups

Businesses today have to balance the aims of a number of stakeholders. This is sometimes difficult because the interests of stakeholder groups can conflict with each other. For example, some stakeholders, such as shareholders, have a financial interest in a business. It is in their interest that the shares in the business increase in value, so that their investments also increase. Other stakeholders, such as environmentalists, are people or groups that actively campaign on issues to do with protecting the natural environment.

If a business successfully launches a new product and all is going well, the shareholders will be very pleased that their cash investment looks like returning a healthy profit. If, however, an environmental group mounts a big campaign to prevent this business operating in the way it does, these two stakeholders are in conflict. Success for environmentalists may mean a loss for shareholders. That said, others may argue that, in the longer term, all businesses gain by protecting our environment.

2.2 Implications
Adapting business behaviour

We live in a world that is increasingly inter-connected. Communication is instantaneous; when an incident happens on the other side of the world, we hear about it within minutes. Is it any wonder, then, that business leaders now fear the consequences of unethical actions by their staff or being accused of an unethical practice?

Most large-scale businesses today take their ethical responsibilities very seriously. They are therefore prepared to adapt their behaviour to avoid accusations of doing wrong, as the following statements show.

- The Go-Ahead Group PLC: 'Every person in the UK is a stakeholder in the public transport industry. The Go-Ahead Group is acutely aware of this, and of our resulting social and environmental responsibilities to the local environments and the people who live in areas where we operate.'

- Marks & Spencer: 'As almost all of our products are made just for us, we can ensure they are produced carefully, in ways that help to protect the environment, the people who make them and our customers.'

- Unilever: 'We are committed to managing our social and environmental impacts responsibly, to working in partnership with our stakeholders, to addressing social and environmental challenges and to contributing to sustainable development.'

Case study: Global suppliers

Europe's largest oil and gas companies plan to survey their suppliers to establish for the first time a global database on supplier corporate social responsibility (CSR) policies. 'The message the companies are trying to give is that your attitudes to corporate responsibility are important to us and also to every player down the supply chain,' said an oil company executive.

The surveys will be self-assessed, but it is expected that the oil companies will audit the information to build up an accurate ranking of suppliers across the world. If successful, the pilot could be extended to 52 other oil and gas companies that use Achilles [a company specialising in identifying, qualifying, evaluating and monitoring suppliers on behalf of major organisations worldwide] to help manage their supply chains. More than 1,000 of the 5,000 suppliers surveyed by UK-based utility companies have already responded.

The moves mark an escalation of individual attempts by large companies to put pressure on their suppliers to adopt ethical and socially responsible policies that echo their own in order to reduce the risk of damage to the reputation of their own brands.

Clothes manufacturers such as NIKE, Inc. and Gap, plus other retailers, have taken a close interest in the employment practices of their suppliers for some time, with UK retailers setting up the Suppliers Ethical Data Exchange to share the results of supplier audits.

The government has repeatedly tried to encourage large companies to use their buying power to ensure that suppliers meet certain health and safety, employment, environmental and wider social standards. The government has used the Company Bill to require directors to operate their businesses 'with regard' to impact on the environment and local community.

In 2006, the Royal Bank of Scotland launched a corporate responsibility report, setting out initiatives for customers, employees, the environment and local communities. The bank spends more than £5 billion a year with suppliers around the world. A spokesperson said that to become one of its main suppliers, businesses have to sign up to its Group Ethical Code for Suppliers, which covers labour rights, the environment, and bribery and corruption.

Source: Adapted from the *Daily Telegraph*, 20 July 2006

1. In your own words, summarise the efforts identified in the article to encourage CSR policies.

2. What are the ethical issues for the suppliers of large-scale oil companies mentioned in the article?

3. Do you agree that this kind of pressure by big companies upon suppliers to adopt CSR policies is likely to work? What are the difficulties involved and how would you try to overcome them?

Responding to ethical pressures

The CSR programmes of businesses are a response to the growing pressures placed on managements to take account of ethical concerns. The case study above shows that several very large companies operating in some significant industries are beginning to exert pressure on their own trading partners to follow socially responsible policies.

Implementing ethical practices

Some household names have begun to implement an ethical stance on issues that affect us all. Take the case study from Walkers crisps (below). This is evidence that one of the UK's major snack manufacturers is working with consumer health in mind. There are other clear indications of this too. McDonald's fast food chains increasingly work to offer healthy options.

Influence of stakeholders and pressure groups

Corporate social responsibility is partly a response to external stakeholder pressure, partly a response to pressure group campaigns and partly recognition that public disapproval could lead to commercial disaster.

Many businesses in pursuit of their primary goals cause damage to the planet. The stakeholders in this, of course, are all of us. Environmental issues are the focus of several well-known **pressure groups** which form to raise awareness of an issue, or several issues.

Key term

Pressure groups – voluntary organisations that exist to create a case that will be listened to by decision makers everywhere. This includes business leaders and politicians.

Case study: Walkers crisps

The text below outlines Walkers' ethical approach.

'A standard bag of Walkers crisps now contains less than a gram of saturated fat. That's just 5% of your guideline daily amount and less saturated fat than half a chocolate digestive! And it's all because we're now cooking our crisps in sunseed oil, one of the healthiest oils there is.

'Our crisps now contain just 8% of your guideline daily amount of salt. We have reduced the salt in our crisps so that a standard bag now only contains 0.5g of salt; that's 8% of your guideline daily amount and the same as a slice of bread!'

Source: Walkers

1. Why did Walkers feel it was necessary to take this step?
2. Which ethical issues would you say are related to this measure?
3. In your opinion, do you feel Walkers will gain from this measure? Justify your answer.

PLTS

Examining the ethical questions that face the whole food and drinks industry will help you to develop your skills as an **independent enquirer**.

Examples of environmental pressure groups include:

- Greenpeace
- ENCAMS (environmental campaigns)
- National Pure Water Association
- Friends of the Earth.

The influence of pressure groups' activity is significant. Their work attracts much media attention and government always takes into account the voice of public opinion. For the modern business, public opinion is vital. The market-orientated company must take care of its public image. Although businesses do not seek votes and they are relatively free (within the law) to pursue unpopular policies and tactics, they do fear public disapproval for commercial reasons. This is one of the reasons why so many CSR policies are clearly outlined.

Impact on competitiveness, reputation and public image

The case study (overleaf) about Timberland, a clothing and footwear company, illustrates perfectly the way in which businesses can use global ethical concerns to boost competitiveness within their market.

Ethical trade

Ethical trade is a way of doing business that takes into account the conditions and practices that occur throughout a supply chain. The case study on Timberland's position in relation to 'workplaces' in their CSR report, shows how a well-established business is prepared to take into account the implications of trading with factories that employ labour in appalling conditions.

Ethical trade has become a growing issue in the past few years because companies with global supply chains – in particular those in the clothing and food sectors – are coming under increasing pressure to ensure decent working conditions for the people who produce the goods they sell.

Value added

A study undertaken by the Institute of Business Ethics showed clearly those businesses with an explicit

Activity: Pressure groups

Investigate the fashion industry pressure group, Labour behind the Label (www.labourbehindthelabel.org). Prepare a report outlining the concerns of this group. Conclude by giving your opinions as to whether you feel it can change things in the fashion industry.

Key terms

Ethical trade – where big companies take account of ethical questions all along their supply chain so that they buy from businesses that treat workers fairly and give them a fair price for their products.

Value added – where value is added to something through work and application of skills and understanding.

Case study: The Timberland Company

Timberland, a leading outdoor footwear and apparel company, produces a bi-annual CSR report. The report not only highlights Timberland's accomplishments and forward-looking goals in its four CSR pillars of energy, product, workplaces and service, but also invites readers to share feedback and ideas for improvement through an online tool called 'Voices of Challenge'.

'"A key goal of our CSR program is to engage our consumers, employees, shareholders and other stakeholders in an on-going dialogue to help us continuously improve our performance. Knowing that few people want to digest 100-page CSR reports, we took a different approach, making the information available in a number of different formats," states Beth Holzman, Manager of CSR Strategy & Reporting at Timberland. "We're hoping to provide all stakeholders, the right amount of information in accessible formats to openly communicate our commitment to environmental and social justice."'

Other highlights of the Timberland report include the following progress against each of its four CSR Pillars:

Energy – Timberland reduced its absolute carbon emissions from owned and operated facilities and employee air travel by 27% over its 2006 baseline, exceeding its goal of 25%. Timberland also became one of the first in the industry to begin measuring and disclosing supply chain emissions for energy use at third-party contract factories.

Product – Timberland scored 1% of its total footwear products using the Green Index® environmental rating system, its program for designing environmental harms out of its products and informing consumers about its products' environmental impacts to spur more sustainable purchasing.

Workplaces – Timberland significantly reduced the percentage of footwear made in high-risk factories from 34% in 2007 to 1% in 2008. Factories receive high-risk ratings if they have high probability and potential for violations such as excessive working hours; debt-bonded or child labour; or lack effective safety mechanisms on machinery.

Service – Timberland employees served over 165,000 hours in the community in 2007 and 2008. In total, employee volunteers planted over 390,000 trees, conserved or beautified over 600 acres of land, and refurbished or installed nearly 400 miles of trails during these two years.

Source: adapted from an article at www.justmeans.com 14 October 2009

1. List and describe the various ethical issues that are mentioned in relation to Timberland.

2. To what extent do you feel that Timberland is adopting an ethical stance in order to improve its own 'competitiveness'?

3. Evaluate the ethical position of Timberland as you understand it. In what ways do you feel that the business will gain from this? Fully explain your response by referring to reputation, competitiveness and public image.

---

commitment to doing business ethically produced profit/turnover ratios that were 18 per cent higher than those without a similar commitment. It concluded that businesses which had set up their own codes of ethics were adding significant value to their business.

Complying with relevant legislation and codes of practice

We have already seen that, in the UK, businesses must comply with a large range of legislative regulations (see pages 252–4) such as those relating to:

- health and safety
- employment
- planning
- environment and pollution.

European Union (EU) laws

The European Union is a political and economic union of 27 nation-states that encompass more than 490 million people. Countries as diverse as Britain and Romania, Cyprus and Slovenia belong to this Union. It is natural that ethical issues that affect us all are the subject of EU law. This law also covers common issues such as employment and environmental pollution. Employment law is an illustration of EU influence in working conditions. The European Union tries to set standards that apply across all member states.

An EU Directive tells a member state that it must implement law in a particular area. The *1993 Directive 93/104/EC* lays down provisions for a maximum 48-hour working week (including overtime), plus rest

The European Parliament building, Strasbourg, is where legislation relating to the EU is debated and passed

periods and breaks, and a minimum of four weeks' paid leave per year for employees. The Working Time Directive (WTD) was introduced to cut down on working hours; there is a clear link between long working hours and health and safety. Working long hours leads to tiredness, and tiredness leads to accidents. However, the UK government negotiated an 'opt-out' from the WTD with the following conditions.

- The worker can agree to do more than 48 hours.
- No worker should be disadvantaged by deciding not to opt out.
- The employer must keep records of all workers who carry out such work.
- Records must be kept available for authorities.

In 2005 the EU voted to stop this opt-out from the Working Time Directive. Despite the WTD, the UK is the only member state in which working time has actually increased over the last decade.

Activity: UK laws

Go to the Business Link website (www.businesslink.gov.uk) and enter 'Code of practice' into the search box on the homepage. Create a presentation about the variety of areas the government tries to monitor and what regulations it uses to do so.

The United Nations logo

UN Declaration of Human Rights

The United Nations Declaration of Human Rights was first produced in 1948, soon after the Second World War. At that time, there was an intense desire to create a better world, based on fairness and justice. Part of the Declaration covered the question of paid employment.

Article 23 of UN Declaration of Human Rights

- Everyone has the right to work, to free choice of employment, to just and favourable conditions of work, and to protection against unemployment.

- Everyone, without any discrimination, has the right to equal pay for equal work.

- Everyone who works has the right to just and favourable remuneration (pay), ensuring for themselves and their families an existence worthy of human dignity, and supplemented (added to), if necessary, by other means of social protection.

- Everyone has the right to form and join trade unions for the protection of his interests.

- Ethical issues can be of worldwide concern or they can be about the relationship between a customer and a business.

UN Global Compact

These days, the UN is trying to influence the global business community in order to protect vulnerable people from exploitation by multi-national businesses. The UN Global Compact calls on businesses to issue regular reports to stakeholders about social and ethical responsibilities. It also makes a commitment that a business will follow ethical policies.

Economic activity

In today's world, there are so many newly emerging industrialising countries, such as China and India, which are opening up their economies and beginning to develop into so many markets. There is a fear that such operations will carry on practices that cause immense damage both to people and to our planet. The question is: how does a global authority like the UN exert influence over these economies? Is climate change now becoming such a serious problem that all countries must agree to do something?

PLTS

Explaining the implications for the business and stakeholders of a business operating ethically will help you to develop your skills as an **independent enquirer**.

Assessment activity 37.2

A successful company manufacturing windows, doors and conservatories has decided to adopt a comprehensive CSR policy and wishes to make maximum PR use of the new set of values. You have been asked to do the following:

1. Explain the implications for the business and its stakeholders of the business operating ethically.
   P2

2. Evaluate the impact of the business's ethical behaviour on its stakeholders and the business.
   D1

Grading tips

1. Consider the benefits of ethical behaviour by businesses. Who benefits the most? Is it the staff, people in developing nations or perhaps the environment? Are products any better? How do consumers benefit? **P2**

2. You should focus on one business and cover as many stakeholders as possible. Look also at the remaining issues in the unit to add to your perspective. Remember, these are your views, but they should be backed up by clearly researched evidence. **D1**

3   Know the social implications of business ethics

Social implications refer to those actions of business that have an effect on society as a whole. These issues relate to a number of areas of activity.

3.1 Areas of activity

Ethics in finance

In financial dealing and payments, there is scope for several kinds of unethical behaviour. Regulations and voluntary codes try to make sure that ethical practices are observed.

The average debt of the typical UK family today is so high that about a quarter of families cannot afford to repay these debts. Businesses in the financial sector, which offer loans which are expensive to repay (resulting in even worse debt for the borrower), are increasingly subject to scrutiny. For example, financial advice given several years ago caused many people to invest in endowment schemes that have failed to result in expected returns. For these reasons, financial advice services have been increasingly regulated.

In business matters, finance is always an area with a great deal of scope for unethical behaviour. The primary purpose of **free enterprise** is to generate profit. Anything standing in the way of this goal can be a target for financial malpractice. There are a number of areas in financial affairs where unethical behaviour arises.

Bribery

Corruption was dealt with earlier in the unit (see page 252). Bribery is a form of corruption. This is the straightforward use of financial muscle to gain unfair advantage over others. An example would be attempting to gain planning permission by giving money to a planning official or councillor. Another would be gaining the award of a contract by giving cash to a decision maker in a business or government department.

Executive pay

One problem that will not go away is excessive pay for top executives. However, US companies now have to include in their annual reports a single figure for the total pay of their executives including salary, perks and pensions. It is a response to public concern about pay rises that are unrelated to effort, plus a number of high-profile cases of failed executives getting pay-offs of up to US$100 million and others having stock options backdated to give them a share of earlier capital gains. This at least tells shareholders exactly what their top executives are earning.

Did you know?

Bonus payments make up a substantial part of the income of banking executives.

Insider trading

Insider trading refers to illegal use of privileged information in dealing on a stock exchange. For example, when a company takeover bid is imminent, shares are rapidly bought up then sold at a big profit. Insider trading is, in theory, detected by the Securities and Exchange Commission (SEC) in the US, and by the Securities and Investment Board (SIB) in the UK. Neither agency has any legal powers other than public disclosure. Nor can they bring prosecutions themselves.

Lobbying

To 'lobby' means to approach an MP or minister with requests for actions or information. The intention is to persuade politicians to adopt a particular cause or issue, in order to benefit it. In business, if a particular company was under pressure to take certain actions, they could informally 'lobby' an important minister in an attempt to gain influence over policies. Lobbying politicians can be a source of corruption.

Key term

Free enterprise – an economic system in which people are free to offer goods and services to meet demand.

Ethics in human resource management

The law is used to ensure that when jobs are advertised, there is no discrimination. People are entitled to feel that job selections are made on the basis of merit rather than on the basis of race, nationality, gender or other unfair grounds. This is why human resources professionals are trained to avoid discrimination of all kinds.

Worker surveillance can be an important question in some organisations. The question is, to what extent is it reasonable for a member of staff to be watched, to have their emails checked, to have calls listened in to? There are important questions of privacy involved. We will look at 'whistleblowing' later (on page 276), a question that is directly relevant to worker surveillance. How safe will staff feel if their management 'snoops' on them?

Ethics in production

The production of goods can lead to ethical problems for business, for example, in animal testing. Around the world, animals are used to help in the development of products ranging from shampoo to new cancer drugs. The number of live experiments in Britain, however, has halved in the last 30 years.

British law requires that any new drug must be tested on at least two different species of live mammal. One must be a large non-rodent. UK regulations are considered some of the most rigorous in the world. The Animals Act 1986, however, insists that no animal experiments should be conducted if there is a realistic alternative.

Almost every medical treatment used on humans has been tested on animals. Animals were used to develop anaesthetics to prevent human pain and suffering during surgery. The ethical questions revolve around the general value of human life in relation to animals. There are also questions about the extent to which animals suffer during testing.

Planned obsolescence

A free market economy means that business produces goods and services that people need or want so that they will pay for them. Businesses try to convince people, partly through advertising and promotions, that they need products. There is nothing unethical in this. However, it is not in the interests of business to produce goods that last forever. To avoid this, planned obsolescence is the deliberate development of products that will need replacing after a time.

Ethics in sales and marketing

Sometimes businesses employ unethical means to try to generate sales. They can do this in a number of ways.

Spamming

This refers to sending emails to thousands of users similar to a chain letter. Email spamming may be combined with email spoofing (see below), which makes it very difficult to determine the originating email address of the sender. Some email systems have the ability to block incoming mail from a specific address. However, because these individuals regularly change their email address, it is difficult to prevent some spam from reaching an email inbox.

Spoofing

This refers to emails that appear to have been originated from one source when they were actually sent from another. Individuals sending junk email or spam typically want the email to appear as though it is from a real address, which may not really exist. This way the email cannot be traced back to the originator.

Raising their own status

This happens when businesses place false recommendations or blogs onto a website. These recommendations either come from paid individuals employed by marketing companies or are employees of the business pretending to be satisfied customers. People engaged in this type of activity are known as 'shills'. Online consumers are being conned into believing that legitimate consumers are recommending a product.

Marketing involves a good deal of public relations. Press releases and positive news stories all serve to raise a company profile and improve it in the eyes of consumers. However, in an age where we are all becoming more concerned about our environment, some businesses engage in crude 'greenwashing' – they try to appear 'greener' than they really are.

Ethics in intellectual property

Intellectual property (IP) law allows people to own their creative work in the same way that they can own physical property. The owner of intellectual property can control and be rewarded for its use. This encourages further innovation and creativity to the benefit of everyone.

The four main types of IP are as follows.

- **Patents for inventions** – new and improved products and processes that are capable of industrial application.
- **Trade marks for brand identity** – of goods and services allowing distinctions to be made between different traders.
- **Designs for product appearance** – a product's appearance is designed by someone with special skills; this is an asset that can be protected by copyright.
- **Copyright for material** – literary and artistic material, music, films, sound recordings and broadcasts, including software and multimedia.

This means that those individuals or business organisations that have invested their time, resources and talents to create something useful or enjoyable for others, have rights to protect it from being stolen. This applies to computer software as well as to music records.

Is downloading music stealing?

Case study: Is downloading really killing the music industry?

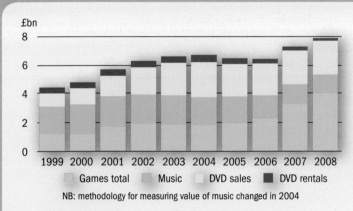

£bn

Spending on games, music, DVD sales and DVD rentals, 1999–2008

NB: methodology for measuring value of music changed in 2004

Legend: Games total | Music | DVD sales | DVD rentals

The music industry feels that illegal downloading is killing it. They feel that every one of the millions of music files illegally downloaded each day is a lost sale. According to research commissioned by the Strategic Advisory Board for Intellectual Property, at least 7 million people in Britain use illegal downloads, worth about £12bn a year.

David Lammy, minister for intellectual property, said, 'Illegal downloading robs our economy of millions of pounds every year and seriously damages business and innovation throughout the UK.' It is something that needs tackling, and we are serious about doing so.

Why does the music industry persist in saying that every download is a lost sale? People only have a limited amount of money. In times gone by, sure, they would have been buying vinyl albums. If you stopped them downloading, would they troop out to the shops and buy those songs? Are people spending their money on something else?

Look at the graph, which shows how spending on games has risen dramatically – from £1.18bn in 1999 to £4.03bn in 2008. Music spending has gone from £1.94bn to £1.31bn, while DVD sales and rentals have nearly doubled, from £1.286bn in 1999 to £2.56bn in 2008. It seems that the culprit is the games industry. Downloaders aren't spending money on the music industry, and in that way they are hurting it. But the lost sales are nowhere near the claims made.

Source: Adapted from an article in *Guardian.co.uk Technology Blog*, 2009

1. What do you feel are the main issues involved in peer-to-peer music file sharing?

2. Do you agree that these type of downloads are unethical? Why?

3. Assess the implications for the music industry if illegal file sharing were left to continue without restriction. Could this have wider social implications?

3.2 Implications

Could you imagine a world where individuals and businesses were allowed to do exactly what they wanted? The implications for everyone would be very serious.

The environment

We saw earlier in the unit (page 250) that, on a global scale, the natural environment is already under threat. It is no exaggeration to say that perhaps the most serious threat facing us comes from climatic changes caused by human activity. One of the major problems today is that economic activity is growing quickly in different areas of the world.

Corporate implications

The desire of an intelligent business leadership to take account of ethical concerns is now an accepted part of good management. When managers establish CSR policies, they are responding to the need to take account of stakeholder concerns. Every one of us is a stakeholder in business activities.

Business managers are required to comply with the law in many areas, including:

- staffing (discrimination, data protection, health and safety and others)
- consumer protection (sale of goods, trades descriptions, consumer credit)

Case study: China

China's industrial development may not be sustainable

In 2004 a Chinese official said that the country's environmental problems had reached crisis levels. The official said China's industrial development was unsustainable because its environment and resources could not cope. Problems such as pollution, acid rain and contaminated rivers had become key policy issues for China.

Is China failing to meet new targets on energy efficiency and pollution? The government set targets to reduce the environmental impact of the country's rapid economic growth. However, only Beijing and five other areas had managed to improve efficiency by at least 4 per cent and cut emissions by at least 2 per cent in the first half of 2006.

The targets, part of a five-year plan, called for energy consumption per unit of GDP to be cut by 20 per cent, and emissions of pollutants to fall by 10 per cent. Chinese officials have not revealed the extent of the failure to reach the targets.

Many Chinese factories seem to be ignoring the law, and pump toxic waste into rivers and lakes. In addition, with the country still focused on fast economic growth, there is little sign that standards are going to improve in the short term.

1. What do you understand by the statement that China's economic development has become 'unsustainable'?

2. What do you consider are the major implications of inaction in environmental matters by the Chinese government?

3. Evaluate the actions that have been taken on a global scale to combat environmental damage from developing economies like China. Do you feel enough has been done?

- the environment (planning, waste management, noise and light pollution, etc.).

Each area creates internal policies, practices, rules and procedures. Without these, businesses can easily fall foul of the law and be fined or suffer worse penalties. Social implications of ethical behaviour affect everyone by ensuring more open, fair and just behaviour.

An example is the Age Discrimination Regulations 2006. Since October 2006, it has been unlawful to discriminate on grounds of age against those in or seeking employment and vocational training. Any business employing staff has to consider this regulation in its selection process.

The regulations apply to employment and vocational training. They prohibit unjustified direct and indirect age discrimination, and all harassment and victimisation on grounds of age, of people of any age, young or old.

Assessment activity 37.3

P3 **M2** **BTEC**

The manufacturing company you work for has taken a strong CSR stance. It wants to put out a press release stressing environmentally friendly processes, sustainability and concern for local good causes. You are asked to do the following.

1. Describe the social implications of business ethics facing the business in its different areas of activity. **P3**

2. Assess the social implications of business ethics facing the business in its different areas of activity. **M2**

Grading tips

1. Consider those ethical issues that you think affect society as a whole. Describe what these issues are and why they are of concern. Relate your thinking on this to a specific business. **P3**

2. Continuing on from P3, describe to what extent you feel that these social issues are a real problem in the case of the particular business you are looking at. Consider what the consequences are for different stakeholders. **M2**

PLTS

Describing the social implications of business ethics facing a selected business in its different areas of activity will help you to develop your skills as an **independent enquirer**.

4 Understand ethical concerns facing different communities

4.1 Communities

We speak of a community to refer to:

- the localities we live in (local communities)
- regional and national areas
- the whole of Europe (the European Union) and beyond (globally).

In today's inter-connected world, we increasingly think of it as one large community.

Local communities

Many businesses are of national importance and their activities have a crucial significance to local communities. Tesco, for instance, is a powerful presence in any community and can have an influence in many different ways (see page 257).

For more than 150 years, the British coalfields offered mining work to the communities around them. However, these communities were scarred for generations

Case study: Buncefield fuel depot

More than 300 tonnes of petrol gushed unnoticed for 40 minutes from the top of a storage tank at the Buncefield oil depot before the spill triggered Europe's biggest fire since the Second World War, an official report into the 11 December 2005 blaze has concluded. A faulty gauge allowed thousands of gallons of unleaded petrol to be pumped into the already full tank at the site near Hemel Hempstead, Hertfordshire. Emergency safety systems failed to stop the tank over spilling. The resulting vapour cloud ignited, injuring 43 people, two of them seriously.

The resulting explosion destroyed 20 similar tanks and sent up columns of black smoke that drifted across southern England. The fire brigade took almost three days to extinguish the blaze and used more than 55,000 gallons of foam, which contained a potentially toxic chemical, perfluorooctane sulphonate.

The Environment Agency said that groundwater at the Hertfordshire site had been contaminated. Spilled fuel and contaminated firewater had passed into the underlying water table; it could be years before the full effects were known.

Some 12 million litres of contaminated water left over from efforts to put out the fire sat in tanks at a sewage treatment works near Rickmansworth whilst experts decided what to do.

1. This was, of course, an accident. Are there ethical concerns? What other concerns might the local community have near the Buncefield depot?

2. What steps could be taken to improve the corporate responsibility of Buncefield?

3. What arguments could you give, despite the accident, to suggest that the Buncefield depot is a good thing to have in an area?

---

because of them. Mining communities suffered a lot of environmental damage, with ugly slag heaps and, in some coalfields, serious coastal damage. Miners suffered long-term health problems too; today many former coal miners still suffer from illnesses caused directly by their job.

Even today, modern businesses leave their mark in many different ways on communities. Despite the environmental and other negative effects, local authorities still welcome new businesses. They bring jobs and cash to areas.

When businesses of any size operate within a locality, there are always ethical concerns. These concerns become highlighted whenever people's worst fears come true – as the Buncefield case study shows.

Regional and national communities

The accident at Buncefield shows that while local people can be in immediate danger from a catastrophic event such as an explosion, an entire region may be affected when an industry faces ethical questions. Environmental issues do not stop at local, national or international boundaries.

However, specific regions tend to contain particular industries. In the UK, the Midlands contained the heart of the British motor industry. Yorkshire, the northeast,

Wales, Scotland, Kent and Nottingham held the bulk of the UK coal mining industry.

When entire industries go through difficulties, there are regional, and often national, effects. The UK car industry suffered from poor planning, inefficiency and bad industrial relations. The coal industry was also troubled by strikes and a national move away from coal as a standard fuel, towards alternatives.

Many communities are faced with serious problems when multi-national corporations set up local operations and later take decisions that are purely commercial. In some cases, complete closure of an important employer leads to significant job losses; in others redundancies. The point is that decisions are taken remotely. On the other hand, multi-nationals often set up in low-wage economies and pay wages that are much higher than those paid by local businesses.

Activity: Multi-national businesses

Investigate the location of multi-national businesses in or near your area. Do you think they are a force for good?

Pressure groups

Environmental pressure groups consistently do exactly what their name suggests; they force issues into the public's attention and therefore pressure both governments and business leaders into action. The two best-known pressure groups are Greenpeace and Friends of the Earth.

Greenpeace campaigns on many issues to defend the natural world. It is committed to halting climate change caused by burning oil, coal and gas. The group investigates, exposes and confronts those who promote dirty sources of energy, including nuclear power, promoting a clean energy future. It supports decentralised energy systems including renewable technologies and energy efficiency.

Friends of the Earth (FOE) seeks to influence policy and practice through what it describes as 'an honest, accurate and open approach'. It does this in the following ways.

- Working local to global – from 200-plus local groups to 70-plus Friends of the Earth International groups, FOE is the only local–global environmental campaign group.

- Solutions-based research – FOE tries to find credible alternatives to problems.

- Enabling campaigning – FOE provides information and tools to help people act.

Did you know?

There are now fewer mountain gorillas in the wild than footballers in the Premier League.

Greenpeace is committed to stopping climate change

Friends of the Earth works locally and globally

The impact of overseeing bodies

It is increasingly recognised that many of the ethical questions that concern us cannot be dealt with just within national boundaries. This means that national, continental and international bodies are taking actions to oversee the activities of business all over the world. Generally, these actions have been based on voluntary measures.

UK government

The UK government has tried to pass laws or create regulations, codes and practices for as many areas of ethics as possible. The government effectively oversees professional practices, as well as selling, trading, employment, health and safety and pollution or waste management. The UK government is also aware of the wider concerns about global warming and has been a supporter of collective efforts to reduce carbon emissions under the Kyoto Protocol.

There are several regulatory bodies that exist in order to protect the ongoing interests of UK stakeholder groups. These include:

- Financial Services Authority (www.fsa.gov.uk)
- Food Standards Agency (www.food.gov.uk)
- Advertising Standards Authority (www.asa.org.uk).

United Nations (UN)

The United Nations (UN) is based in New York – although the land it uses is international, not American, territory. The UN is made up of 191 countries from around the world and was set up in 1945 after the Second World War as a way of bringing people together to avoid war. In fact, the UN logo shows the world held together in the 'olive branches of peace' (see page 264).

On page 264, we saw that in 1948 the UN issued its Declaration of Human Rights which sets out the basic expectations that anyone, wherever they are, should be entitled to expect from employment.

In December 2009, world leaders gathered in Copenhagen, Denmark to try to reach agreement on ways of working together in order to reduce climate damage from human activity. At the Copenhagen Summit, the UN secretary-general, Ban Ki-moon, urged all countries to formally sign on to the Copenhagen Accord to start tackling climate change and step up work toward a legally binding treaty. He also urged richer nations to contribute to a multi-billion dollar fund to help poorer countries cope with global warming.

The EU, WTO and WHO

As we saw on page 262, the EU now covers almost half a billion people in 27 nations. The EU can issue directives to member states, effectively instructing them to implement law.

The World Trade Organization (WTO) is an international body whose purpose is to promote

Case study: Car scrappage

There are 30 million motor vehicles on Britain's roads and around two million are scrapped each year. Previously, car owners paid about £50 to have their vehicles scrapped, which encouraged some people to dump cars illegally. However, under new EU laws, all this has changed.

The End of Life Vehicles Directive, which forces member states to legislate, intends to reduce pollution and waste by encouraging more recycling of materials from scrapped cars. Manufacturers will cover the cost. As a result, the government and environmentalists hope fewer cars will be dumped.

The European legislation sets a target of 80 per cent of the materials in old vehicles to be reused or recycled, rising to 85 per cent in 2015. The change was brought in despite protests from car manufacturers, who said when the law was proposed it would bankrupt them.

Two companies, Autogreen and Cartakeback, will handle the UK's scrapped vehicles. They will issue certificates of destruction to the owners, so that the vehicles can be deregistered from the government's DVLA (Driver and Vehicle Licensing Agency) database.

1. Why should the scrapping of old motor vehicles should be a concern to the European Union?

2. What other ethical issues does the EU appear to be involved in?

3. What arguments, if any, could you put forward to say that it is important the EU acts on these issues?

free trade by persuading countries to abolish import taxes and other barriers. As such, it has become closely associated with globalisation. The WTO is the only international agency overseeing the rules of international trade.

The World Health Organization (WHO) is a branch of the UN that promotes physical, mental and social well-being across the world. It funds international health research, co-ordinates inter-governmental health policies and monitors standards of health globally.

Corporate social responsibility

Some globally known corporations work hard to involve the local populations in their corporate activities. Levi Strauss, the jeans manufacturer, has a training and education programme involving over 12,000 employees worldwide. The Levi Strauss Foundation engages in local charitable causes and offers matched funding to help local people.

4.2 Issues

The consequence of business activity across the world is having a dramatic effect on many local communities. Some of these communities are primitive tribal peoples whose entire way of existence is threatened by business corporations seeking more profit. Many others are agricultural/rural communities.

The South American Amazon Basin is a vast area, the majority of which is in Brazil. The area used to contain more than two million square miles of rainforest. Over the last 30 years, the Brazilian government has allowed deforestation to permit industrialisation and the creation of a network of roadways. This has had a serious impact on the scattered communities living there, as well as on the forest itself.

The same process has occurred in Africa, where commercial logging, mining, drilling and clearing for living space have all led to large areas of deforestation.

In the Philippines, mining companies are not only granted mineral mining rights, they are also granted a logging concession allowing them to chop down trees to supply timber for its pit props and sluices.

The problems associated with deforestation and mining are dramatic for local populations.

- Tribal groups suffer loss of land.
- There is huge disruption to their local ways of survival.
- This can result in loss of cultures.
- There is damage to the health of those living in these communities, not least because of pollution of the local water supplies.

How does deforestation in the Amazon rainforest affect the people living there?

Case study: Shell and the Ogoni People of Nigeria

On 6 June 2001, the Shell Oil pipeline, which passes through the Baraale community, home to the Ogoni people of Nigeria, ruptured and started spilling crude oil into nearby forests, farmlands and houses. Aseme Mbani, chief of the community, was in his farm when the pipeline ruptured.

'I was working when I saw crude oil rushing into my cassava farm. Then I went to the pipeline and I saw where it was leaking. It flowed into my house and flooded my entire home with crude oil.' He had to abandon the house.

The chief took steps to ensure that Shell repaired the ruptured pipeline. 'I reported the matter to the Shell contractors in charge of the pipeline and also to the police. After that, we wrote Shell a "Save Our Soul" letter. When there was no response, I went to Shell to report the matter at a section they call "Ogoni Re-entry". They told me they had seen the letter I wrote. They said we should suffer the spillage because we caused it. They said we had been cutting pipelines and we should reap what we sow.'

Chief Mbani said the oil continued to leak and he kept 'repeating and repeating' his visits to Shell to urge them to act fast before the situation worsened. But Shell never responded.

In 2009, Shell paid a settlement totalling almost £10 million as 'a compassionate payment to the plaintiffs and the estates they represent in recognition of the tragic turn of events in Ogoni land.'

Source: ERA Field Report No. 89 'Shells Oil Spillage'

1. In what ways, if any, do you think the local people in the Ogoni community of Nigeria benefit from Shell Oil activities on their land?

2. Explain why multinationals like Shell should have a responsibility to people like the Ogoni.

3. How might Shell benefit from addressing issues like this?

Globalisation

The world has become inter-connected. Business markets now extend around the globe with modern communication systems making this possible.

Globalisation means that the world is developing into one huge inter-dependent economy. For example:

- the British service sector (banks, IT services, etc.) is able to deal with customers from a call centre in India

- a sportswear manufacturer can design its products in Europe, make them in Southeast Asia and sell them in North America.

Making use of employees or production facilities abroad is called outsourcing; and this is where the anti-globalisation arguments really begin. If these practices replace domestic economic activity with an economy that is heavily influenced or controlled from another country or continent, then the process of globalisation can also be seen as a surrender of power to the big corporations, or a means of keeping poorer nations in their place.

For some of its critics, globalisation has come to be symbolised by:

- low-paid sweatshop workers

- genetically modified seeds forced on developing world farmers

- the selling-off of state-owned industry to qualify for International Monetary Fund (IMF) and World Bank loans

- increasing dominance of US and European corporate cultures across the globe.

Not everyone agrees that globalisation is necessarily evil, or that globalised corporations are running the lives of individuals, or are more powerful than nations. Some say that the spread of globalisation, free markets and free trade into the developing world is the best way to beat poverty there.

Key term

Globalisation – where the economies of the world are becoming more dominated by a few multinational businesses.

Cultural imperialism

Culture governs every aspect of our lives including:

- our dress sense
- our manners
- our outlook and opinions
- our art and architecture
- our education
- our lifestyle.

To govern culture, it seems, is to govern the world. But what is **cultural imperialism**?

Imperialism means dominating another country to achieve your own aims. Cultural imperialism refers to the tendency for Western business corporations to impose Western ways of life on other cultures around the world. Britain was an imperialist nation for many years when it had an overseas empire. Cultural imperialism is a very divisive topic. In other words, it can cause a great deal of disagreement. Some people argue that countries with dominating cultures such as the USA are forcing their own culture on others through unfair trade practices. Others argue that nobody can be forced to accept cultural imports.

However, some complaints are not easy to dismiss – particularly those surrounding companies rather than countries. Look at the accusations that follow.

- Western media companies have been using large budgets and aggressive 'monopoly-like' practices to steadily push their smaller, less aggressive, competitors onto the sidelines, both at home and abroad.
- While demanding increased access to markets, Western producers and distributors have been very protective of their domestic front. They keep their home audiences largely oblivious to the existence of other products and use their dominant market positions to make it difficult for smaller distributors to bring products into the Western market.

Key term

Cultural imperialism – local ways of life are being influenced and altered through the effects of Western values and practices spreading all over the world.

- Western producers and distributors have been protecting their domestic markets by releasing only selected products themselves, or only releasing products after they have been 'adapted' or 're-branded' to meet Western cultural norms.

Ecology

Just as there are concerns about global or Western-dominated businesses imposing their own cultural assumptions on local cultures around the world, so there are concerns that economic developments are wiping out local wildlife and bio-systems. An ecological system links plants and animals which exist naturally and in harmony in an area. Any interruption to this delicate balance can result in both plants and animals dying out.

Fair trade

Fair trade is not only about trading fairly, it is also about development. With fair trade, producers receive an agreed and stable price that covers the cost of sustainable production. In addition, producer organisations receive an extra payment, known as the Fairtrade social premium, to invest in social, environmental or economic development projects.

The Fairtrade logo on a product informs consumers that the producer has been paid an agreed and stable price

Guarantees a **better deal** for Third World Producers

FAIRTRADE

The Fairtrade Foundation was established in 1992 as an independent certification body that licenses the Fairtrade mark to products that meet international standards which are set by Fairtrade Labelling Organisations International (FLO). Certified producer organisations and registered traders must comply with these standards to ensure better terms of trade and decent working conditions.

In addition, producers must institute process requirements to encourage their organisations to continually:

- improve working conditions for workers and product quality
- increase the environmental stability of their activities
- invest in the development of their organisations and the welfare of their producers.

Fairtrade trading standards stipulate that traders must:

- pay a price to producers that covers the costs of sustainable production and living
- pay a premium that producers can invest in development
- make partial advance payments when requested by producers
- sign contracts that allow for long-term planning and sustainable production practices.

Child labour

UNICEF (the United Nations Children's Emergency Fund) has said that globally:

- 352 million children aged between five and 17 years are engaged in some kind of employment
- 97 per cent of all working children employed in developing countries (many in enforced labour), work in extremely bad conditions.

Children continue to be forced into labour because:

- they do not cost very much to employ
- in some cases, the money they earn can mean the difference between survival or starvation for their family.

Child exploitation is therefore largely caused by poverty. In the 43 countries with an average family income of US$500 or less per person, child labour runs at 30–60 per cent. Where average income is between US$500 and US$1,000, the figure falls to 10–30 per cent of all children.

Whistleblowing

Sometimes in a workplace, whether it is a private business or a public service organisation, corruption can occur. An example of corruption would be a manager giving a close relative confidential information so that they win a moneymaking contract. What happens if another member of staff finds out about this and feels that something should be done about it?

The Public Interest Disclosures Act 1998 made it an offence to discipline anyone who made a disclosure about something believed to be in the 'public interest'. This is **whistleblowing**, alerting everyone to something that is wrong.

Key term

Whistleblowing – informing managers or other authorities about unethical practices going on within an organisation.

Assessment activity 37.4 P4 M3 BTEC

The newly appointed managing director of the company you work for wishes to take a strong stand on social responsibility. In the past, local people have complained about lorries and vans travelling in the area. They have also complained about smells from the factory. The managing director wants full awareness and has asked you to complete the following tasks.

1. Describe the ethical concerns facing the communities in which the business operates. P4

2. Explain ethical concerns facing the communities in which the business operates and suggest measures that could be taken to improve corporate responsibility. M3

Grading tips

1. Select a particular business or industry, then describe the ethical concerns that are generated by its activities. These concerns are likely to be local ones. Example: a forest or woodland is being lost; a local ecological system is disrupted. P4

2. Give a full explanation of why there are concerns about the activities of the business. What steps, if any, could the management of the business take to minimise the concerns? M3

PLTS

Extending your thinking on ethical issues facing the communities and suggesting ways of improving corporate responsibility will help you to develop your skills as a **creative thinker**.

Just checking

1. In your own words, write an explanation of what is meant by 'business ethics'.
2. Explain what is meant by 'sustainability'.
3. What is 'corruption'?
4. Who are the 'stakeholders' in a business? How would you distinguish 'stakeholders' from 'shareholders'?
5. Why might there be a conflict of interest between different stakeholders in a business?
6. How can pressure groups influence ethical questions?
7. What are the main areas of legislation in the UK that influence the ethical behaviour of businesses?
8. What is 'planned obsolescence'? Why is it an ethical concern?
9. Give a brief outline of an ethical issue that affects each of the following:
   - the local community
   - the regional community
   - the national and international community.
10. What is meant by corporate social responsibility? Is it important and why?
11. What is 'globalisation'? Is it important?

edexcel

Assignment tips

1. The web is an excellent source of information about worldwide ethical questions (look for pressure group websites!).

2. When looking at ethical issues it is a good idea to categorise them, for example, environmental, sustainable production, waste, deforestation, etc. Remember to think local too! Your responses will be more impressive if you show local concerns as well as international.

3. Present your work in an imaginative way. Don't just use reports – use images, charts, tables and pie charts too.

38 Business and the economic environment

The economic environment may seem a bit of a mystery. You may have heard terms such as 'economy', 'GDP', 'recession', 'growth' and inflation' on the news without knowing what they really mean or how they affect people. In this unit, you will discover what these terms, and more, are actually referring to as well as how they affect businesses. You will look at different aspects of the UK economic environment and how recent changes have affected it. You will also use what you have learned to apply it to a chosen business. This will allow you to see how business and economic environments are linked together.

The government plays a major role in the economic environment and ultimately aims to control it. You will explore the role of government in detail and learn how the public and voluntary sectors also have a big impact on the economy as a whole and stimulate demand in the private sector.

It is not only events in the UK that affect businesses. The European Union is a major influence on the business environment. You will learn about the different policies that affect the UK that come from the EU and also the way that international economies influence the UK economy through globalisation.

Learning outcomes

After completing this unit you should:

1. understand the impact on businesses of changes in the economic environment
2. know how government spending impacts on businesses
3. understand fiscal and monetary policies and the effects on spending
4. know how the international economy affects UK businesses and competition.

Assessment and grading criteria

This table shows you what you must do in order to achieve a **pass**, **merit** or **distinction** grade, and where you can find activities in this book to help you.

To achieve a **pass** grade the evidence must show that the learner is able to:	To achieve a **merit** grade the evidence must show that, in addition to the pass criteria, the learner is able to:	To achieve a **distinction** grade the evidence must show that, in addition to the pass and merit criteria, the learner is able to:
P1 explain the effects of changes in the economic environment on a selected business **See Assessment activity 38.1, page 299**	**M1** analyse the implications of government policies for a selected business **See Assessment activity 38.1, page 299**	**D1** evaluate the impact of changes in the economic environment on a selected business **See Assessment activity 38.1, page 299**
P2 identify how government policies impact on a selected business **See Assessment activity 38.1, page 299**		
P3 identify the impact of government spending on a selected business **See Assessment activity 38.1, page 299**		
P4 explain how both fiscal and monetary policy decisions have affected a selected business **See Assessment activity 38.2, page 306**	**M2** analyse the effects of fiscal and monetary policies for a selected business in terms of the market it operates in **See Assessment activity 38.2, page 306**	**D2** suggest and justify elements of fiscal and monetary policies that would help a selected business achieve its objectives **See Assessment activity 38.2, page 306**
P5 describe the impact of international factors on a selected business **See Assessment activity 38.3, page 317**	**M3** assess the impact of changes in the global and European business environment on a selected business **See Assessment activity 38.3, page 317**	

How you will be assessed

To achieve this unit, you will need to select a local or national UK business and examine how it is affected by the UK economy, and government spending and policy, as well as influences from the EU and the rest of the world. Assessment activities are provided throughout this unit, as well as research activities to stimulate your thinking and ideas for assessment.

Lenny, 16, BTEC student

I now find watching the news on television very interesting, especially when it is about business. Before studying this unit, hearing expressions like 'GDP', 'inflation', 'fiscal policy' and 'trading blocs' didn't really make much sense to me, but now I really feel well informed and even find myself having an opinion on what is being reported!

Knowing about the economic environment means that I now know how changes in things like interest rates or budget deficits affect businesses and the country as a whole. Sometimes changes end up affecting me as well. Although I never would have thought it, this unit has made me much more interested in government and politics too. It has made me realise how important things like voting are and how I, together with other young people, can get involved in influencing the way that the country is run.

This unit has also helped me appreciate how the UK is linked to the economies of the EU and the rest of the world. When something happens in another country, it really can affect the UK economy in ways that I can now understand.

1. What do you think is meant by inflation?

2. Why is it important for the economy that young people vote in local and general elections?

3. How might interest rates affect you as a young person?

1 Understand the impact on businesses of changes in the economic environment

There are many different elements of the economic environment that have a significant impact on businesses. In this unit you will learn about these different elements and how exactly they influence the economic environment, as well as how government policy is used to influence them. Whilst you are reading this section and carrying out the activities in preparation for assessment, it is important that you think of a business that you will be able to study in more detail.

1.1 Economic environment

Every country has its own **economy** which has features that can be measured in different ways to see how they are changing. You will learn about these different features and their measures in this section, which will enable you to explain changes in a specific business that you have chosen. The economic environment of a country has a significant effect on its businesses, as the trade that is happening between that country and other countries affects how much money is passing in and out of the country. This then affects the cost of goods and prices. In this section we will be focusing on the economic environment in the UK.

Business cycle

When economists make judgements about the economy, they use a number of different indicators to measure how the country is doing compared to another point in time, for example, last month, last quarter or last year. They also use these indicators to make judgements about the UK economy compared to other economies around the world. You will learn about how

these indicators are worked out on pages 283–8. All economies are known to go through different stages that are cyclical, as shown in Figure 38.1.

The business cycle shows how we can expect to see increases and falls in the production, income and expenditure of the country over a period of time. Economists use specific terms to describe different parts of the business cycle, as shown in Table 38.1 (below).

The UK economy moves between boom and recession over time because during a boom the demand for products eventually gets so high that manufacturers and other suppliers cannot satisfy it. This leads to rising prices. As costs rise, including those paid to employees for their wages, as most people will be employed the result is rising inflation. (You will learn more about inflation and deflation on page 284.) People also borrow more, so the demand for credit also goes up and becomes more expensive.

Eventually, with so many costs increasing, the price of products or services becomes so high that demand starts to fall as people are unable to pay for them. This then leads to productivity falling as businesses do not need to make as many products or offer as many services and start to cut costs. They may at this point start to reduce the numbers of staff that they have or reduce selling prices to try to increase demand. Profits also start to fall. Unemployment starts to go up and the government has to spend more money on benefits and methods of creating a demand for products or services to try to prevent unemployment levels from getting higher.

Once an economy has reached recession, it can be difficult for it to get out of because of the cycle of recession itself, as shown in Figure 38.2. The most usual way for an economy to be stimulated to recover from recession is by some form of external stimulus, perhaps from the government or another investor. You will learn more about how this is done as you work through this unit.

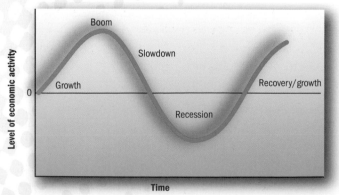

Figure 38.1: The business cycle

Key term

Economy – the way that trade, industry and the wealth of a country is measured.

Table 38.1: Business cycle terms

Term	What it means
Boom	There is a high level of economic growth. Demand for products is high. Employment levels and wages are rising. Sales and profits are high. The UK demand for imports from other countries is high. The number of products being made is high. Interest rates are increasing. Investment levels are high. GDP growth is higher than the UK trend rate for economic growth, which has tended to be around 2.5 per cent in the past.
Slow down	Economic growth is slowing, but output is still going up.
Recession	The economy has contracted and continues to contract. People start to save rather than spend, so demand falls. Investment falls. Unemployment rises. Government spending rises, for example, on unemployment benefits and initiatives to stimulate demand. Prices fall. Interest rates fall. Negative GDP growth for two or more consecutive quarters.
Recovery	When the economy has reached the lowest point in a recession the next stage is recovery. Recovery often needs some kind of stimulus to start it, for example, a cut in taxes, a reduction in interest rates or investment by other countries.

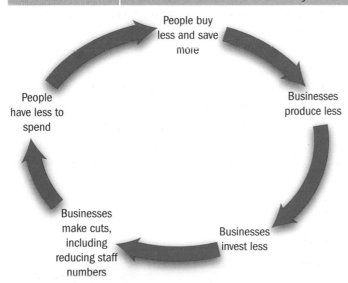

Figure 38.2: The recession cycle

Indicators

Knowing the different stages of the business cycle is very important in understanding how the economy is measured. There are five different indicators of an economy's status which can be measured to indicate how well it is doing. These are:

1. changes in Gross Domestic Product (GDP)
2. rates of inflation and deflation
3. employment rates
4. trade surpluses/deficits
5. balance of payments.

Changes in Gross Domestic Product (GDP)

The indicator that is used to measure how much is being made in the UK is known as the Gross Domestic Product (GDP). Changes in the GDP indicate which stage of the business cycle the UK economy is in (see Figure 38.3 overleaf). GDP is the measure of business activity in the country as a whole for a particular quarter. Although it is only shown as one measure there are in fact three parts to it.

- GDP Output measures the value of the products and services that have been created through the economy, for example, through farming or manufacturing.
- GDP Income measures the total income generated by the production of goods and services in the economy.

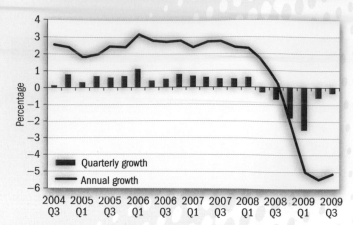

Figure 38.3: UK GDP Growth 2004–2009 (source: Office for National Statistics)

- GDP Expenditure measures the total expenditure on all finished goods and services that have been produced in the UK economy.

The combination of these three different measures is used by the government to work out what is happening to the economy as a whole. This information can then be used to make plans. The Office for National Statistics produces economic data and it is published to organisations including banks, industry leaders and the media. GDP statistics are used not only to record what has happened already, but also to predict what is going to happen in the future.

Activity: The UK economy

In pairs, look at the graph in Figure 38.3 which shows UK GDP Growth between 2004 and 2009. Then answer the following questions.

1. Which stage of the business cycle was the UK economy in during Quarter 1 of 2006?

2. Which stage of the business cycle was the UK economy in during Quarter 1 of 2008?

3. Which stage of the business cycle was the UK economy in during Quarter 1 of 2009?

4. What was starting to happen in Quarter 3 of 2009?

Now visit the Office for National Statistics website at www.statistics.gov.uk to obtain the latest information on GDP growth to find out the current situation in the UK economy.

Activity: The likely effects of the business cycle on Warburtons

Warburtons is a successful bakery firm based in Bolton with locations all over the UK. Like all other businesses in the UK, it is affected by events and changes in the UK economy. Use the knowledge that you have learned so far to carry out some research into the likely effects of changes in the GDP over the past 10 to 20 years on Warburtons. What kind of changes are booms and recessions likely to have had on this business? You can visit the Warburtons website at www.warburtons.co.uk.

Rates of inflation and deflation

Inflation and deflation relate to the measurement of prices in the UK economy. Inflation is measured by the Consumer Price Index (CPI), which looks at prices in the economy as a whole using standard measurements that have been agreed across Europe. The Retail Price Index (RPI) was traditionally used to measure inflation before the change over to the CPI and includes mortgage interest payments, unlike the CPI (see Figure 38.4 opposite).

The CPI index measures the average price changes of a 'basket of goods' over a period of time. The price of the basket of goods is measured each month and the Office for National Statistics uses the new prices to work out how much the goods have changed in price. If the prices have gone up, this is known as inflation; if the prices have gone down, this is known as deflation.

When inflation is going up, it means that the price of goods is going up, so this may lead to consumers not being able to buy the things they want or businesses cutting costs, for example, by making employees redundant. This leads to unemployment rising and a further fall in the demand for goods. Because inflation makes it more difficult for people to afford to buy things, employees often ask to be paid more so that

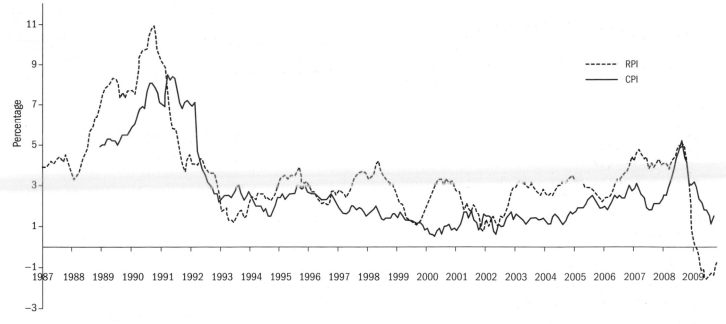

Figure 38.4: CPI and RPI – percentage changes year on year, 1987–2009 (source: Office for National Statistics)

they can cover their costs. If a pay increase is not equal to inflation, it means that in real terms those employees are being paid less, but if they have a pay increase that is equal to or higher than inflation, this can lead to higher costs for the business, which in turn leads to prices having to go up. Everything has a knock-on effect. When business costs go up and the prices of goods have to rise, this is known as cost-push inflation. When prices go up because the product is in short supply, for example, when the economy is in a boom, this is known as demand-pull inflation.

As inflation is a measure of prices going up, it is usual that inflation is a positive increase, as costs usually go up rather than go down due to the value of money. You may remember that when you were younger prices seemed a lot less, but actually, if you compare them to what they would be worth today, you may be surprised as although prices have gone up, wages have gone up too and you can still afford them.

Activity: What is your money worth?

Using the Measuring Worth website (www.measuringworth.com), find out how much something that cost £1 when you were born is worth now. Then consider the effect of the changes in the value of money on businesses and the assets they own.

Sometimes, as you saw in the graph in Figure 38.1, there may be a time in an economy when there is deflation. Deflation is when the price of goods and services goes down for a period of time. This often shows that the economy is in a period of recession.

Although falling prices may seem like a very good thing, it can cause problems. Because prices are pushed down, the costs for businesses need to be reduced so that they can survive. This means that businesses may need to cut costs and become more efficient, which can lead to redundancies. Deflation also means that people may put off buying more expensive products because they believe that they will become cheaper in the future. This too can make it difficult for businesses to survive.

Activity: The likely effects of inflation and deflation on Warburtons

Use the knowledge that you have learned so far to carry out research into the likely effects of the changes in inflation and deflation over the past 20 years on Warburtons.

Employment rates

Employment rates are also indicators of the performance of the economy. You have already learned that during a boom, employment levels will be high and during a recession unemployment levels will be high (see Figure 38.5). Employment rates affect businesses and the economy as a whole in several different ways.

When employment levels are high, it may be more difficult for an employer to recruit suitable staff. This is because there may not be many suitable people looking for work. Those already working for the business may ask for higher wages as a result of levels of inflation. This may make it difficult for the business to manage costs. However, when employment levels are high the government will receive more money in taxes from those who are working and paying tax and National Insurance.

When unemployment levels are high, people may not be able to afford to buy goods from businesses and so sales may fall. The government will need to spend more money looking after people, including payments for benefits. The government will also receive less money through taxes. High levels of unemployment are bad for an economy because it means that more people are not contributing to the economy.

In developed countries with high levels of technology, unemployment may take place for structural reasons, such as machines being able to do work that was previously done by people.

Trade surpluses/deficits

Another indicator that shows how the UK economy is doing is the measurement of trade surpluses or trade deficits with other countries. A trade surplus means that the value of exports from the UK is greater than

Activity: The likely effects of employment and unemployment on Warburtons

Use the knowledge that you have learned so far to carry out research into the likely effects of the changes in employment and unemployment rates over the past 20 years on Warburtons.

the value of imports. A trade deficit means that the value of exports from the UK is less than the value of imports.

When trade deficit occurs, it means that a country is importing more than it exports. In simple terms it means that the country is spending more than it is earning. However, trade deficit is not always a major problem as the country may be able to make up the difference with investment from investors in other countries. The UK has had a trade deficit for a number of years and throughout 2009 the size of the deficit increased.

Figure 38.6 shows the deficit between what was being imported against what was being exported for goods and services until the end of 2008. It shows that the UK was exporting more services than it was importing and had done so for the previous ten years. However, for imports of goods the opposite was true. Combining goods and services together means that overall the UK has a deficit.

The UK's trade deficit has a number of effects on UK businesses. Importing goods from overseas is likely to mean that they are cheaper and this may help

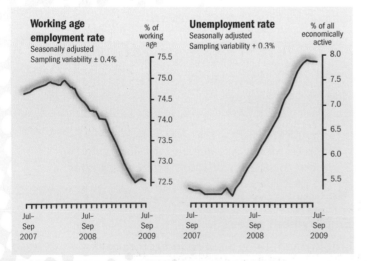

Figure 38.5: Employment statistics, 2007–2009 (source: Office for National Statistics)

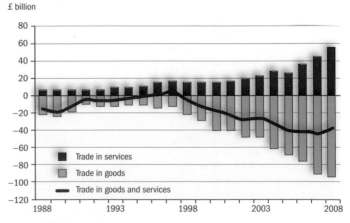

Figure 38.6: Balance of UK trade in goods and services, 1988–2008 (source: Office for National Statistics)

businesses in the UK to cut costs. This may include those businesses that are offering services. However, UK manufacturing companies may find it more difficult to survive if consumers buy the imported goods as prices are likely to be cheaper than similar goods made in the UK.

Balance of payments

The balance of payments is the difference between the amount of money that is coming into the country against the amount of money that is going out. The balance of payments includes all the financial imports and exports, including those that are trade as well as investments. Like a trade deficit, a negative balance of payments indicates that more money is flowing out of the country than is flowing into the country.

Looking at Figure 38.7 (below), the current account shows all of the payments in and out of the country, including trade and investment. A negative number

A Summary of balance of payments in 2008

£ million

	Credits	Debits
1. Current account		
A. Goods and service	421 501	459 899
1. Goods	251 102	343 979
2. Services	170 399	115 920
2.1. Transportation	20 880	20 376
2.2. Travel	19 598	37 256
2.3. Communications	4 639	4 122
2.4. Construction	1 127	904
2.5. Insurance	8 036	1 073
2.6. Financial	52 828	14 209
2.7. Computer and information	7 040	3 055
2.8. Royalties and licence fees	7 361	5 500
2.9. Other business	44 697	24 404
2.10. Personal, cultural and recreational	2 091	959
2.11. Government	2 102	4 062
B. Income	263 703	236 763
1. Compensation of employees	1 032	1 738
2. Investment income	262 671	235 025
2.1. Direct investment	69 169	10 638
2.2. Portfolio investment	68 104	73 309
2.3. Other investment (including earnings on reserve assets)	125 398	151 078
C. Current transfers	15 422	29 032
1. General government	5 512	14 606
2. Other sectors	9 910	14 426
Total current account	**700 828**	**726 884**
2. Capital and financial accounts		
A. Capital account	5 590	2 197
1. Capital transfers	4 589	1 297
2. Acquisition disposal of non-produced, non-financial assets	1 001	900
B. Financial account	−637 053	−655 204
1. Direct Investment	52 451	72 528
Abroad		72 528
1.1. Equity capital		23 405
1.2. Reinvested earnings		36 091
1.3. Other capital		13 032
In United Kingdom	52 461	
1.1. Equity capital	49 218	
1.2. Reinvested earnings	15 923	
1.3. Other capital[2]	−12 680	
2. Portfolio Investment	240 586	−128 620
Assets		−128 620
2.1. Equity securities		−60 774
2.2. Debt securities		−67 846
Liabilities	240 586	
2.1. Equity securities	44 045	
2.2. Debt securities	196 541	
3. Financial derivatives (net)		−17 746
4. Other Investment	−930 130	−580 028
Assets		−580 028
4.1. Trade credits		−158
4.2. Loans		−122 407
4.3. Currency and deposits		−461 054
4.4. Other assets		3 591
Liabilities	−930 130	
4.1. Trade credits	−	
4.2. Loans	−348 261	
4.3. Currency deposits	−576 783	
4.4. Other assets	−5 086	
5. Reserve assets		−1 338
5.1. Monetary gold		−
5.2. Special drawing rights		−24
5.3. Reserve position in the IMF		802
5.4. Foreign exchange		−1 923
Total capital and financial accounts	**−631 483**	**−868 007**
Total current, capital and financial accounts	**88 133**	**72 887**
Net errors and omissions	**3 554**	

1 Other capital transaction on direct investment abroad represents claims on affiliated enterprises less liabilities to affiliated enterprises
2 Other capital transactions on direct investment in the United Kingdom represents liabilities to direct investors less claims on direct investors

Figure 38.7: Summary of balance of payments, 2008 (source: Office for National Statistics)

indicates that more money is being paid out than is coming in. The capital account shows all international capital transfers and any assets that have been bought or sold, such as property or gifts. The capital account has had a surplus since 1996. The financial account shows international money that is flowing in or out of the country relating to business investments in land, stocks and shares. This account may include government-owned assets, such as reserves including gold or assets owned by foreign investors.

To make the balance of payments balance, the amount of money that is held in the current account should balance against the capital and financial accounts added together. When the UK has a deficit current account, it means that it is buying more goods and services rather than investing money in capital assets. If the UK is borrowing money to fund the current account, this will show as an inflow of foreign capital in the balance of payments.

If a country like the UK has a negative balance of payments, this means that the outflow of money is greater than the inflow. For businesses that are established in the UK, this may mean that it is harder for them to export their products to other countries. It may also mean that it is more difficult for them to access finance to invest or make their businesses more efficient. In the longer term, this may also lead to them being less competitive as they are unable to become more efficient and therefore compete with overseas companies, especially in industries that involve manufacturing.

Activity: The likely effects of the balance of payments on Warburtons

Use the knowledge that you have learned so far to carry out research into the likely effects of a negative balance of payments during 2008 on Warburtons.

Conflicting objectives

The five different indicators that can be used to measure how the economy is doing (see pages 283–8) help the government to work out which stage of the business cycle the economy is in. You may have realised that some of the indictors are interlinked and that positively affecting one indicator may have a

negative effect on another. This is a challenge that the UK government, the Governor of the Bank of England and business leaders have to face to make sure that all the indicators are as positive as possible.

If the government wants to increase the number of people in employment that are able to pay tax, it must also be mindful that full employment can lead to inflation as more people are in work and therefore demanding products or there are fewer people available to work and therefore they can ask for higher wages.

PLTS

Researching the scrappage scheme will help you to develop your skills as an **independent enquirer**.

Functional skills

Researching and producing your scrappage scheme presentation may help you to develop your **ICT** skills.

'Ripple effects' of downturns in particular industries

You have already learned that there are some economic influences that affect the whole of the UK economy, for example, levels of inflation. Some industries have such a big influence on the UK economy that if they are showing a downturn in production, the consequences of this are felt in other industries and potentially across the economy as a whole. Particular industries that have this impact include housing, construction and manufacturing.

Housing

The housing industry has such a large impact on the UK economy because around two thirds of people in the UK own their own home. If there is a downturn in the price of houses, this has a knock-on effect on the wider economy. This is because if house prices fall, people may lose confidence in spending and, therefore, this will affect the demand for goods and services. Houses are the only form of wealth that many people in the UK have and they are often used as security. If their house price falls, people feel less secure. Banks and building societies may be less willing to loan money to people to buy new houses.

The UK car industry

In the 2009 Budget, the government introduced a voluntary discount scheme that supported motor dealers to give motorists £2,000 towards a new vehicle if they traded in their old one. The car had to be over ten years old and to be going for scrap. The idea of the scrappage scheme was to boost demand and support the UK car industry, as well as the manufacturers of car parts produced in the UK. The scheme was introduced because car sales were falling.

The scheme was also designed to help reduce carbon emissions as newer cars are more environmentally friendly than older ones. The scheme was expected to have cost more than £400 million by February 2010.

Think about it!

1. Which of the economic indicators do you think the government was trying to improve in the UK car industry?

2. Using quality newspapers, journals and websites, such as the BBC website (www.bbc.co.uk), find out the benefits of the scrappage scheme. Find out, too, the drawbacks or disadvantages of the scheme, particularly in relation to the balance of payments and areas of the economy that were adversely affected by the scheme.

3. Put together a short presentation that makes a judgement about whether or not you think the scrappage scheme was the most appropriate scheme to run during 2009.

A fall in the housing market will also affect those other industries that depend on its sales, such as removals, estate agency or retail sales of items for the home, such as new kitchens or bathrooms. A decline in the sales of these items means that the businesses selling them then have to cut costs, which may include redundancies, therefore leading to higher unemployment and a reduction in overall demand across the economy. A fall in the housing market may also lead to foreign investors not wanting to put their money into the UK and, of course, UK buyers may also affect other economies around the world by not wanting to buy there either.

Construction

The construction industry is linked to the housing industry because houses need to be built and this is done through their construction. A decline in the price of houses leads to fewer people wanting to buy a first home or move from one home to another. Therefore, a decrease in the demand for houses will mean that the construction industry is affected. If demand for the construction of houses, or other buildings, falls because businesses and home owners are trying to cut costs, construction-related industries will also be affected. These include construction material businesses, electricians, plumbers and painters. This can lead to higher unemployment.

Manufacturing

The effect of a decline in manufacturing may be felt in a number of different ways in the UK economy. Firstly, if manufacturing companies need to reduce costs, it is likely that they will make redundancies and this may lead to a loss of skills in the industry, as well as a rise in unemployment. A reduction in demand for products and services across the economy is also likely to occur. A reduction in goods to sell for export will affect the balance of payments by making it even more negative. If manufacturers cannot produce goods for the UK, they will need to be imported and this again will lead to a more negative balance of payments. If manufacturing declines, it is less likely that foreign investors will want to bring their money to the UK to invest in new processes and equipment. This may, therefore, affect the value of the UK pound and cause to it becoming weaker.

Structural adjustments

When people look at the economy as a whole, they often refer to its structure. This means the overall make-up of the economy. The structure is divided into three sectors:

- the primary sector, which consists of activities that directly relate to natural resources, including farming, mining, oil extraction and fishing
- the secondary sector, which consists of activities that include manufacturing and construction
- the tertiary sector (also known as the service sector), which consists of activities that relate to services, such as banking, education, communications, hotels and catering and transport.

In the past, the UK was referred to as being an industrial economy. This meant that most of the output and employment came from the primary and secondary sectors. Since the 1960s, the amount of manufacturing has steadily declined and more output and employment now comes from services industries. This can be seen in Figure 38.8, which shows the changing structure of the UK economy. As you can see, services have significantly increased since 1970 compared to manufacturing when comparing gross value added (GVA), which is the contribution that each producer, individual or sector makes to the

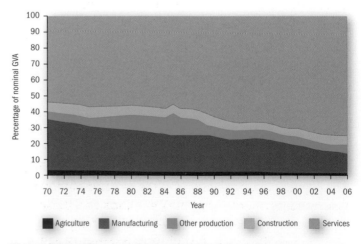

Figure 38.8: The changing structure of the UK economy, 1970–2006 (source: Office for National Statistics)

Activity: GDP and sectoral output

Look at Figure 38.9, which shows GDP and sectoral output.

1. In pairs or small groups discuss what is happening to:
    - overall GDP
    - services output
    - construction output
    - manufacturing output.

2. Select a business in your local area that you are familiar with. Explain how these changes may affect the business and present your ideas and discussions to another pair or group.

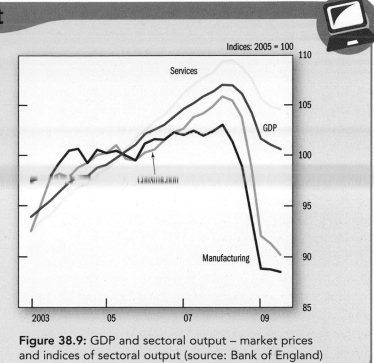

Figure 38.9: GDP and sectoral output – market prices and indices of sectoral output (source: Bank of England)

UK economy. The UK economy, like others around the world, changes over time due to changes in demand for UK products. For example, during an economic boom when people have more money in their households, they are more likely to demand services such as hotels or communications at a higher level compared to other sectors, for example, those supplying food, which would not see such high growth. Such changes affect the structure of the economy and levels of output and employment in the different sectors. This means that businesses will be affected by those changes as demand for their products or services is affected by structural changes in the economy as a whole.

Welfare considerations

As you should know by now, employment rates greatly impact on businesses, and during economically challenging times businesses need to cut costs and offer more services or produce more goods in order to be competitive. This means that the economic environment affects the way that businesses operate. Employees who are working make tax and National Insurance payments from their earnings and these are used to fund public services, such as hospitals and schools. Businesses also make contributions on behalf of their employees, including payments towards

pension schemes. The money taken from employees and businesses not only goes towards paying for public services, but also funds benefits for those people who are unemployed, unable to work or retired.

Activity: Taxes

Carry out some research into all the different ways that employees and businesses pay taxes, both directly and indirectly. Produce a short guide or leaflet for someone who is just starting your course.

Difficult economic times have a number of different effects on businesses. Firstly, there may be pressure on individuals and businesses to raise more money through taxation so that money is available to run services and fund benefit payments. If there are more people out of work, this is likely to affect the demand for products and services so businesses need to cut costs at the same time. The government may need to raise money through borrowing and this may cause the Bank of England interest rate to go up, which will mean that a business has to pay higher interest on any loans that it has. You will learn more about the welfare state and social policy later in this unit.

1.2 Government policy

At a minimum of every five years, an election has to be held and a government voted in by the people of the UK to run the country. The government produces a set of policies that it uses and develops to influence the UK economy. These are divided into nine key areas and each of these influences the way that businesses operate. We will look at each of these in turn in this section.

Activity: Government and elections

Find out the answers to the following questions and produce a poster that displays your answers.

- Who is the current Prime Minister?
- Which political party is currently in power?
- How long have they been in power?
- Find out more about that party and what they believe in.

Economic policy

Economic policy means the policies that the government has to deal with such as economic growth, unemployment and inflation. A government will put together a package of measures that it believes will deal with these issues, but as you have already learned sometimes the objectives of each measure will conflict.

Economic growth is very important to governments as it means that the living standards of the population increases. The benefits of good **standards of living** are people bringing in an income, increased demand for products and services, revenue from taxes and low rates of unemployment leading to less poverty.

Key term

Standards of living – the quality of people's lives in terms of income and material comforts. It is measured using the real national income per capita. This is calculated by dividing the GDP by the total population and shows whether the standard is going up or down per person.

Unemployment policy is closely linked with economic growth because if the economy is growing, then more people are likely to be needed in work and therefore fewer people should be unemployed. If a government's objective is to have as many people employed as possible, this means it is working towards full employment (which equates to less than 3 per cent of the population being unemployed). Economic growth does not necessarily lead directly to reduced levels of unemployment because it depends on the type of growth that is created and the type of jobs that are needed. This means that unemployment policy also needs to link with other policies, such as those on education, skills and training. Higher levels of employment, as you learned on pages 285–6, also means that more people will be contributing to the UK economy as a whole.

Did you know?

In December 2009, the (then) Chancellor of the Exchequer, Alistair Darling, announced a package of measures to try to tackle unemployment. These included internships and guarantees of places in education or training for every 16 and 17 year old in the UK. This was due to the level of young people being NEET (Not in Employment, Education or Training) exceeding one million people, i.e. 1 in 10 of people aged 16–19.

Activity: Unemployment policy

Carry out research into current government policy on unemployment. Then find out how it might be affecting a business in your area through incentive schemes for employers, such as internships, apprenticeships or training. Produce a display for your classroom on the different opportunities that are available that directly link to government policy.

Industrial policy

Industrial policy relates to government policy that is designed to enhance and increase industry in the UK. This is linked with economic policy as a whole, but focuses more on jobs and skills. In April 2009, the government published a policy document called

Building Britain's Future – New Industry, New Jobs. The document outlined key ways that the government's industrial policy was being shaped to support:

- rising incomes
- low carbon economies and greater resource efficiency
- new technologies
- demographic changes.

Policy documents like these highlight the way that governments plan to deal with issues that directly relate to industry. Industrial policy is also strongly linked to competition policy.

Activity: *Building Britain's Future – New Industry, New Jobs*

Find out how the demographic changes that are outlined in the above industrial policy might impact on a business in your area. You can access the document from the Department for Business, Innovation & Skills website at www.bis.gov.uk/files/file51023.pdf.

Competition policy

Government policy towards competition also has a big influence on the economy. In December 2009, the UK government's attitude towards competition was that it brought a number of different benefits, including the good use of the economy's resources through enterprise and efficiency and good performance on pricing, quality and choice. However, there was also recognition that competition policy needs to make sure that one or two businesses do not dominate a market and that the competition is as fair as possible.

Activity: The Treaty on Open Skies

The UK government signed up to The Treaty on Open Skies, which allows greater competition between airlines across the world. Find out more about the treaty by carrying out research in books, journals and online. Then write a short summary of the impact that the treaty had on competition between airlines around the world.

To ensure that competition takes place within the UK, the Competition Act 1998 is used to stop anti-competitive practices such as:

- price fixing, where businesses get together to agree prices
- businesses becoming too dominant in the market place
- businesses that supply goods and services to some businesses but not others
- selling goods or services at different prices for different groups of customers
- forcing rivals out of business
- limiting supplies to make sure prices go up.

These UK anti-competitive laws are also supported by EU laws that prevent such practices taking place. The Office of Fair Trading works to investigate anti-competitive practices and ensure that competition continues in the UK economy. Sector regulators are used to ensure that anti-competitive practices are dealt with and these regulators include Ofcom (communications industries), Ofwat (water and sewerage providers) and Ofgem (gas and electricity providers). If companies are found to be operating in a non-competitive way, their cases may be referred to the Competition Commission for full investigation.

Activity: The Competition Commission

Visit the Competition Commission's website at www.competition-commission.org.uk and look at some of cases that have been referred to the Commission under their current inquiries section (click the Investigations link). Select one case and produce a short presentation that you can give to other students in your class on why the case was referred and what the outcome was. Use presentation software or diagrams to help you deliver your presentation. Consider the effect of the inquiry on the businesses involved and others in the sector in which they are trading.

Fiscal policy

Fiscal policy covers the spending and taxation decisions of a government. Governments can change tax rates, the type of taxes that they impose and what they decide to tax. The aim of fiscal policy is to influence **aggregate demand** by increasing the government's own spending and/or by reducing taxes. For example, the less tax people pay on their incomes – income tax – the more money they will have to spend and this will increase demand. Increasing income taxes will decrease the amount of money people have to spend, but the government will have more money for public spending.

Keeping a balance between the amount of money available for public spending and the level of taxation is important as changes in either can affect aggregate demand and therefore, unemployment levels and inflation. You will learn about fiscal policy in more detail on page 300.

Social policy

Social policy means the polices that the UK government put in place for welfare and social protection. It relates to social services and the welfare state. It directly links to the economic environment because it relates to issues such as health, employment, community care, housing, crime and social disadvantage.

Social policy affects the level of benefits that are given to people, whether they are **means-tested** or universal (given to everyone), the level of investment that is made into public services, such as hospitals, and investment in programmes for housing and crime prevention. Social policy affects businesses because it ensures that employees are treated equally in terms of their age, gender, race, sexual orientation, disability, religion or beliefs. The National Minimum Wage is part of social policy as it sets minimum levels at which employees must not be paid.

As the UK is part of the European Union, it is also supported by EU social policies. These include social measures that support the development of areas of the EU and funds are provided to help with this.

Key terms

Aggregate demand – the total demand for goods and services in an economy.

Means-tested – an assessment of whether or not someone qualifies for financial help by taking into account their level of individual or household income.

Activity: The ESF and Gloucestershire

In June 2009, Gloucestershire First, the Gloucestershire Development Agency, was awarded £500,000 by the European Social Fund (ESF) to help small and medium sized businesses in the area cope with difficult economic conditions. The money awarded was to be used to support businesses with 20 or less employees to help them cope with making staff redundant. Employees facing redundancy or those already made redundant were offered support in finding new jobs or training if necessary.

1. Produce a factsheet about the European Social Fund and how it has been used in the UK to help people, areas and businesses.

2. Find out what the allocation is in your area and how the fund is being used.

PLTS

Researching the European Social Fund will help you to develop your skills as an **independent enquirer**.

Education and training policy

Government policy on education has a very large impact on the way that businesses operate and the level of skills in the population. On page 293, you learned about the UK government's publication *Building Britain's Future – New Industry, New Jobs*, which has a strong focus on education and training in order to help improve the economy.

Education and training needs to link with industrial policy to make sure that people are being trained for employment in areas that will help the economy. Education and training policy will dictate the type of qualifications that are studied and which qualifications money is invested in. It also includes support for different types of training, such as literacy and numeracy skills, as well as funding for students wanting to study in higher education. In 2007 the government published a policy document called *World Class Skills: Implementing the Leitch Review of Skills in England* which describes how the government planned to improve skill levels in the population to 2020.

Activity: World Class Skills

Access a copy of the *World Class Skills: Implementing the Leitch Review of Skills in England* policy document. Choose one of the goals or recommendations described in the document that interests you and then write a short report about how its influence would affect an employer in your area.

Education and training policy is very closely linked to funding, so governments have to prioritise which groups should receive different amounts of funding, from pre-school learning all the way through to learning opportunities in the community and for the elderly. These groups all have important needs and so ensuring that the money is used as effectively as possible is very important.

Sometimes government policy is so important that a policy is made law. This happened with the Education and Skills Act in 2008, which was a landmark piece of legislation, mainly because it raised the compulsory participation age of young people in education or employment with training from 16 to 18.

Activity: Raising the compulsory participation age

Find out more about the Education and Skills Act 2008 and interview a local employer to find out their views about it.

- How will the change in the compulsory participation age affect the employer?

- What are the advantages and disadvantages to their business and industry?

- Overall, what does the employer think about the change in the school leaving age?

Transport policy

Transport policy covers many different areas and links not only with economic policy, but also has obvious links with environmental policy. Transport policy covers:

- road
- air
- train
- shipping.

Within each of these, it also substantially affects levels of crime, taxation and congestion. Transport policy is considered at national and regional levels to try to ensure that the UK has good transport systems that help businesses to operate as efficiently and effectively as possible. Transport policy influences the amount of tax that is paid as fuel duty. It also influences the level of tax vehicle owners pay to drive their vehicles on the road. Security in public areas, such as bus or train stations, is also covered as well as an increase in the number of British Transport Police who take part in initiatives to reduce crime and the fear of crime for public transport users.

Did you know?

The Department for Transport is responsible for all policies relating to transport. Why not visit the website at www.dft.gov.uk and find out more about what it does?

Activity: Vehicle tax

In April 2010, there were a number of changes made to the way that vehicle tax was charged. Visit the UK government website Directgov at www.direct.gov.uk and click on Motoring to find out more about the changes.

1. What might be the potential affects of these changes on local businesses in your area?

2. What will the effects on customers be, if any?

Regional policy

Regional policies are those that are appropriate to a particular region of the UK. In 1994 the government divided England into a number of different regions (see Figure 38.10 overleaf) and developed policies according to the needs of those particular regions. Each region often has different issues that need to be addressed and regional policy allows this to happen.

Environmental policy

Government policy with regards to the environment is very closely linked with transport and industry policy because these areas need to complement one another

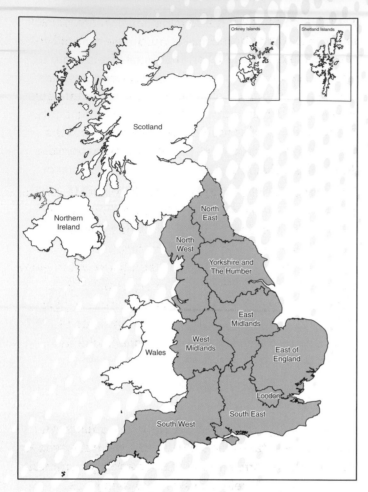

Figure 38.10: Regions of England by government office

rather than conflict. Government environmental policy is led by the Department for Energy and Climate Change (DECC). In 2008, the UK government greatly enhanced its environmental policy by changing the law through the Climate Change Act. This Act includes the following targets:

- a UK-wide climate change risk assessment must be completed every five years
- a programme must be put in place to reduce climate change risks
- public authorities and some companies, for example, those that supply water and energy, must report on what they are doing to reduce climate risk
- a climate strategy has to be published.

Activity: DECC

Access the DECC website at www.decc.gov.uk and carry out some research into the environmental policy developments that are happening in the UK as a whole and in your area. Consider how these environmental policy changes might affect businesses in your area.

Activity: Government Office Network

Access the Government Office Network website at www.gonetwork.gos.gov.uk and find out what is happening in the regional government office for your area and how businesses operating where you live are being affected by these actions.

Environmental policy is significantly linked to climate change

2 Know how government spending impacts on businesses

You have already learned how government spending impacts on businesses by looking at government policy. Policy and spending are very closely linked as spending usually follows policy. Government spending has a huge impact on demand in the economy and we will look at this now in greater detail so that you will be able to measure the impact on local and national businesses.

2.1 Government spending

Government spending is influenced by the type of government that is in power and the type of role that it sees for itself. Most modern governments across the world believe that it is important for them to stabilise their economies by spending money in different areas to stimulate or reduce aggregate demand. In this section, you will learn how government spending impacts on businesses positively and negatively, including the impact on business confidence.

Public services via central and local government agencies

Public services are any services that are provided by the government, such as education, health and the police. The level of investment in public services depends on the government's priorities for the UK as a whole and also the priorities for a particular area.

Many public services are run by both central and local government. For example, the National Health Service is run centrally, but local areas also have primary care trusts that look after care needs in their area. Local authorities look after the education needs of local people, while the Department for Schools and Families considers the way that the service operates as a whole.

The Audit Commission is a central government agency that monitors local government agencies to compare how they are doing and how wisely government money is being spent. In December 2009, it launched measures to make it easier to compare local government spending via the Oneplace website.

Activity: Oneplace

Access the Oneplace website at www.oneplace.direct.gov.uk and take a look at the Area assessment for where you live. How is your area doing? How is government money being spent locally? What are the priorities in terms of public spending? How might local government spending affect businesses in your area?

Private and voluntary sector business organisations

Private and voluntary sector business organisations are also affected by government spending. If the government invests in a particular sector and area,

this leads to business being generated for the private sector. For example, in Southampton the new police headquarters for the city opened in 2010. For the previous two years, Kier Brazier (www.kier.co.uk) was involved in the construction of the building that cost around £31 million. Jobs were created to support the development and other local businesses benefited from increased trade from the construction workers during the building phase.

Government spending also affects the voluntary sector because grants are more readily available for such organisations when government spending is high. In March 2010, the government announced that £38 million worth of grants had been given out in more then 15,000 small grants to voluntary organisations. If spending is cut, these organisations may struggle to find alternative funding particularly in times of economic difficulty when contributions to charity may decline.

Deficit funding

Deficit funding is where the government spends more than it takes in taxes. This means that the government then needs to borrow money from banks, government bonds or through selling assets. The difference between the amount of money that the government is spending and the amount of tax revenue that is being received is called the public sector net cash requirement (PSNCR). If the PSNCR continues over a number of years, it is then called the government debt.

If there are not enough people in work to pay taxes, the government may need to boost spending to increase aggregate demand itself and try to break the cycle. In November 2009, the PSNCR was £81.6 billion, which was £62.5 billion higher than in 2008/09 and the highest level so far since records began. It was expected that the borrowing would continue to increase to £175 billion by April 2010. As a result, the Chancellor of the Exchequer announced a package of measures to reduce the amount of borrowing, including the Fiscal Responsibility Bill which was passed by Parliament in February 2010.

Like an individual or business, if government borrowing and debts become too large it may become impossible for the government to pay the money back. This is known as 'defaulting on a debt' and with economies so interlinked, this often affects other countries. In 2008, due to a banking crisis in Iceland, the government there came close to bankruptcy as debts spiralled out of control. Many other countries were affected by this, including charities that had invested money in Iceland to try to get a high return on their donations.

Did you know?

Naomi House, a children's hospice in Hampshire, and The Cats Protection League both lost significant amounts of money due to the collapse of the Icelandic banking system. Naomi House lost £5.5 million and The Cats Protection League lost £11.2 million as a result.

Government spending and the multiplier mechanism

As you have already seen, an increase in aggregate demand affects government spending on the factors that affect that demand. Increasing government spending to increase aggregate demand has benefits known as the 'multiplier mechanism' or 'multiplier effect'. As government spending stimulates demand, it makes investment in the economy more attractive to business people. This is because they will want to invest their money in the economy in order to make more money. The opposite is true if aggregate demand is reducing as business people are likely to feel uncertain about investment. The level of confidence in the economy is often referred to as 'business confidence'.

The multiplier mechanism shows that one change in demand has an effect on other areas of demand, just like the rippled effects within different industries such as construction that you read about on page 290.

An example of how the multiplier mechanism works can be seen in the following example. A local business owner loses a contract and decides that they will need to significantly reduce their workforce as a result. With many local people now out of work and with a reduced income, local shops begin to suffer a drop in trade. The shops then need to buy less stock and their suppliers need to produce less, which then affects their employees. If government spending can help to stimulate demand in the original business owner's industry sector, then the multiplier effect is reduced and many of the negative effects are avoided.

Activity: London 2012 Olympics

Consider how the holding of the Olympics in London in 2012 stimulates demand via the multiplier effect. What areas of business will be affected and how?

Local impacts of funding

As well as spending money on regional areas, it is also possible for governments to spend money in local areas or in local partnerships. One such example is the Partnership for Urban South Hampshire (PUSH), which is a partnership of local authorities that considers government funding that is needed in the local area. You have already learned about the Audit Commission and the role it plays in local government spending.

Many types of local funding are now completed on what is known as a bid basis. This means that an area will bid for funding to help with a particular problem and then report back on how successfully that funding has helped to solve the problem.

Private Finance Initiatives

Private Finance Initiatives (PFIs) are one way that the government has sought to increase spending in conjunction with businesses. It involves awarding contracts to private sector organisations and businesses which, together with local authorities, will then provide a service that was previously provided by the public sector. For example, in December 2009, a PFI was signed between Hampshire County Council, West Sussex County Council and Southampton City

Council to replace and maintain 250,000 streetlights at a cost of £225 million. The service will be carried out by private contractors Tay Valley Lighting Limited and Southern Electric Contracting. The PFI will benefit local people as there will be better use of energy, the potential for reducing the carbon footprint and safer streets, which should in turn lead to reduced crime. By carrying out this work as a PFI, the private contractors will pay for the streetlights, but will be paid back over a number of years.

In some cases, PFIs mean that an asset such as a school or hospital effectively remains owned by the private sector and money needs to be paid to that owner to use those facilities over a number of years. However, it is important to recognise that not all PFI initiatives have been successful. In December 2009, a report into a PFI between HM Revenue & Customs and

Mapeley STEPS Contractors Limited concluded that it did not provide value for money for the tax payer when buildings were sold to the contractor to be maintained and then were leased back. It also highlighted some of the risks that were associated with PFIs.

Activity: Local Private Finance Initiatives

Investigate a PFI in your area.

- Which organisations are/were involved?
- What are/were the benefits for your area?
- Are there/were there any disadvantages from using a PFI in this situation?

Assessment activity 38.1

For the first part of the assessed work for this unit, you must demonstrate that you have gained understanding of how businesses are affected by the economic environment. You will need to make particular reference to how changes in the economic environment affect a selected business of your choice, and how government policy and spending also affects it.

1. Explain the effects of changes in the economic environment on your selected business. **P1**
2. Identify how government policies impact on your selected business. **P2**
3. Identify the impact of government spending on your selected business. **P3**
4. Analyse the implications of government policies for your selected business. **M1**
5. Evaluate the impact of changes in the economic environment on your selected business. **D1**

Grading tips

1. Make sure that you choose an appropriate business for this assignment. You should know the business well or have access to published data. You can use this business throughout your assessed work.

2. You are expected to investigate a wide range of government policies and their impact on your business, so you will need to carry out a significant amount of research. You may find it helpful to go back through the headings in this unit and identify which policies have had the biggest impact on your chosen business. **P2**

3. You will need to consider the impact of spending at a local, national and European level, including any effects on aggregate demand and the economy as a whole. You will need to explain the multiplier effect in the context of your business by tracing the knock-on effects of changes in demand and how these affect output, purchasing, overheads and growth. **P3**

3 Understand fiscal and monetary policies and the effects on spending

You have already learned a lot about government spending and how governments need to try to balance their budgets, like everyone else. **Fiscal policy** considers these budgets in more detail by looking at spending in direct relation to total tax revenues.

Key term

Fiscal policy – the government's policy towards public spending, taxes and borrowing.

3.1 Fiscal policy

Fiscal policy is based on the approach that was first developed by the economist John Maynard Keynes. Keynes believed that by changing levels of taxation and government spending, the government could influence productivity levels. As you are already aware, government spending influences government borrowing and debt.

The UK government's approach to fiscal policy up to December 2009 was that it should borrow to invest for future needs, and that current needs should be met by tax revenues. However, due to the economic downturn in the UK, the level of public sector net cash requirement (PSNCR) had risen to £81.6 billion and was expected to continue to increase to £175 billion by April 2010. As you now know, the Chancellor of the Exchequer announced a package of measures to reduce the amount of borrowing, including the Fiscal Responsibility Bill. This became law in February 2010 and the idea behind the Act was to limit the amount of government borrowing.

In the past, the UK government was committed to what was known as the 'Golden Rule', which states that government borrowing should never be more than 40 per cent of national income. However, due to the recession, UK banks that needed money to avoid collapse and falling tax receipts the government broke this rule and government own borrowing escalated. The Fiscal Responsibility Act was introduced to try to sort out this situation.

Direct and indirect taxation

Direct and indirect taxation are the two different methods the government uses to gain income. Direct taxes are those that are paid by individuals and business on their income or profit and include the following.

- **Income tax** is paid on all income and is calculated in two ways: 20 per cent of income is taxed for lower earners and 40 per cent of income is taxed for higher earners. Most people are entitled to a personal allowance, which means that a proportion of their income is not taxable. In 2009/10 the top of the lower income band was £37,400, so anyone earning over this amount pays 40 per cent income tax. Tax also comes from the interest received on savings in the bank and again is paid at 20 per cent or 40 per cent, depending on the earnings of the person with the savings. Rises or reductions in income tax can affect the general level of spending in the economy.

- **National Insurance contributions** are a further form of tax that is based on income. National Insurance contributions build up to enable people to claim benefits if they need to and also form a state pension for when they retire. Employers and employees both have to pay National Insurance contributions to the government.

- **Corporation tax** is a tax on company profits. Most businesses try to pay the least amount of Corporation tax that they possibly can and this can be done through reinvesting back into their company for the future. In 2009, the main rate of Corporation tax was 28 per cent.

Indirect taxes are those that are taken indirectly from individuals by being added by businesses to the prices charged to the customer.

- **Value Added Tax (VAT)** is a tax that is charged on most goods and services that VAT registered businesses provide in the UK. It is also added to some goods that are brought into the UK from countries outside of the European Union. VAT is chargeable on most goods and services, including business gifts, staff meals and sales of services. From December 2008 to December 2009, the

Chancellor of the Exchequer decided to reduce VAT from 17.5 per cent to 15 per cent to stimulate spending. On 1 January 2010, the VAT rate reverted back to its original figure.

- **Excise duty** is a form of tax that is paid on particular goods, including alcohol, tobacco and fuel. Excise duties are often added to goods that are luxuries, seen to be harmful to health or may damage the environment. The duty is designed to raise money, but also to reduce demand for them.

- **Air passenger duty** is a tax paid by airlines per flight operated. The duty used to be paid per person, but this was changed in November 2009 to per flight instead. It also increased in price, which meant that flight prices went up. The increase in this duty was done to raise extra funds, but also for environmental reasons.

Activity: Air passenger duty

Conduct some research to find out what the advantages and disadvantages are of paying air passenger duty per flight rather than per person?

Activity: Indirect taxes

What other indirect taxes are there, for example, business rates? Produce a poster or leaflet giving details about these taxes and their impact on a selected business.

Capital allowances

Businesses have the ability to claim tax allowances on things that they have purchased or investments they have made. These claims are made against the taxable profits made by the business and help to reduce tax payments. Capital allowances may be used on plant and machinery, other equipment and research and development. The allowances help businesses to keep reinvesting in themselves for the future.

Activity: Capital allowances

Visit the Business Link website at www.businesslink.gov.uk and find out more about capital allowances and their rates. Consider how changes in capital allowances might affect a business in your area.

Impact of changes on costs, aggregate demand and tax free allowances

As you have already learned, any changes in costs affects aggregate demand and therefore can increase or decrease the amount of government spending that is necessary. Fiscal policy needs careful control to ensure that the economy is as stable as possible. Tax free allowances are used to help increase or decrease the level of tax that is being paid. A tax free allowance means that an amount can be earned or gains received before tax is paid on the remaining amount.

Potential annual revision

Each year tax allowances are reviewed in light of government spending and the economy as a whole. The latest allowances and rates are announced by the government and then administered by HM Revenue & Customs. As you have seen, it is possible for the government to change taxation for a short time if this is felt to be necessary (see temporary reduction in VAT earlier).

Public finances

Public finances are affected by fiscal policy because the amount of public money that is spent and the level of taxes that are collected has a big impact on the overall health of what is commonly referred to as the 'public purse'. Careful monitoring and movement of tax levels tries to achieve stability in the economy. The charts shown in Figures 38.12 and 38.13 (overleaf) make it possible for us to see where government spending has been allocated and also government receipts. It is possible to see the difference between spending and income that makes up public borrowing for 2009/10.

Public sector borrowing

As fiscal policy controls changing levels of taxation and spending, it also influences public sector borrowing. When public sector borrowing is high, it can mean that the amount of money that is available for other businesses to borrow becomes limited. This means that it may be harder for a business to borrow money to invest in new technology or growth. Limited borrowing can also lead to increases in interest rates as people want to borrow more money than there is available. Higher interest rates usually mean higher costs, which are passed on to customers and may affect demand.

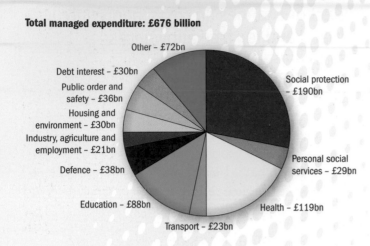

Total managed expenditure: £676 billion

Figure 38.12: Government spending by function, 2009–2010 (source: Office for National Statistics)

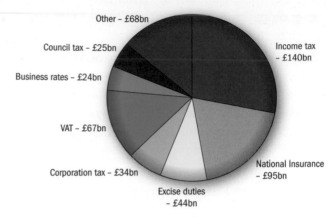

Total receipts: £498 billion

Figure 38.13: Government receipts, 2009–2010 (source: Office for National Statistics)

Comprehensive spending review

The last comprehensive spending review took place in 2007 when the UK government announced government departmental expenditure limits (DELs) until 2011. The spending review also required those departments to consider efficiencies and value for money so that government spending could be focused in the best possible way.

Activity: Comprehensive spending review

Using the HM Treasury website (www.hm-treasury.gov.uk), carry out research into a government department and see what was agreed in the last comprehensive spending review. How might the spending review and departmental limit affect businesses in your area?

Pre-Budget Report

Every year, a Pre-Budget Report is delivered in the autumn by the Chancellor of the Exchequer. The report gives an update on what has happened in the economy and in public finances so far during that year. It also sets out the direction of government policy in the time running up to the Budget in the spring of the following year. The first Pre-Budget report was introduced in 1997 and its purpose was to outline to businesses and individuals the direction of the UK government's focus with regards to spending.

What were the focus points of the last Budget?

The Pre-Budget Report in 2009 announced that in 2010 the government was intending to increase National Insurance contributions, increase some duty on vehicles and that some benefits, including child benefit were due to increase.

Activity: Pre-Budget Report

Using the HM Treasury website at www.hm-treasury.gov.uk, look at the Pre-Budget Reports that have been issued each year since 1997. Read some of the statements that have been made in them and what they meant for businesses in your area.

Budget

In March of each year, the government publishes a budget that outlines government spending proposals for the next three years and also provides a measure of the budget position for the past year. The budget position shows the variation between government spending and tax revenue (see deficit funding and PSNCR on page 297).

- A balanced budget occurs when government spending and tax revenue are equal.
- A budget surplus occurs when government spending is less than tax revenue.
- A budget deficit occurs when government spending is more than tax revenue.

A budget surplus means that the government can pay off its debts. A budget deficit means that it will have to borrow more to finance its spending. When a budget announcement is made, it highlights any changes in taxation that will be coming into force, taking into account statements that were made in the Pre-Budget Report the previous autumn.

Re-distribution of income

Re-distribution of income is where money is moved from people who are able to earn money in larger amounts to those who are poorer. Fiscal policy enables this by taxing higher wage earners at higher levels than those on lower incomes and also by providing additional support and benefits to help lower income households. Such measures try to move people from poverty. Examples of such measures include Child Tax Credits which are paid to families with up to a maximum household income of £59,000 (in 2010) and Educational Maintenance Allowance (EMA) given to students who are living in families with household incomes of less than £30,810 (2008/09).

Table 38.1: Eligibility for Educational Maintenance Allowance (source: Directgov)

Your household income (for financial year 2008–09)	How much EMA you get
Up to £20,817 per year	£30 per week
£20,818 – £25,521 per year	£20 a week
£25,522 – £30,810 per year	£10 a week

The Bank of England is a major influence on spending in the UK

3.2 Monetary policy

Monetary policy works in a different way to fiscal policy, but also seeks to help support an economy. Monetary policy works by influencing:

- the rate of interest that is offered by the central bank within which it is operating
- money supply
- the way that the exchange rate works in a country.

In the UK the central bank that controls the rate of interest is the Bank of England.

Aggregate demand and trading conditions

Changes in interest rates, the value of currency and the supply of sterling (£) all affect aggregate demand in the economy. Demand in turn then affects businesses, which has a knock-on effect on the way that businesses trade and their ability to make profits and invest. Trading conditions are also affected by the value of currency since this affects imports and exports.

Monetary policy

By the end of 2009, the Bank of England Monetary Policy Committee had cut base interest rates to 0.5 per cent, which was the lowest that they had ever been. The base interest rate is the rate that is used by banks to lend to each other. The rate also influences the amount that banks charge to lend money to individuals and to businesses, as well as the amount of interest that is paid on savings and investments.

Having a low base rate means that people are less likely to want to save their money and will want to spend it instead, which creates demand for products and services. This then leads to the multiplier effect (see page 298). However, as having a low base rate means that fewer people are saving, this may affect the supply of money in the economy. Due to the banking crisis in 2009, a number of banks needed help to continue lending to customers and this led to a reduced supply of money in the economy. Although interest rates were low between the Bank of England and the other commercial banks, the amount customers needed to pay did not immediately reduce as there were more people wanting to borrow money than there was money available. Commercial banks were also more cautious at lending money following the bad debts that caused the crisis in the first place.

Part of monetary policy also concerns the supply of money and what is called 'quantitative easing'. This is when more money is released into the economy. When the money supply is increased, more people have money to spend, potentially leading to an increase in aggregate demand. As most modern economies are now linked to the global economic cycle of other economies, changes in national income and expenditure in other countries also affect our economy.

Monetary policy also relates to exchange rates, in this case the value of sterling (£) against other currencies such as the US dollar or the euro.

Activity: The United States recession

Carry out some research into the United States recession that started during 2008. Find out how the impact of the recession in that economy affected the UK economy and businesses operating within it.

Interest rate changes and investment decisions

By keeping interest rates at a low level, aggregate demand is stimulated as more money is available for people to spend. It is also cheaper for businesses to borrow money and invest in their own businesses.

Interest rate changes can also affect whether or not external investors want to invest in the country. A fall in interest rates may affect the confidence of investors from overseas who want a larger return on their money. They may decide to withdraw their money from the UK economy if they believe they can get a higher return elsewhere. Business confidence may also affect the value of sterling as fewer people from overseas may want to buy sterling if they believe the currency is losing value.

When the value of sterling is lower against other currencies, it makes imports more expensive and exports cheaper. If this situation continues, the UK net aggregate demand should rise due to the multiplier effect. This, of course, does depend on the type of goods being imported and exported, as well as the ability of UK exporters to increase their sales overseas.

The Bank of England can influence the value of interest by changing interest rates or by dealing in foreign exchange to try to influence its supply and therefore value. Reducing the exchange rate can occur by lowering interest rates or selling sterling. Raising interest rates and buying foreign currency will have the opposite effect as this will reduce aggregate demand and reduce inflation.

Activity: Exchange rates

Find out the value of sterling against the US dollar and the euro over the past 12-month period. How does the decrease or increase in value against each currency affect a selected local business in your area?

Inflation

Inflation, as you learned on page 284, is the measurement of the increase in prices. The target for the UK government is to keep inflation at around 2 per cent to support employment and economic growth. Two per cent inflation gives stability to the economy so it is just as bad to be below 2 per cent as it is to be above it. Monetary policy influences inflation

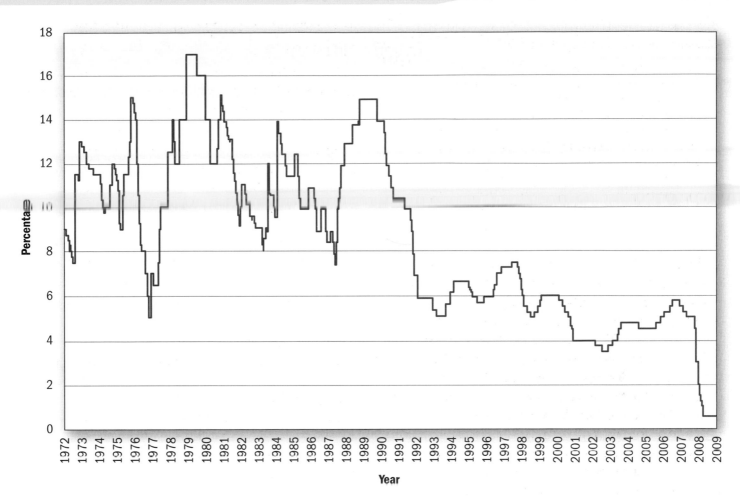

Figure 38.14: Changes in Bank of England interest rates, 1972–2009 (source: Bank of England)

because rates of interest affect spending and therefore demand. Monetary policy also affects the supply of money, again influencing demand and costs, and therefore inflation.

Employment levels

Employment levels are also affected by monetary policy. Keeping inflation at around 2 per cent means that wage increases should be around this level too. This controls cost-push inflation. Low inflation tends to mean that workers are more secure in their jobs because costs are kept stable. If inflation levels are high, the cost of wages is high and employers may try to control this by reducing their employee numbers, which then leads to a reduction in aggregate demand.

A good supply of money in the economy means that businesses should feel confident to invest in the future by taking on new employees. If more people are working, aggregate demand is likely to go up and, therefore, business confidence should go up again as more spending takes place.

Impacts of actual and anticipated changes

Actual changes in interest rates affect the levels of business investment, but anticipated changes can also affect the economy. This may be through what are known as 'second-round effects'. This is where businesses that are not directly affected by a change in interest rates are instead influenced by other businesses they work with which are, and so they will see changes in demand or customer spending. Anticipated changes in monetary policy may also affect the UK economy even if these changes do not actually take place. For example, a predicted increase in interest rates may encourage investors to buy more sterling, which will increase its value without the actual change in interest rates taking place. A predicted reduction in interest rates may make business owners wait until the rate is actually published to make finance decisions, as finance may then be cheaper to obtain. In this way, anticipated change may affect the demand for borrowing.

Assessment activity 38.2

P4 M2 D2 BTEC

You must now consider how fiscal and monetary policy decisions have affected your chosen business. Use the same business that you chose for Assessment activity 38.1 to build on your understanding.

1. Explain how both fiscal and monetary policy decisions have affected your selected business. **P4**

2. Analyse the effects of fiscal and monetary policies for your selected business in terms of the market it operates in. **M2**

3. Suggest and justify elements of fiscal and monetary policies that would help your selected business achieve its objectives. **D2**

Grading tips

1. In your explanation of fiscal policy make sure you include all the possible types of taxation

that affect your selected business, including all the different types of direct and indirect taxation. **P4**

2. To fully develop your explanation of how monetary policy decisions have affected your business, you should consider the effects of rising and falling interest rates, the CPI measurement of inflation and the effect of exchange rates, if these are relevant to your business. **P4**

3. Analysing the effects means looking at the pros and cons of each before you then go on to suggest and justify elements of fiscal and monetary policies that would help your particular business. You could use your analysis for M2 to highlight areas for you to consider carefully as part of your justifications. **M2 D2**

4 Know how the international economy affects UK businesses and competition

By now, you should know that businesses are greatly affected by the UK economic environment. But increasing links between economies throughout Europe and the rest of the world means that the international economy is now also a major influence on the way that UK businesses trade.

4.1 European factors

European factors have a big influence on the UK economy because the UK is part of the EU. The influence of the EU itself and individual EU countries affects the way that UK businesses perform.

Role of European Union (EU)

The European Union began 1950 and was originally known as the European Communities. France and the Federal Republic of Germany were the first members, but membership has since increased to 27 member states with other potential entrants wanting to join.

Table 38.2 details some of the key events in the history of the European Union.

The purpose of the EU is to allow the free movement of people, goods and services throughout member states. The EU, as a whole, had a population of 497,455,000 on 1 January 2008, of which 61,186,000 were from the UK. Figure 38.15 opposite shows the population of the EU by age.

From a business point of view, having a European Market that links economies means that there is no need to pay any customs or excise charges to other member states. It also means that goods can be brought into the EU from countries such as the US and China as a whole and then be broken up and distributed to a number of countries, again, without having to pay extra costs to the individual states involved. This has meant that costs have decreased for countries trading within the EU and for countries outside the EU that trade with it.

Table 38.2: Significant dates and events in the history of the EU

Period in time	Significant event	Number of member states
1950s	France and Germany join together to pool their coal and steel resources. Belgium, Italy, Luxembourg and the Netherlands join the community.	6
1973	Three new member states join: Denmark, UK and the Republic of Ireland.	9
1981	Greece joins the communities.	10
1986	Spain and Portugal join the communities.	12
1990	East Germany and West Germany reunify, with Eastern Germans becoming part of the EU.	12
1992	New powers are given to the community, now known as the European Union, to work together and increase co-operation.	12
1995	Three new member states join: Austria, Finland and Sweden.	15
2004	Ten new member states join: Cyprus, the Czech Republic, Estonia, Hungary, Latvia, Lithuania, Malta, Poland, Slovenia and Slovakia.	25
2007	Bulgaria and Romania join the EU.	27
2007	Croatia, Macedonia and Turkey apply to join the EU.	27

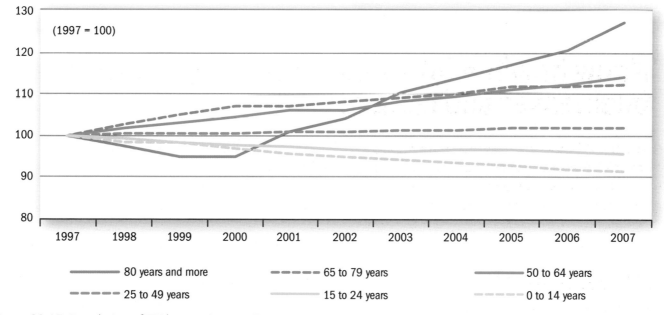

Figure 38.15: Population of EU by age (source: Eurostat)

Creating a single market involved passing more than 1,000 pieces of legislation as part of preparations for integration. It also meant that EU countries had to start developing ways for their businesses to deal with company law, business rules and accounting principles in a similar way so that they would be able to trade more efficiently across the EU. Removing barriers to trade has made it easier for businesses to set up and operate across the EU whilst giving protection to customers everywhere with the same EU laws regardless of which countries they are living in and which businesses they are working with.

In November 2009, the first President was appointed to lead the European Council. This was Herman van Rompuy and he was the Belgian Prime Minister at the time. The purpose of having a President was to have a leader to draw all the strengths of the different states together. His appointment was made as the last country that was needed to ratify the Lisbon Treaty did so in 2009.

Activity: The Lisbon Treaty

Produce a display for your classroom or a poster that shows everything that you can find out about the Lisbon Treaty. Consider in your work how the Lisbon Treaty affects you as a citizen of the EU and how it might affect a national or local business that you know.

Herman Van Rompuy, the first EU President

Performance of European Union economies

The EU has encouraged its 27 member states to work extremely closely through the single market, and this means that as time has moved forward the economies of the individual countries have moved closer together and are more closely linked. Many of the 27 member states use the same currency, the euro, so this means no exchange rate fluctuations between them.

As you can see from Figure 38.16 (opposite), the different countries within the EU have very different economies. Some have done very well and others

have had mixed performance. This led, in 2008, to a group of economies in the EU being referred to as PIGS, those of Portugal, Italy, Greece and Spain. These economies were grouped together as they had large deficits and high levels of unemployment. More recently, Ireland has also joined this group of economies so that PIGS has now become PIIGS.

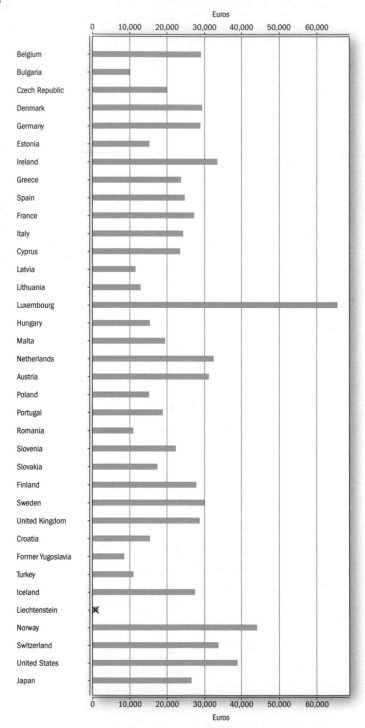

Figure 38.16: Gross Domestic Product (GDP) per capita in euros on current market prices (2007) for EU member states compared to some non-EU member states (source: Eurostat)

Activity: European economies

Activity: European economies

Choose one member state of the EU and find out what you can about its economy. Research its interest rates, inflation level, GDP and currency value, as well as its overall economic strength. Produce a fact pack about that country's economy and ask other students in your class to share what they have found about different economies.

Did you know?

In 2009 Poland was one of the only economies in the EU to show growth. Most other EU members' economies were contracting.

European policies

There are a number of different European policies that affect UK businesses and we will look at each of these now.

Agriculture

The Common Agricultural Policy (CAP) is one of the oldest policies that was developed by the EU and seeks to benefit its members by:

- encouraging the production of safe and high-quality food throughout the union
- supporting the upholding of thriving rural communities
- giving farmers incentives to take good care of the environment.

The CAP aims to make sure that there is sustainable agricultural production in the EU that helps the economic and social environment of the EU. Agricultural land represents a large part of the EU and it is important to ensure that sustainable agricultural production takes place from an economic, social and environmental point of view.

Business, growth and employment

The European Commission (EC) works with the member states to help achieve business success, growth and employment. In November 2009, the EC launched a consultation paper called EU 2020 to investigate ways to invest and grow that are smarter and greener. The EU has policies to promote employment and to invest in schemes that support countries or regions within countries to develop and grow. To support business growth and opportunities for employment, part of the focus of the European Commission is on Enterprise and Industry policies.

Activity: European Commission Enterprise and Industry policies

Find out which different policies are operated by the EU on Enterprise and Industry by carrying out some research online. You could start by accessing the European Commission website at europa.eu.

Education

The European Commission has also set out policies in relation to education within the 27 member states. The objectives and targets from the European strategy and co-operation in education and training identify four long-term strategic objectives:

- making lifelong learning and mobility a reality
- improving the quality and efficiency of education and training
- promoting equity, social cohesion and active citizenship
- enhancing creativity and innovation, including entrepreneurship, at all levels of education and training.

The education benchmarks for EU members by 2020 are:

- at least 95 per cent of children between the age of four and the age for starting compulsory primary education should participate in early childhood education
- the share of 15-year-olds with insufficient abilities in reading, mathematics and science should be less than 15 per cent
- the share of early leavers from education and training should be less than 10 per cent
- the share of 30–34-year-olds with tertiary educational attainment should be at least 40 per cent
- an average of at least 15 per cent of adults (age group 25–64) should participate in lifelong learning.

Economics and finance

EU countries are closely linked in economic and financial terms. Some are linked through monetary union, which you will learn about later in this unit, and others are linked by budgets that are set across the EU. All countries have to pay into the EU budget, but the amount each pays depends on its income, the amount of tax paid and the resources that the country has. Financial regulations and rules are in place so that the money in the budget is distributed fairly amongst the different countries. The data is also published so that all the member countries can see how the budget has been shared out.

The EU works towards growth and increasing the number of jobs in each of the member states. The EU as a whole also wants to create security and deal with certain issues as a group of countries, such as ageing populations across the EU and globalisation. You will learn more about globalisation on page 316. As the EU countries work together, their economies are seen to be of 'common concern' and advice is given by the Council of Europe to make sure that the policies of the individual countries support each other through integrated guidelines and assessment of reforms.

Activity: Financial operation in the EU

Find out what the following organisations do to support economic and financial policies in the EU.

- European Investment Bank (EIB)
- European Investment Fund (EIF).

Environment

Like the individual member states of the EU, the EU as a whole has many different policies on the different ways to protect the environment. These policies relate to:

- air
- European climate change
- pollution
- land use
- noise
- sustainable development
- waste.

Having policies on the environment means that businesses in member states must know about them and conform to them. These policies help to support the overall aim of the EU to protect the environment.

Activity: Environment policy

Think of a business that you know well that operates in your local area or choose a nationally operating business. Choose one of the environmental policy areas listed above or another from the EU that relates to the environment and produce a poster showing the effect of that policy on your selected business.

Science and technology

The European Commission's Joint Research Centre (JRC) carries out research and develops policy on science and technology. There are a number of areas that the JRC considers across the member states, including the extent to which genetically modified organisms are used in foods and other products. The JRC also investigates the way that technology may help to support and improve the lives of EU citizens. In November 2009, the JRC was investigating nuclear energy, the impact of Web 2.0 and biodiversity, amongst a number of other important topics for the EU.

Activity: Joint Research Centre (JRC)

Access the European Commission JRC website at www.jrc.ec.europa.eu and read the latest newsletters on science and technology developments. Choose one area of scientific or technological research and consider its impact on a local or national business that you know. What are the potential positive and negative impacts of this research for your business?

Regional

With 27 member states in 2009, the EU has a huge number of people who live across 271 regions. This means that there are huge differences between the living standards of those people. Part of EU policy is to reduce social differences and so regional policy has been developed which focuses on member states that need extra help. As Table 38.3 shows, in 2009 the EU gave different regional funds to help some of its member states.

Table 38.3: EU regional funds in 2009

EU regional funds	Some of the member states who received them
Cohesion funds – given to countries with a gross national income that was lower than 90 per cent of the EU average	Greece, Portugal, Cyprus, Estonia, Hungary, Malta and Poland
Conversion assistance – given to regions with less than 75 per cent of GDP per inhabitant	Cornwall and Isles of Scilly, West Wales and the Valleys
Phasing out assistance – given to regions that would have received assistance when the EU was a smaller number of countries (15) but did not benefit as there are now 27	The Highlands and Islands of Scotland

External relations

Having a President of the European Council means that member states are able to work together as a group to co-ordinate external relations across the rest of the world. In November 2009, the first EU Trade Commissioner was appointed. Baroness Catherine Ashton was chosen from the UK and her role is to develop policy and promote and negotiate on behalf of the EU with important and powerful countries, such as the United States, China and India. Baroness Ashton is also Vice President of the European Commission and as such her role is also to oversee foreign policy, like the role of the Secretary of State in the US, who in November 2009 was Hilary Clinton.

Baroness Catherine Ashton, EU Trade Commissioner and Vice President of the EC

Activity: Regional policy

Access the EU regional policy website at www.ec.europa.eu/regional_policy and find out more about how EU regional policy works and the types of funds available.

Social

Social policy, as you learned on page 294, refers to policies and guidelines that affect the way people live, such as welfare policies that cover things like social security and housing. A key focus of EU social policy is to combat discrimination and work towards equal treatment of people across all member states. EU social policy also seeks to support social mobility across member states so that EU citizens can move between them. It also promotes the enhancement of human rights within the EU and campaigns for improvements across the rest of the world. The European Union Agency for Fundamental Rights (FRA) works within the EU to campaign on different issues involving fundamental human rights. For example, 2010 was the European Year for Combating Poverty and Social Exclusion across the EU, welcomed by the FRA, which was carrying out research into youth experience of discrimination, social marginalisation and violence.

Activity: The FRA

Visit the FRA website at www.fra.europa.eu/
fraWebsite/ and find out more about how it
campaigns for improvements to the rights
of members across the EU. Consider how
the FRA works within the framework of the
Lisbon Treaty, which you learned about on
page 308.

The Economic and Monetary Union (EMU)

All 27 member states of the EU are linked into the
Economic and Monetary Union either by being within
it or by being affected by it. Eleven member states
changed their currency to the euro in January 1999,
with Greece joining in January 2001. In January 2002,
euro notes and coins were introduced as national
currencies were gradually withdrawn. The countries
that trade in euro are known as the 'eurozone'. Another
four countries have joined since 2002.

The benefit to member states of being part of the EMU
is that there is enhanced economic stability throughout
the EU. However, in 2009 the UK had still not joined
the EMU in full and was unsure when and if the UK will
join. There are a number of potential advantages and
disadvantages to joining and these are outlined below.

Arguments for the UK joining the EMU

- Risk of currency changes either in favour or against
  UK businesses would be gone.

- Interest rates in the UK would be exactly the same
  as those in the rest of the eurozone (the rate in the
  EU in 2009 was 0.25 per cent base rate compared to
  0.5 per cent in the UK).

- Charges to change currency will be avoided.

- Many businesses are already trading in euro and
  there is an indication that many more will start to do
  so in order to take payments from customers and
  suppliers, so whether or not the UK officially
  adopts the euro it is likely to become common
  place anyway.

- It would be easier to compare prices between the
  UK and other EU member states and prices will be
  lower as additional costs are avoided.

- Britain needs to trade within the eurozone and be
  part of it if it is going to be an effective member of
  the EU.

Table 38.4: EU member states that joined the EMU and their previous currencies

Country	Currency before transfer to euro
France	Franc
Germany	Deutschmark
Spain	Peseta
Italy	Lira
Ireland	Punt
Greece	Drachma
Belgium	Belgian franc
Luxembourg	Franc
The Netherlands	Guilder
Austria	Schilling
Portugal	Escudo
Finland	Markka
Slovenia	Tolar
Slovakia	Koruna
Malta	Lira
Cyprus	Pound

- Moving round Europe will become much easier,
  including buying products online from different
  member states both to and from the UK.

Arguments against the UK joining the EMU

- Interest rates and other economic conditions, such
  as levels of taxation and public spending, will be
  dictated from the ECB (European Central Bank) and
  therefore may not be right for the UK.

- The UK will lose the benefit of exchange rate
  fluctuations to make additional profits.

- The UK has a history of using the pound and should
  not give it away.

- It may weaken links with business partners in the
  US and the rest of the world if the exchange rate in
  euro is not as good as the rate in pounds.

- When the euro is introduced, prices will become
  higher (this was noted in several EU member states
  as retailers and other suppliers rounded up their
  prices upon introduction of the euro).

4.2 Global factors

As you have now learned, the EU is a key influence on business and the economic environment and links together the economies within Europe. However, all economies across the world are also now strongly linked to each other through their stock markets and through the supply of money on a global basis. The links between world economies can have positive and negative effects on the UK economy due to the huge investment that takes place across borders.

The World Trade Organization (WTO)

The World Trade Organization (WTO) was made up of 153 member governments in 2009. The organisation seeks to support the negotiation of trade by helping to sort out trade problems between countries. The purpose of the organisation is therefore to promote trading and to sort out any disputes. There are ten benefits that the WTO associates with the negotiation of trade.

1. The system helps promote peace.
2. Disputes are handled constructively.
3. Rules make life easier for all.
4. Freer trade cuts the costs of living.
5. It provides more choice of products and qualities.
6. Trade raises incomes.
7. Trade stimulates economic growth.
8. The basic principles make life more efficient.
9. Governments are shielded from lobbying.
10. The system encourages good government.

Activity: WTO

Find out which member governments are currently part of the WTO and how the organisation works by visiting the WTO website at www.wto.org.

Trading blocs

A trading bloc is a group of countries that work together to increase trade amongst each other and to take advantage as a group from economic benefits. Trading blocs can make trade with other countries not included in the preferential trading deal more difficult.

The North American Free Trade Agreement (NAFTA), for example, supports trade between the United States, Canada and Mexico and so fees and other charges are reduced making free trade easier. The EU acts as a trading bloc and allows some other countries to work with it to trade more easily.

Activity: Trading blocs around the world

There are a number of different trading blocs around the world which negotiate and work together. Find out more about these trading blocs:

*   G20
*   APEC
*   The Cairns Group.

Consider how they affect the prices of goods coming into the EU and the UK. How might they affect a UK national or a local business that you are familiar with?

Stock market fluctuations

Stocks and shares are traded throughout the world through different stock exchanges that exist in countries. You will have probably heard of many of the stock exchanges, including the London Stock Exchange. Others exist all over the world, including those in New York, Hong Kong and Abu Dhabi. As trade is now much more global and investors move money between countries to try to make as much profit as they can, changes (or fluctuations) in the value of stocks and shares in one country can have a big impact on those in another. The housing slump in the USA has had a big effect on securities around the world and contributed to the banking crisis in the UK during 2009.

Activity: The 2009 UK banking crisis

Carry out some research into the 2009 UK banking crisis. Find out why the UK government decided to lend the banks money and why the US housing market so directly affected the UK stock market.

Credit availability

After the Second World War, the International Monetary Fund (IMF) was set up to help economies around the world achieve financial stability. In 2009 there were 186 member countries, so nearly all the countries of the world are part of the IMF. As countries trade with each other for goods, services and exchange rates, the IMF tries to make sure that all economies are as stable as possible. The IMF also helps to control the amount of credit that is available in its member countries. This is because the amount of credit that is available across the world can affect the price that different countries pay to borrow money, and also the amount that businesses have available to them to invest and grow. If a country has problems paying its international bills, the IMF is able to give them loans to try to avoid their economy having serious problems, which then can lead to a ripple effect on other economies. This is what happened when the US economy had troubles in 2008 which led to economic problems in the UK and other countries in 2009. Countries are also asked to lend money to the IMF so that it can then be offered to other countries in greater need.

Activity: The IMF

Find out more about the IMF by visiting its website at www.imf.org.

Global warming

You have probably heard a lot already about global warming. This is because it is a big issue for the people, economies and businesses of the world. As the temperature of the world increases due to the greenhouse gases released by human activities, it is predicted that there will be huge differences in sea levels. This will have massive effects on different parts of the world, such as flooding, which will mean that lots of people will be at risk of losing their homes and businesses and property prices will be affected in these areas. There is, therefore, a need to continue looking at cleaner energies so that greenhouse gas emissions are reduced as much as possible. The forms of transport we currently use may need to be reconsidered so that the most environmentally friendly

ones are encouraged and big polluters are stopped. As the effects of global warming will be felt all over the world, businesses will also be affected by changes in competition and imports and exports.

Political stability and war

Political instability, such as the frequent changes in government and leadership and periods of social unrest and troubles that occur in some areas of the world, has a big impact on the way that trade happens between countries. Wars, too, have an impact due to the support that is needed in a country to help deal with poverty and the large movements of people between countries. Political instability and war affects the ability of a country to trade with others which often negatively affects the economy of that country, as well as those around it. For example, if a country relies heavily on its exports of raw materials to other countries, political instability or war may mean that it can no longer supply the materials or get them out of the country. This then affects not only the economy of the country producing the raw materials, but also the economies of those countries that rely on the materials.

Activity: Political stability

During 2009, the following countries were deemed to be some of the most politically unstable, involved in a conflict or both. Choose one of the countries and find out more details about their political instability or war it was experiencing and whether or not the situation has changed.

- Zimbabwe
- Somalia
- West Bank and Gaza
- Sudan
- Iraq.
- Guinea
- Afghanistan
- Cambodia
- Sri Lanka

Industry-specific developments

Developments across the world in the oil, gas and motor industries have a major impact on the competitiveness of UK businesses. The worldwide price of oil and gas affects the prices of production all around the world. This is because most products or services, in one form or another, are affected by oil prices, whether it is due to the production of a product, the offering of a service or the movement of goods or services from one place to another.

The UK used to be one of the world's largest suppliers of natural gas and still produces a significant amount in the North Sea. However, its supplies are diminishing rapidly and the UK increasingly relies on imports. This reliance affects the production and distribution of gas as well as its costs. When natural resources, such as oil and gas, become more scarce their price usually goes up, which of course affects any business that relies on them, whether directly or indirectly. With the availability of natural resources set to decrease in the not too distant future, it is important for the oil and gas industries to consider the sustainability of these resources.

The UK motor industry is responsible for a significant proportion of the research and development that goes into new and cleaner types of fuel. The search for more environmentally friendly fuels is a major issue for all countries across the world as part of the need to help reduce the impacts of global warming.

Environment

You have already learned that trading blocs and other agreements between countries help the world's economies to work together to help each other. You should also have realised by now that the increasing threat of global warming and other environmental problems means that all countries need to commit to becoming more clean and green in their business practices. Key meetings of world leaders regularly take place in an effort to help protect the environment and the planet as a whole. The following initiatives are all part of the United Nations Framework Convention on Climate Change and are a major part of a global attempt to help the environment.

Rio Earth Summit

The Earth Summit was a very large and important conference held in Rio, Brazil in 1992. Leaders from countries all over the world attended and together made some very difficult decisions that they hoped would positively affect the environment. Agreements were made to support work in areas of biological diversity, climate change, forest management and sustainable development.

Kyoto Protocol

This is an agreement that was adopted by many countries in Kyoto, Japan in 1997 to set targets and to support work that aims to reduce carbon emissions and to support investment in and development of cleaner energy in developing countries.

Copenhagen Climate Conference

The 15th United Nations Climate Change Conference took place in Copenhagen in December 2009. The Copenhagen Accord is a draft and last-minute agreement that was given to those attending the conference, but it has been heavily criticised and at the time of the conference it did not commit any countries to any actions. The conference was viewed by many as a failure because of its lack of achievement.

> **Activity: The Copenhagen Accord**
>
> Carry out some research to find out more about the Copenhagen Accord and the issues surrounding it. Find out where other UN Climate Change Conferences have been held and what was discussed there, as well as any agreements made. What impacts did these agreements have on the UK economy and the businesses operating within it?

Genetically modified products

Genetically modified (GM) foods are those foods that have had their molecular biology (genetics) changed in some way. Genetic modification is carried out because it allows certain crops and other foods to give higher yields, be resistant to diseases and pests, survive droughts or grow in difficult conditions. In Europe there has been a mixed response to GM foods, with some people protesting against them because they feel they are not safe and others feeling quite happy to eat them. In developing countries, GM foods have been viewed more positively, especially where problems caused by drought and disease are common, as they are seen as a way of feeding the populations and avoiding famine. In the United States, there are already more than 40 different types of GM plants.

Activity: GM foods

Hold a debate in your classroom, with half of the class supporting the adoption of GM foods in the UK and the other half opposing it. You will need to prepare by carrying out some research individually or in pairs before the debate. Ask your tutor or another visitor to your classroom to lead the debate and help decide the outcome.

Outsourcing

'Outsourcing' is where a business asks another company or a group of companies to carry out work on its behalf. Outsourcing on a global level means getting people in other countries to do work that used to be done in the UK. Companies in many developing countries are now able to offer high quality services, but do not cost as much as UK companies offering similar services.

China and India are both popular countries for global outsourcing and it is expected that the economies of both will continue to grow as a result, particularly in the industry sectors of computer science, software engineering and business processing.

Globalisation

You have probably heard it said that the world is getting to be a smaller place. Of course, this does not mean that it is actually getting physically smaller, rather it is recognition of the fact that countries all over the world are communicating more and more effectively across boundaries and that the economies and businesses that operate in different countries are now more closely linked. This is globalisation, and it means that if something is working well in one country, it will have an effect on other countries across the world, and vice versa.

Emerging economies

Emerging economies are those that are growing rapidly, for example the economies of China and India. The opposite of an emerging economy is a developed economy, like those in the UK or the USA. 'Tiger economies' are also economies that are rapidly growing, but the term was originally used to refer specifically to the economies of South Korea, Singapore, Hong Kong and Taiwan, where extremely rapid economic growth resulted in major reductions in poverty and the countries having some of the fastest growing economies in the world. During its rapid growth in the 1990s the Republic of Ireland was referred to as the Celtic Tiger as its economy grew significantly and many jobs were created for the Irish people.

There are other ways in which the economies of countries can be grouped together. For example, the economies of Brazil, Russia, India and China are grouped together and known as BRIC economies because they share some common characteristics. They have all been growing rapidly and also have large rural populations. However, the approaches to business methods and growth in these economies are completely different. In 2003 it was predicted that these economies were growing so rapidly that by 2050 they are likely to be the four wealthiest economies in the world.

Activity: BRIC economies

Choose one of the four BRIC economies (Brazil, Russia, India or China) and produce a fact pack on the current status of that economy. Include information on how that economy is influencing or affecting a national or local business near you.

Assessment activity 38.3

P5 M3 **BTEC**

For the final Assessment activity of this unit, you will need to consider the impact of international factors on your selected business. You should, therefore, review all of the information and activities you have covered so far.

1. Describe the impact of international factors on your selected business. **P5**

2. Assess the impact of changes in the global and European business environment on your selected business. **M3**

Grading tips

1. As you have worked through the final section of this unit, you have learned about many of the different international factors that affect UK businesses. To ensure that you give a full description of these factors and their impacts on your selected business, make sure that you include as many different topic headings in your work as you can. **P5**

2. In order to properly assess the impact of changes in the global and European business environment on your chosen business, you should consider the many different pressures on UK businesses from things like global warming and the increasing influence of BRIC economies. Consider the ways that your chosen business has been affected by pressures outside of their control and also how they have exploited opportunities that have become available. **M3**

Just checking

1. What is meant by the business cycle?
2. What does GDP output measure?
3. What is the difference between CPI and RPI?
4. How is deflation measured?
5. Why might it be difficult for an employer to recruit suitable staff when employment levels are high?
6. What is meant by a trade surplus?
7. Name and explain one of the effects of the UK's trade deficit on a UK business.
8. Describe what is meant by the balance of payments.
9. Who is the governor of the Bank of England and what role does he play?
10. Why does the housing industry have a large impact on the UK economy?
11. How does a decline in the manufacturing industry affect the UK economy?
12. Name the three sectors of the economy.
13. What is meant by 'standard of living'?
14. What impact did the Treaty on Open Skies have on competition?
15. Explain what is meant by social policy and its effect on the economy.
16. What is the difference between direct and indirect taxation?
17. What is the difference between monetary policy and fiscal policy?
18. Name all members states of the EU.
19. Who was the first President of the European Council?
20. Who and what are the PIIGS?

edexcel

Assignment tips

1. You will need to use your analytical and evaluation skills to complete this Assessment activity. Remember that to 'analyse' means to look at the positive and negative aspects of something, in this case government policies, and to 'evaluate' means to make a judgement about something, the impact of changes in the economic environment and how they have affected your business overall.

2. In order to analyse the effects of fiscal and monetary policies for your business, you will need to look at the pros and cons of each. You will then be able to suggest and justify elements of fiscal and monetary policies that would help your particular business. You should, therefore, use your analysis for M2 to highlight areas for you to consider carefully as part of your justification for D2.

3. Make sure that you keep up to date with what is happening in the economy by reading good quality newspapers and also watching the news. Websites like those provided by the Bank of England (www.bankofengland.co.uk) provide up-to-date information on what is happening in the economy and decisions that have and are being made.

4. Business and the economic environment is a more complex unit than you may have studied before. Remember to keep looking back through the unit and re-reading sections to help you complete your assignments effectively.

Glossary

Acceptance – the formal agreement to accept an offer.

Aggregate demand – the total demand for goods and services in an economy.

Aim – broad statement of intent providing a direction for a business, from which more specific objectives could be set.

Ambience – the atmosphere of the event.

Attendee – a person who is going to attend an event.

Authority – the power a person has in their role.

Bailor – the person providing the hire.

Balance Sheet – a financial statement of a business or institution that lists the assets, debts, and owners' investment as of a specific date.

Biography – the life story of a person written by someone else.

Break even – when costs are equal to income so there is no profit or loss.

Break-even point – approximate sales volume required to cover costs, below which production would be unprofitable and above which it would be profitable.

Capacity – the legal power to enter into a contract.

Capital – cash or goods used as an investment in a business.

Capital intensive – this is where a business has a lot of machinery involved in the production process.

Cash flow – money coming into a business from selling its products and the money it spends on all aspects of production.

Caveat emptor – from the Latin term meaning it is 'let the buyer beware'. Today used to mean that a buyer is purchasing a product 'as is' and should be aware of defects in it.

Clicks and bricks – businesses that offer online services via the web as well as the traditional retail outlets (offline) staffed by people.

Communication channel – the method that is used to communicate.

Conditions – essential parts of the contract.

Consideration – the value attached to the promises on a contract.

Consumer contract – a contract made between businesses and members of the public for consumer goods such as food, clothes and furniture.

Contract – an enforceable agreement made between two or more parties.

Contracting – a reduction in the number of employees.

Corporate governance – the people and procedures for taking the major decisions within a business.

Corporate social responsibility (CSR) – the policy of a business towards all stakeholders that takes their interests into account.

Corruption – not following fair and equal procedures to make decisions; attempting to persuade by using cash or opportunity.

COSHH (Control of Substances Hazardous to Health) – the regulations dealing with chemical use in the workplace.

Counter-offer – an offer that invalidates the original offer.

Creditor – a business or person the company owes money to.

Cultural imperialism – local ways of life are being influenced and altered through the effects of Western values and practices spreading all over the world.

Customer relationship management – an integrated information system that can be used to plan, schedule and control pre-sales and post-sales.

Cyclical trend – a change that recurs on a regular basis.

Data mining – a technique that describes the process of exploring large amounts of data with the objective of revealing hidden relationships or patterns that provide an insight into customer behaviour.

Date of incorporation – the date a company comes into existence.

Delegate – the name given to a person who is attending an event. This term is used particularly with conferences.

Direct competitors – competition between two or more businesses that offer essentially the same products and services.

Duress – when a person enters into a contract against their will.

Economy – the way that trade, industry and the wealth of a country is measured.

Employment Tribunal – a formal meeting with a panel of three people, including a judge, who will listen to claims made by an employee against their employer. It is like a court hearing but less formal.

eRetailing – selling of retail goods on the Internet.

Ethical trade – where big companies take account of ethical questions all along their supply chain so that they buy from businesses that treat workers fairly and give them a fair price for their products.

Ethical values – the standards that are held and are set by a business or individuals that control their behaviour.

Evacuation assembly area – a designated place to meet if the building has to be evacuated.

Excess capacity – when an organisation has too many goods or services on offer compared to the number of customers. Maximum capacity means that the organisation is working to the highest level that it can.

Exclusion clause – a term in a contract that tries to exempt or limit the liability of a party who is in breach of contract.

Executed consideration – an act in exchange for a promise.

Executory consideration – a promise yet to be fulfilled.

Expanding – An increase in the number of employees.

Express terms – clauses in the agreement that are agreed to by the parties.

Extended marketing mix – an addition to the traditional marketing mix of product, price, place and promotion (the four Ps) to include three further Ps, related more to marketing services, i.e. people, physical evidence, processes.

Fire marshal – person appointed by an employer to ensure an area of a building has been evacuated in the event of fire in the workplace.

First aider – person responsible for giving emergency treatment to employees injured in the workplace.

Fiscal policy – the government's policy towards public spending, taxes and borrowing.

Fixed assets – a tangible long-term asset held for business use such as equipment and furniture.

Fixed costs – a cost such as rent and insurance, which does not depend on production or sales levels.

Flat organisational structure – one that has fewer hierarchical layers and therefore fewer levels of management above employees. Compare this to a hierarchical or pyramid structured organisation which have many hierarchical layers and therefore many levels of management employees.

Formal – an event that is carried out in a more serious and structured way.

Franchisee – holder of a franchise; a person who is granted a franchise.

Franchisor – company or person who grants franchises.

Free enterprise – an economic system in which people are free to offer goods and services to meet demand.

Global warming – the gradual warming of the planet's surface caused by carbon dioxide build up in our atmosphere. It has the effect of changing the climate in the long term.

Globalisation – where the economies of the world are becoming more dominated by a few multinational businesses.

Gross Domestic Product (GDP) – the sum total of the value of the country's output over the course of a year.

Gross profit – total revenue of a business minus the cost of goods it sold.

Gross salary – the salary before any deductions are made, for example, tax or National Insurance. Net salary is the amount the employee receives after deductions have been made.

Health and Safety at Work Act 1974 – the key piece of legislation concerning health and safety in the workplace.

Health and safety representative – a person appointed by a business or trade union who focuses on protection of workers from harm in the workplace.

HM Revenue & Customs – the government department responsible for collecting taxes as well as paying tax credits and child benefit.

Implied term – part of the contract not necessarily included by the parties but automatically included by law to protect the parties.

Indemnity clause – a term in a contract between two parties, where one of the parties agrees to protect the other party against liabilities such as damages, loss or injury, in respect of a third party.

Indirect competitors – competition among suppliers of different types of products and services that satisfy the same needs.

Inflation – the overall general upward price movement of goods and services in an economy.

Informal – an event where speech and dress are much more relaxed and the rules or procedures are not as strict.

Interpersonal skills – skills that are used to deal with other people, such as dealing with their feelings through body language or tone of voice.

Invitation to treat – indication that a person might be open to receive an offer; this is not legally binding.

Jurisdiction – to have the power to hear cases.

Knowledge-based economy – economy based solely on the production, distribution and the use of knowledge.

Labour intensive – here, a business uses a lot of people in the production process.

Learning curve – the process of gaining experience and knowledge as a result of learning from mistakes.

Leaseholder – person who has bought the right to occupy the business property for a certain period of time.

Lien – the right to retain possession of goods until they are paid for.

Limited company – a business that is owned by shareholders, all of whom have limited liability for the business debts.

Limited liability – shareholders lose no more than the value of their shares if the business should fail.

Liquidated damages – damages agreed at the negotiation stage.

Macro-environment – the economy, technology, society, government and the competitive environmental factors that can influence an organisation but that are outside of its direct control.

Mall – a large, frequently enclosed, shopping complex which contains a variety of shops, businesses and restaurants that are accessible by common passageways.

Malpractice – any occasion when someone does not follow accepted normal practice (usually to gain advantage).

Manual handling – lifting and carrying things at work.

Market place – the world of commercial activity where goods and services are bought and sold.

Market share – amount of a product or service (usually expressed as a percentage) that a business sells in a given market area.

Means-tested – an assessment of whether or not someone qualifies for financial help by taking into account their level of individual or household income.

Memorandum of Association – the document which sets out the purpose of the company.

Mind map – a diagram used to represent words, ideas, tasks or other items linked to and arranged around a central key word or idea.

Minors – people who are under 18. They are generally unable to make contracts.

Misrepresentation – a set of untrue facts made by one party which are relied on by the other party when entering into the contract.

Mistake – when a person enters into a contract after getting the facts in the negotiation wrong.

Mitigation – something done in order to reduce losses.

Multi-tasking – carry out a number of different tasks at the same time.

Net profit – income after all expenses and taxes have been deducted.

Objective – making a judgement without having feelings attached to it.

Offer – a promise that is intended to be followed.

Offeree – the person receiving an offer.

Offeror – the person making the offer.

Operational activities – the day-to-day actions taken by a firm to achieve its primary purpose.

Overdraft – an agreement with a bank to allow the business to spend money it does not have at that moment.

Own brand – a name, a symbol or a design used to identify a specific retailer and make it appear different from its competitors.

Pension – a payment that is given to a person when they retire. The pension may be a company scheme that the employee has paid into during their employment, a private scheme that they have arranged themselves or a state pension which they pay into through National Insurance contributions.

PESTLE analysis – a model used by organisations to understand the external environment in which they operate. PESTLE stands for: Political, Economical, Sociological, Technological, Legal and Environmental.

Pressure groups – voluntary organisations that exist to create a case that will be listened to by decision makers everywhere. This includes business leaders and politicians.

Privity of contract – the relationship between third parties to a contract. It is a legal concept denying third parties the right to sue on a contract.

Profit and loss account – an account compiled at the end of an accounting period to show gross and net profit or loss.

Profitability – to earn a profit; the positive gain from a business operation after deducting all expenses.

Promisee – the person receiving the promise.

Promisor – the person making the promise.

Recession – a period of general economic decline; usually defined as a fall in GDP for two or more consecutive quarters.

Remedy – solution for the victim of a breach of contract.

Repudiate – treat the contract as if it is over and invalid.

Reservation of title – retaining ownership of the goods until the contract is completed.

Retail positioning map – a model used to identify where a retail store sits in the market compared to competitors.

Revenue – total amount of money received by the company for goods sold or services provided during a certain time period.

RIDDOR (Reporting Injuries, Diseases and Dangerous Occurrences Regulations) – the regulations dealing with accidents/injuries or dangerous occurrences in the workplace.

Risk assessment – a document used to record hazards, risk of harm and the controls put in place to minimise the risk and harm.

Rogue trader – a trader operating as a legitimate business without the necessary skills and abilities to do the job.

Shareholders – individuals or organisations that own or hold a share in a business.

Situation analysis – assessment of the organisation's current and future strengths, weaknesses, and opportunities.

Soft copy – a version of a document, such as a pdf, that can be emailed or uploaded to a website.

Stakeholder – a person, group or organisation that affects or can be affected by an organisation's actions.

Standard form contract – a contract made between parties using their standard set of terms.

Standards of living – the quality of people's lives in terms of income and material comforts. It is measured using the real national income per capita. This is calculated by dividing the GDP by the total population and shows whether the standard is going up or down per person.

Stock Exchange – the market place where company shares are bought and sold.

Stock market – a general term for the organised trading of stocks through exchanges and over the counter.

Supply chain – the network of retailers, distributors, transporters, storage facilities and suppliers that participate in the sale, delivery and manufacture of a particular product.

Supply of goods and services – services that do not have consumer contracts, where one party actually provides a service to the other, such as a plumber or hairdresser.

Tenant – person renting the business property.

Terms – the parts of the contract agreed to by the parties.

Title – the legal right of ownership.

To reserve title – to retain ownership of the goods.

Trade description – a description made by a seller about the goods they are selling.

Transferor – the person who is providing the goods or services.

Trend – the general direction in which something tends to move.

Ultra vires – to act outside of one's powers.

Uncontested – when the other party does not disagree.

Undue influence – when a party exerts pressure on another to enter into a contract due to the nature of their relationship or position.

Unlimited liability – business owners are personally responsible for all the debts of the firm and their personal assets can be seized to pay company debts.

Unliquidated damages – damages awarded which were not agreed on the contract.

Value added – where value is added to something through work and application of skills and understanding.

Venue – the place where an event takes place.

Warranties – important terms of the contract, but not so important that they are classed as essential.

Whistleblowing – informing managers or other authorities about unethical practices going on within an organisation.

Woolf Reforms – a series of changes to the civil courts led by Lord Woolf.

Bibliography

Unit 16
Books

Bovee, C. and Thill, J. (2008) *Business in Action with Real Time Updates*, Prentice Hall

Kirton, M. (ed.) (1994) *Adaptors and Innovators: Styles of Creativity and Problem-Solving*, Thomson Learning

Parsloe, E. and Wray, M. (2000) *Coaching and Mentoring: Practical Methods to Improve Learning*, Kogan Page

Torrington, D. et al (2007) *Human Resource Management*, Financial Times/Prentice Hall

Journals

Business Review

Personnel Review

Websites

- www.acas.org.uk – Advisory, Conciliation and Arbitration Service
- www.adviceguide.org.uk – Citizen's Advice Bureau, guides to the workplace
- www.businesslink.gov.uk – Business Link, advice for businesses
- www.cbi.org.uk – Confederation of Business and Industry
- www.cipd.co.uk – Chartered Institute of Personnel and Development
- www.coachingnetwork.org.uk – The Coaching & Mentoring Network
- www.dti.gov.uk – Department of Trade and Industry, advice on coaching and mentoring
- www.investorsinpeople.co.uk – Investors in People
- www.managementqualifications.co.uk – Management Qualifications
- www.mindtools.com – Mind Tools
- www.mybusiness.co.uk – My Business, information and resources on management issues for small businesses
- www.personneltoday.co.uk – Personnel Today, human resource information provider
- www.statistics.gov.uk – UK National Statistics
- www.thecareerbreaksite.com – Career Break Site

Unit 18
Books

Bowdin, G. et al (2006) *Events Management*, Butterworth-Heinemann

Craven, R. and Golabowski, L. (2006) *The Complete Idiot's Guide to Meeting and Event Planning*, 2nd edition, Alpha

Friedmann, S. (2003) *Meeting & Event Planning for Dummies*, John Wiley & Sons Ltd

Wolf, P. et al (2005) *Event Planning Made Easy*, McGraw-Hill

Journals

Event Journal

RSVP

Websites

- www.britishchambers.org.uk – British Chambers of Commerce, which organises many business events
- www.businesslink.gov.uk – Business Link, government support for business
- www.cfa.uk.com – The Council for Administration
- www.evolutionevent.com – Event management company website with case studies of events organised for major companies such as Microsoft and BT
- www.primetimeevents.co.uk – Event planning website with lots of ideas many events for business
- www.speednetworkinghampshire.co.uk – Speed Networking Events, networking for business
- www.times100.co.uk – The Times 100, free learner and tutor materials and case studies

Unit 21
Books

Abbott, K. et al (2002) *Business Law*, Thomson Learning

Beale QC, H. (ed.) (1994) *Chitty on Contracts*, Sweet & Maxwell

Keenan, D. and Riches, S. (2004) *Business Law*, Longman

Sparrow, A. (2001) *The E-commerce Handbook*, Fitzwarren Handbooks

Turner, C. (2008) *Contract Law*, Hodder Education

Turner, C. (2007) *Unlocking Contract Law*, Hodder Education

Websites

- www.acas.org.uk – Advisory, Conciliation and Arbitration Service
- www.hmcourts-service.gov.uk – Her Majesty's Court Service, information about court proceedings
- http://home.clara.net/pauljspence/STOE.htm – Example of a standard form contract
- www.moneyclaim.gov.uk – Money Claim Online, advice for making civil court claims
- www.oft.gov.uk – The Office of Fair Trading, government department that ensures businesses trade fairly
- www.stay-legal.com – Stay Legal, business carrying out checks into the legality of website traders
- www.tradingstandards.gov.uk – Trading Standards Institute, government website checking trading practices
- www.verdict.co.uk – Verdict Research, business research consultants

Unit 27
Books

Atkin, B. and Brooks, A. (2000) *Total Facilities Management*, Blackwell Science

Health and Safety Executive (1997) *Successful Health and Safety Management*, HSE

Ridley, J. (2004) *Health and Safety in Brief*, Butterworth-Heinemann Ltd

Stranks, J. (2005) *Health and Safety Law*, 4th Edition, Prentice Hall

TUC (2003) *Your Rights at Work: A TUC Guide*, Kogan Page

Websites

- www.bifm.org.uk/bifm/about/facilities – British Institute of Facilities Management, Facilities Management Introduction
- www.britsafe.org/feedcontents.aspx?id=100093 – British Safety Council, BSC Annual Survey 2008
- www.businesslink.gov.uk/bdotg/action/layer?topicId=1073956105 – Business Link, Create and operate a health and safety policy
- www.employment-studies.co.uk/pubs/summary.php?id=hse589 – Institute for Employment Studies, Work and Enterprise Panel 2, Business Survey 2007
- www.getreading.co.uk/news/s/2037242_kfc_closed_due_to_vermin_infestationLaura Herbert – getreading.co.uk, KFC closed due to vermin infestation
- www.hpa.org.uk – Health Protection Agency
- www.hse.gov.uk/contact/faqs/manualhandling.htm – HSE, Manual handling FAQs
- www.hse.gov.uk/coshh – HSE guidance for COSHH
- www.hse.gov.uk/PRESS/2008/coiw48508.htm – HSE news story: Warning on handling hazardous materials after HSE prosecution
- www.hse.gov.uk/press/2009/coise0210tex.htm – HSE news story: Machinery manufacturer fined after worker loses fingers
- www.hse.gov.uk/PUBNS/indg184.htm – HSE, Signpost to the Health and Safety (Safety Signs and Signals) Regulations 1996
- www.hse.gov.uk/pubns/indg293.pdf – HSE Welfare at Work: Guidance for employers on welfare facilities
- www.hse.gov.uk/pubns/whswindx.htm – HSE, Workplace Health, Safety and Welfare
- www.hse.gov.uk/riddor – HSE guide to RIDDOR
- www.news.bbc.co.uk/1/hi/uk/7824291.stm – BCC News story: Primark linked to UK sweatshops
- http://news.stv.tv/scotland/east-central/132045-fleas-hit-fife-council-office – STV News story: Fleas hit Fife Council office
- www.timesonline.co.uk/tol/news/politics/article2093977.ece – Times Online news story: Red tape cost more than sick miners got in compensation
- www.wind-watch.org/documents/wp-content/uploads/goineshagler-noisepollution.html – National Wind Watch, Noise Pollution: A Modern Plague

Unit 29

Books

Alexander, N. and Doherty, M. (2008) *International Retailing*, Oxford University Press

Blanchard, D. (2007) *Supply Chain Management Best Practices*, John Wiley & Sons

Brittain, P. and Cox, R. (2004) *Retailing: An Introduction*, FT Prentice Hall

Chopra, S. and Meindl, P. (2006) *Supply Chain Management: Strategy, Planning and Operation*, Prentice Hall

Cook, S. (2008) *Customer Care Excellence: How to Create an Effective Customer Focus*, Kogan Page

Court, Y. et al (2006) *Online Retailing: The Impact of Click on Brick (Future of Retail Property)*, British Council of Shopping Centres

Cox, R. and Brittain, P. (2004) *Retailing: An Introduction*, FT Prentice Hall

Dunne, P. and Lusch, R. (2007) *Retailing*, South-Western College

Harris, E.K. (2006) *Customer Service: A Practical Approach*, Prentice Hall

Levy, M. and Weitz, B. (2008) *Retailing Management*, McGraw-Hill

Spector, R. (2002) *Amazon.com: Get Big Fast*, HarperCollins

Websites

- www.amazon.co.uk – Amazon.co.uk, online shopping website
- www.argos.co.uk – Argos, online shopping website
- www.asda.co.uk – Asda, online shopping website
- www.bootsthechemist.co.uk – Boots the Chemist, online shopping website
- www.brc.org.uk – The British Retail Consortium, information on environmental, transport and planning issues
- www.chemistdirect.co.uk – Chemist Direct, online shopping website
- www.communities.gov.uk/pub/821/PlanningPolicyStatement6PlanningforTownCentres_id1143821.pdf – Planning Policy Statement 6: Planning for Town Centres
- www.johnlewis.com – John Lewis, online shopping website
- www.londis.co.uk – Londis
- www.marksandspencer.com – Marks and Spencer, online shopping website
- www.mcdonalds.co.uk – McDonald's
- www.oft.gov.uk – The Office of Fair Trading
- www.pcworld.co.uk – PC World, online shopping website
- www.qvcuk.com – QVC, online shopping website
- www.retail-week.com – Retail Week, an informative trade weekly that provides information on current retail developments
- www.spar.co.uk – Spar
- www.statistics.gov.uk – UK National Statistics
- www.tesco.com – Tesco Online, shopping website
- www.times100.co.uk – The Times 100, a learner and tutor business studies resource centre
- www.waterstonescoffee.co.uk – Coffee @ Waterstone's
- www.whsmith.co.uk – WHSmith.co.uk, online shopping website

Unit 36

Books

Barrow, C. (2007) *Starting a Business For Dummies, 2nd Edition*, John Wiley and Sons

Belsch, G. and Belch, M.A. (2008) *Advertising and Promotion – An Integrated Marketing Communications Perspective*, McGraw-Hill

Brassington, F. and Pettitt, S. (2007) *Essentials of Marketing*, Financial Times/Prentice Hall

Cave, S. (2002) *Consumer Behaviour in a Week*, Hodder Arnold

Chaffey, D. (2003) *E-Business and E-Commerce Management*, FT Prentice Hall

Clow, K.E. & Baack, D.E. (2009) *Integrated Advertising, Promotion and Marketing Communications: Global Edition*, Pearson

Dibb, S., Simkin, L., Pride, W. M. and Farrell, O.C. (2005) *Marketing Concepts and Strategies*, Houghton Mifflin (Academic)

Hall, D., Jones, R. and Raffo, C. (2004) *Business Studies, 3rd Edition*, Causeway Press Ltd

Kotler, P., Armstrong, G., Wong, V. and Saunders, J. (2008) *Principles of Marketing* Financial Times/Prentice Hall

Lester, D. (2008) *Starting Your Own Business*, Crimson Publishing

Lowe, M. (1999) *Business Information at Work*, Europa Publications

McClave, H.J. (2008) *Communication for Business*, Gill & Macmillan Ltd

Morris, M. (1985) *Starting a successful business: Start up and grow your own company*, Kogan Page

Needham, D. and Dransfield, R. (1994) *Marketing: Everybody's Business – Covering European and International Marketing*, Heinemann

O'Kane, B. (2006) *Starting a Business in Britain: A Comprehensive Guide and Directory*, Virgin

Palmer, A. (2009) *Introduction to Marketing: Theory and Practice*, Oxford University Press

Proctor, T. (2005) *Essentials of Marketing Research*, FT Prentice Hall

Rickman, C.D. and Roddick, A. (2007) *The Small Business Start-up Workbook: A Step-by-step Guide to Starting the Business You've Dreamed of*, How to Books Ltd

Stokes, D. and Lomax, W. (2007) *Marketing: A Brief Introduction*, Thomson Learning

Stuart, B.E., Sarow, M.S. and Stuart, L. (2007) *Integrated Business Communication: In a Global Marketplace*, John Wiley & Sons

Websites

- www.amazon.co.uk – Online shopping
- www.bbc.co.uk – The British Broadcasting Corporation
- www.bized.co.uk – A business education resource site
- www.brc.org.uk – Trade Association for the British Retail Industry
- www.businessballs.com – Free business resources – free career help, business training, organisational development
- www.businesslink.gov.uk – Free government run organisation offering advice and information for businesses
- www.businesscommunication.org – Business communication resources
- http://cnx.org – An education resource site
- www.freemarketingzone.com – Free advice on all aspects of marketing
- www.lessonplanet.com – Education website offering learning materials
- http://news.bbc.co.uk/1/hi/business – The business pages of the BBC website
- www.thetimes100.co.uk – The Times 100 case studies
- www.marketingminefield.co.uk – Advertising and Marketing Guide
- www.marketingonline.com – MarketingOnlineLive.com
- www.marketingteacher.com – Free marketing resources for learners, teachers and professionals
- www.statistics.gov.uk – Official UK statistics
- www.tesco.com – Tesco's main website
- www.tutor2u.net – Free marketing resources for learners, teachers and professionals

Unit 37

Books

Gillespie, A. (2002) *Business in Action*, Hodder & Stroughton

Websites

- http://anitaroddick.com/aboutanita.php – AnitaRoddick.com, Anita Roddick (1942–2007), founder of The Body Shop, explains her ethical stance
- www.bbc.co.uk/news – BBC news website
- www.bis.gov.uk – Department for Business, Innovation & Skills
- www.business-ethics.com – Business Ethics, site that deals with a range of business ethics questions
- www.co-operativebank.co.uk – The Co-operative Bank, the website of an ethical business
- www.csreurope.org – CSR Europe, information on corporate social responsibility
- www.ethicalconsumer.org – Ethical Consumer, campaigning website on behalf of ethically minded consumers
- www.foe.co.uk – Friends of the Earth
- www.greenpeace.org.uk – Greenpeace
- www.hse.gov.uk – The Health and Safety Executive
- www.hse.gov.uk/workers/whistleblowing.htm – HSE, whistleblowing at work

- www.ibe.org.uk – Institute of Business Ethics
- www.telegraph.co.uk – Daily Telegraph
- www.thebodyshop.co.uk – The Body Shop
- www.tuc.org.uk – Trades Union Congress

Unit 38

Books

Gillespie, A. (2002) *Business in Action*, Hodder & Stroughton

Marcouse, I. and Lines, D. (2003) *Business Case Studies*, 2nd edition, Hodder Arnold

Sawyer, M. (2004) *The UK Economy: A Manual of Applied Economics*, 16th Edition, Oxford University Press

Whitaker's Almanack (2009) 141st Edition, A & C Black Publishers Ltd

Journals and newspapers

The Economist

Financial Times

Business sections of broadsheet newspapers

Websites

- www.bized.co.uk – Biz/ed, business studies resources for tutors and learners
- www.britishchambers.org.uk – British Chambers of Commerce, information on exporting
- www.businesslink.gov.uk – Business Link, information on importing and exporting
- www.cabinetoffice.gov.uk – UK Cabinet Office
- www.dft.gov.uk – Department for Transport
- www.direct.gov.uk – Directgov, follow the links to information for businesses
- http://europa.eu – The official website of the European Union
- www.imf.org – International Monetary Fund
- http://news.bbc.co.uk/1/hi/country_profiles/default. stm – BBC News website, up-to-date country profiles
- www.statistics.gov.uk – UK National Statistics
- www.times100.co.uk – The Times 100, a learner and tutor business studies resource centre
- www.un.org – The United Nations
- http://unfccc.int/2860.php – United Nations Framework Convention on Climate Change

Index

A

acceptance (of an offer) 83–84
action planning, health & safety 156–57
activities at business events 64–66
administrative skills 219
advice for small businesses 229
after-sales service 177–78, 188
age discrimination regulations 6, 269
aggregate demand 294, 297, 298, 301, 303, 304
agricultural policy 309
aims of business 208
air passenger duty 301
ambience 58
Animals Act (1986) 266
appraisal systems 37–38
atmospheric pollution 137
attendees, business events 47
Audit Commission 297
audits
   personal skills 14, 218, 220
   small business competition 211–12
authority 49
   delegating 30–31, 39–40
automation, impact on work 12
autonomy 40
awareness raising, health & safety 155

B

bailor, hirer of goods 103
balance of payments 287–88
balance sheet 234, 235
barriers to entry 198
benchmarking 36, 155
best practice guidelines, risk assessment 153
bonuses 21
break even 56–57
break even point 210
budgets
   business events 56–57, 72
   government 303
   health and safety 151
   pre-budget report 302
   start-up businesses 229, 230
building works, dangers of 128
business cycle 282–83, 284
business ethics 246–47
business event management
   documents needed 47, 48
   follow up 70–75

health, safety and security 66–67
   legal requirements 48
   organisational procedures 47–48
   organiser's role and skills 46–51
   prior arrangements 55–58
   programme, setting up 47
   resources 62
   running an event 64–70
   scheduling 62–64
   support requirements 68
   troubleshooting 68–70
   types of event 46, 52–55
   venues 46, 58–61
business planning 208–209
business proposals 239–41
business targets 36
business trends 210–11
business types 206–208

C

cafeteria incentive schemes 24–25
capacity (legal) 87
capacity (production) 12, 40
capital 210
capital allowances 301
capital intensive businesses 6
car scrappage scheme 272, 288, 289
career breaks 24
cash flow 207
cash-flow forecasting 232–33
caveat emptor 102
Charter Mark 33–34
child labour 276
childcare, employee reward 21
citizens as stakeholders 257
Civil Procedure Act (1997) 109
clicks and bricks retailers 163
climate change 250–51, 264, 271, 272, 315
Climate Change Act (2008) 296
co-operatives 223
codes of behaviour/conduct 29–30
communication
   channels, business events 57–58
   with customers 185
   open communications 31
   skills of event organisers 49
   in the workplace 32
communities, ethical concerns 269–73
Companies Act (1985/1989) 88–89
competence 40

competition
   government policy 258, 293
   in the labour market 10
   new businesses 209, 215
   in retailing 197–200, 258
Competition Act (1998) 194, 293
competitive edge 209
comprehensive spending review 302
Computer Misuse Act (1990) 144
conditions of a contract 94
conferences 54
confidentiality issues, business events 67
consideration, contract law 85
construction industry 290
consultation, business events 57
consumer contract 97
Consumer Credit Act (1974) 81
consumer motivation 215
Consumer Price Index (CPI) 284–85
Consumer Protection Act (1987) 228, 253
Consumer Protection (Distance selling) Regulations 2000 (as amended) 98, 227
consumer protection law 98, 101–104, 227, 228, 252–53
contingency plans 50
contraction of workforce 4
contractors, health & safety 150
contracts 80
   acceptance 83–84
   capacity 87–88
   communication of offers 83
   consideration 85–86
   counter offers 82–83
   factors invalidating 89–92
   invitations to treat 82
   offers 82
   organisations using 88–89
   privity of 86
   remedies 106–10
   and statutory consumer protection 101–105
   types of 80–81
   see also standard form contracts
contracts of employment 26–30, 228
Contracts (Rights of Third Parties) Act (1999) 86–87
Copenhagen Climate Conference 315
Copyright, Designs and Patents Act (1998) 144